CRUDE WORDS

contemporary writing from venezuela

RAGPICKER PRESS
LONDON

CRUDE WORDS
contemporary writing from venezuela

First published in 2016 by Ragpicker Press Ltd
70 Frederick Place, London SE18 7BH

ISBN 978-0-9929161-2-1
eBook ISN 978-0-9929161-3-8

Text design, typesetting and eBook design
by Adam Lowe and Jonathan Penton
Copyedited by Alexa Radcliffe-Hart
Cover design by Ernesto Muñiz
Photographs by Tim Girven with the exception of
'Savoy, puro sabor venezolano' by Yavn Isaacs

Printed & bound by T. J. International, Padstow, Cornwall.

CRUDE WORDS

contemporary writing from venezuela

edited by
MONTAGUE KOBBÉ, TIM GIRVEN
& KATIE BROWN
with a foreword by
ALBERTO BARRERA TYSZKA

 Ragpicker Press

Contents

6

7

EDITORS' NOTE

This project started where all good things do: at the pub, with like-minded people bouncing ideas off each other. One of those ideas was to highlight the much-neglected and recently booming literary scene in Venezuela – it fit beautifully with Tim's fascination for all things Latin American, especially non-fiction writing; it resonated, quite obviously, with Montague's heritage, born and raised in Caracas; and it cried out loud for Katie, a fellow patient of the Venezuelan literary bug, though consigned to the fiction ward, to be brought onboard. Two years later, having read through over three hundred thousand words in submissions, liaised with close to one hundred authors, gone through the gruelling process of selection – the most painful stage of the entire project without a doubt – and engaging with what amounts to a not-so-small village to translate, edit and produce *Crude Words*, we can finally present English readers with this unprecedented showcase of almost totally unknown talent from abroad.

Like any selection, literary or otherwise, the criteria of inclusion we used relied heavily on subjective consideration and doubled up as a device of exclusion. Such is the nature of choice, which must always be incomplete and imperfect. This is by no means meant to be an exhaustive anthology of contemporary Venezuelan authors, nor is it an authoritative compendium of the very best Venezuelan writing today. Rather, this is a selection – nothing more, nothing less – of the literary endeavours emerging from Venezuela at this difficult juncture, as the country faces a consuming economic and social crisis. And yet, though just a sample, we, the editors, remain as wide-eyed – perhaps more, as a matter of fact, after all the research and hard work of the past two years – at the quality of the work contained in these pages, as moved by the realisation that set this whole project in motion: the undisputable fact that there is a vast pool of talent out there – not all undiscovered, some perfectly established – which remains utterly unavailable to English readers. With *Crude Words* we hope to have gathered at least a small glassful from that pool.

A word on the methodology: although some interesting collections of translations have appeared online in recent years – notably Palabras Errantes' *Voices From the Venezuelan City* project and the Venezuelan special edition of *Words Without Borders* – the only contemporary writers to have seen their work in print in English are Alberto Barrera Tyszka, Ana Teresa Torres and Israel Centeno. Faced with the enormity of a whole country's literary production we proceeded by approaching the authors that stand out in our appreciation and asking them to submit a piece of writing of their choice – that which they considered the most appropriate calling card to an English audience – and to provide us with a brief list of recommended authors we ought to approach. In this sense we must give special thanks to Carlos

Sandoval, Héctor Torres, Willy McKey, Eduardo Sánchez Rugeles, Victoria de Stefano and Freddy Gonçalves Da Silva for their priceless assistance both pointing out authors previously unknown to us and also helping us to get in contact with them. Without their keen and continued support this book would have looked very different.

The collection you are holding in your hands now grew from the original target of twenty texts to the final – and still hopelessly insufficient – thirty with natural ease. In fact the hard thing was to find a cut-off point and to stick to it. The themes into which the selection is subdivided, on the other hand, emerged spontaneously from the submissions. There is clearly a dominating presence of male writers over female ones: this too is a reflection of the demographic distribution with which we were presented by the texts we received. Whether this is merely a result of the group of authors we approached or an accurate reflection of the writing establishment in the country is impossible for us to tell.

Finally, a word of caution regarding politics: from the conception of this project it has been our intention to refrain from making a political or ideological statement, be it implicit or explicit. Having said that, any gesture – and certainly one of this magnitude – gains significance when placed against the backdrop of as highly politicised a society as Venezuela's. We are aware as well as apprehensive of this fact. Even more so in light of our commitment from the very start to looking in detail at the effects of the huge and unprecedented diaspora experienced in Venezuela over the last decade, which was always going to translate into a platform for dissident voices. We would have liked to have welcomed more authors from the other side of the divide but our efforts to recruit them went unheard. Nevertheless, we have deliberately chosen informative and thorough texts that together offer an in-depth analysis of the origins of Venezuela's crisis, dating back to the 1980s, long before the emergence of Hugo Chávez, and the ultimate consequences of the political game on the everyday life of common people.

We couldn't finish this introductory note without a heartfelt thank you to all the people involved in the making of *Crude Words*. To every writer who submitted material for our consideration, we are humbled by their desire to publish with us and grateful that they allowed us to look at their work; to every author who generously accepted to be included in this collection and every translator who contributed their time to be part of this extended family (including Rachael McGill, whose brilliant translation didn't make it to the book in the end, through absolutely no fault of hers), to Ernesto Muñiz for his fantastic cover art, and to all those who have encouraged us along the way, a sincere and massive thank you.

FOREWORD:
TO READ A COUNTRY

ALBERTO BARRERA TYSZKA
Translated by Tim Girven

There is one characteristic that makes Venezuela radically different from the rest of Latin America: it is an oil country. By this I mean to say that Venezuela produces almost only and exclusively oil – setting it apart even from Mexico, Brazil, Ecuador and Colombia. Oil is the country's principal and essential source of income, and it is the fundamental motor of the economy. More than just a circumstance, it is the definition of a country, of an identity. Almost a century ago now, Venezuela began undergoing a profound transformation that took it from being a rural, peasant society, to becoming the only oil-state in the entire region. Perhaps an example is more illustrative: in Venezuela, at least until the beginning of this year (2016), filling a car's petrol tank to the brim cost significantly less than a small bottle of drinking water.

This condition of being an oil-state, the owner of the largest gas reserves in the world, has produced a society that has certain ideas and criteria about wealth and work, about social mobility and the role of the state, which are very different from those of other countries in the continent. Many years ago, the collective certainty that we were a rich, immensely rich, country took firm root in Venezuela. We came to think that this wealth was a talent, something that required no further effort, something that didn't even need to be cultivated. And so we began to believe that all we had to know was how to share out this wealth that already existed, a wealth that we – as if by birth right – already had. Perhaps something in this can explain how and why, in the second half of the twentieth century, Venezuela – a nation of fewer than twenty million inhabitants – managed to become the world's foremost importer of Scottish whisky.

The flip side of the coin is profoundly Latin American. Despite the enormous wealth, the monetary flows and a remarkable state ever capable of sponsoring populist politics, Venezuela has never ceased to share the principal tragedy that unites all Latin American nations: inequality. And the country's reality remains marked by the natural consequences of this tragedy: poverty, impunity, violence… But to enable a reading of the country, another fundamental characteristic needs to be added to this context: its militarist tradition. Before the forty years of representative democracy, from 1958 to 1998, Venezuela had been subject to a process of confrontation and domination by successive military rulers for a century and a half. Civilian life, as a nation, is a fragile and – relatively speaking – decidedly recent invention.

It is in this context that one has to locate Hugo Chavez's appearance in Venezuela's history. In the midst of an economic crisis and the failure of the traditional political parties, the emergence of a military leader onto the political scene was neither outrageous nor particularly surprising. Chavez proposed a new narrative of the country from the perspective of the poor, in the voice of the labouring classes, and thereby resuscitated the dream of the millionaire country, the fantasy of an easy wealth that only needed to be recuperated and shared out by a strongman, by a leader in uniform. Somehow, he modernised the continent's worn-out tradition, reinvented Latin America's old and well-known military *caudillismo*.

In 1992, Hugo Chavez attempted a coup d'état and failed. But his public surrender before the television cameras transformed him into a media phenomenon. His military defeat and his launch into the space of public spectacle occurred simultaneously. He quickly discovered that the mass media could be as powerful as martial weaponry. Chavez won the elections of 1998 and, from that moment on, began to produce a profound change in Venezuelan society. He turned himself into an invasive presence, a protagonist who took advantage of his electoral majorities to change laws, transform the state, and occupy all public institutions. With a leftist discourse, he gave ever more political punch to the military and concentrated ever more power on himself, developing the cult of his personality into public policy. Somehow, Chavez converted his popularity into a modern form of tyranny.

Chavez's political discourse was always full of truths. But his political practice steadily constructed a personalist and authoritarian regime, designing a country dependent upon his individual diktat and only sustainable during oil's boom-times. He turned populism into an emotional experience and presented the country with a radical choice: you're either with me or against me. You either love me blindly or hate me blindly. He banished discernment from the political debate. He generated a politics of affect and opened the door to irrationality. And then, when he was already speaking from the reaches of posterity, sickness suddenly appeared. An unforeseen and precipitate death left the country in a strange orphanhood. Subsequently the fall in oil prices hastened the resounding failure of his model. Today Venezuela has the highest inflation in the world, and inequality and poverty remain the principal signs of our identity.

Fortunately for us all, reality is always more complex than it appears. More plural, stranger, less predictable. The first great virtue of this anthology is precisely its diversity. It offers a deliberately multiple register in terms of issues and genres, but also in terms of tone and narrative possibilities. The majority of the texts brought together here were written in recent years, in a polarised and tumultuous Venezuela. The country breathes in these pages; but so too do many other (possible) countries, many other realities and many other ways of speaking them. A country that lives besieged and a country that tries to find itself from exile; a country of endless problems and a country that recognises itself in its pleasures; a country – above and beyond any economic or social indicator, beyond any utopia too – that continues writing itself from the perspectives of fear, of death, but also from that of sex, or from that of love. It is, definitively, a country written from the perspective of its wounds, a country that has more questions than statements.

Umberto Eco once said, with regard to *The Name of the Rose*, that when you can't theorise something, the best option is to try to narrate it. This book manages to bring together a fascinating selection of different types of stories and *crónicas* (reports) so as to offer a justly complex and distinct narrative of Venezuela. It is an extraordinary effort, a doorway that only good writing can offer: where ambiguity manages to overcome the kingdom of stereotypes, to defeat the Manichean moralism which aims to turn history into a mere paean. Here is a country that survives its own headlines. A country to be read.

THE ART OF LOVE: SEX, PORN & CONFLICT

CORNY OR PORNY

GUSTAVO VALLE
Translated by Joanna Josefina Thomas

Life is sweeter when it's imprecise. Let there be no more spreadsheets, no more non-negotiable fees, inflexible timetables or strict formulas for social grace and order. A lack of precision is playful. It's loaded with that sensuality envied by organised societies. Estimations and ambiguity may be the tools of improvisation and disorder, but also of humour and seduction. Exactitude fails when it comes to questions of courtship and love. What could be further from love than the precision of a Swiss watch? To fall in love we must play the game of subtle misdirection, fleeting gestures: let us graze past each other in the dark, and let all become clear only after a long journey. And, as the games of seduction have their counterparts in the actions of daily life, so imprecision becomes the way of life for some societies, making its home in their procedures, rules and structures. This is the case for Venezuela, the flag bearer of Latin American sentimentality.

It's no coincidence that the national pornography industry has failed in Venezuela. Explicitness – in all its many forms – is simply not enjoyed. Directness is considered unfriendly, and clarity is just dull. We prefer the party streamer to the straight line. We play at misdirection, we avoid the issue, and we're as evasive and slippery as a fish.

But a country without its own porn industry is a country with problems. And what's more, those nations whose consumption of pornography is reliant on imports never quite manage to fulfil their own particular brand of debauchery; an inexcusable form of sexual dependency. Here in Venezuela there are no creole porn stars, no top-shelf magazines, no home-grown producers of X-rated films. Our eroticism enjoys robust Catholic health, and full-frontal nudity is reserved for Maragall's statues in Los Caobos Park.

In Venezuela we like coquetry with an edge but not prostitution; further evidence of our corny, prudish spirit. Audacity and frankness are the domains of drunks and children, who together make up the most honest group in the country. Venezuela clings with its last breath to non-explicit eroticism, a phenomenon attributable to the fact that we are a village of true romantics.

Our inherent corniness has saved us, for the time being, from vulgarity. But at what price? That very corniness is, in fact, a form of vulgarity in itself, though one that produces pity instead of revulsion. Adherence to the corny is a mechanism for moral preservation, and, as all such mechanisms, it will eventually disappear. Our method is to seek the destruction of all defences through sentimentalism. We favour affectionate, extortionate betrayal. This is our armour against the myriad pains of love (true sentimentalists cannot conceive of abandonment). It offers effective protection against sadness by creating the wonderful illusion of a world apart; a world in which we can postpone the arrival of a harsher reality.

Yet our reality isn't hard, it is soft and pliable. It lacks an outline, and has no rules to support it. Our dedication to inexactitude makes us value approximations. We cultivate love and humour (and all other inexact sciences) over any other discipline. We hate rigour because it seems too severe, and we're a society who wants, at any price, to be happy. So we feed a reality full of oracles, speculations, estimates and simulations. We Venezuelans, today more than ever, live a life of constant postponement, where everything will be fixed at some unseen point in the future. We have faith in this future because we're a hopeful country. Which is to say, we're irredeemably corny, practicing a form of optimism that strains against the bounds of logic and clarity. We prefer promises to actions, since the former are vague whilst the latter are definite. We love ambiguity because we are – or believe we are – romantics and seducers, and surely there is no such thing as a pessimistic romantic. When all is said and done, who has ever known an optimist who enjoys pornography?

THE PRINCESS OF ESCURUFINÍ

EDNODIO QUINTERO
Translated by Montague Kobbé

1

She was blood of my blood: my first cousin. I met her at our maternal grandparents' country home on an occasion when most of the clan had come together, a huge horde arrived from all corners – merry, witty, with a tangled diction, as if they were all wealthy expats – and branded with an identical Semitic nose. I can't recall the reason for that tribal reunion, perhaps we were witnessing the agonic passing of a hardy great-aunt called Margarita – a hairy old spinster – or maybe it was Cousin Asiloé's boozy wedding – she'd married a Colombian horse trader whose perfect and permanently exposed dentures featured a double row of shiny gold teeth.

I can't remember if we were in that huge country home surrounded by *bucare, guamo* and coffee trees for a funeral or for the birth of the ninetieth grandchild to grace the lives of our grandparents – old, nonagenarian relics who reeked of urine and refused to die. But I will never forget that among the loud gaggle of cousins and a whole bunch of rascals whose kinship I would have been unable to establish, running around all day in and out of the yards, lodgings and hallways as if they were being chased by the devil himself, from that very first day I noticed my cousin I fell madly in love with her. Although I still recall her sweet name I shall in what follows refer to her as Helena, just like the beautiful and treacherous wife of Menelaus. She became the centre of my life. Helena was my sun.

That hot and rainy August, which my memory insists on displacing with a dry month of February, I knew happiness. I would wake up early and run like an unbridled horse in search of breakfast – homemade corn *arepas*, scrambled eggs, fresh milk and *natilla* – a real delicacy that Aunt Isabel, my mother's sister, prepared with great care and not too much salt. Then I would splash around in water-filled canoes – the animals' drinking troughs – which the smaller ones among us used as bathtubs. Clean and fresh following the cleansing ritual, I'd be ready to face the long and promising day. Afterwards, all dressed up in my dandy clothes and with my straight Motilon Indian hair neatly combed in a style that suited me, I'd sit in the hallway like the guard of a royal palace. Softly whistling to myself, I would wait until Helena – my flower – made her entrance at the threshold of the day.

All day long I endeavoured to be near her, I followed her steps like the Earth follows the Sun, and though she never seemed disturbed by my presence I believe she wasn't too happy either to have me hanging from her skirt tails as if I were her shadow or her faithful lapdog. I think she tolerated me, and perhaps she looked at me from the heights of her maddening beauty with some scorn, as the astral king might look upon one of his satellites. I never told her about my infatuation, since at the age of seven we still can't find the words to name that fever which makes us wake up in the middle of the night with a cold sweat and turns us into stuttering idiots when confronted with the object of our desire. For me it was enough to dance the dance of the jaguar for her or to recreate the flight of the hare from the pack of wolves. I played the role of the quick and agile hare, and once out of reach of the wolves I hung from the branch of a *manteco* tree, in which position I'd be possessed by the spirit of Tarzan. I'd turn somersaults in the air and when my tricks and pirouettes made her laugh I suddenly became – thanks to that unique smile – the single most joyful being on this blue planet, the most remote place in the Milky Way where my cousin and I had very recently landed. So, what could I say to Helena, who was barely a week younger than me, although I wouldn't find that out until much later. Yes, we were exactly the same age and we also shared the misfortune of being only children. But during that first meeting, what was I to say to her? Please, do tell me.

Something happened at the end of the family reunion. As if the gods of our ancestors had listened to my fervent prayers, the country home gradually emptied out. My big-nosed relatives, with their herd of squirts and a few golden-tressed girls, started to pack up their belongings and disappeared in their carriages pulled by chestnut mares or grey nags. Fate, which sometimes behaves like a cunning old man, left

Helena and me all by ourselves. The adults rushing about in the big house from sunup to sundown were like puppets hung on the wall – for us, they didn't count.

This was the state of affairs when, on a bright early September afternoon, my cousin and I reached the top of a hill from where the country home looked as if it were one of those little houses that adorned nativities during Christmas. We had never been so far away from the family nest. Our escapade filled us with huge excitement, as evidenced by the blush on my cousin's cheeks. I was beside myself with joy but feared my cousin might get scared by the sound of my heartbeat – roaring like a river in spate – and run away. Covered in sweat we sat by the shade of a flaming *bucare* tree to catch our breath. I was spellbound by the tip of my shoe, which gleamed like a gold tooth, and by the scent of cinnamon and bay leaf emanating from my cousin next to me, which cloaked me like a protecting mantle.

I suppose she spoke first, although I would be unable to reproduce the exact words she said, let alone the mutterings I produced as answers. I can, however, picture myself with my cousin, entering a copse on the far side of the hill, in search of a bush they call *uvito* – little grape – the flowers of which we would use to make a garland to adorn Helena's hair. What for? Did she think she was the princess of Escurufiní, the lost corner where we found ourselves? No: my first cousin, the beautiful Helena, had decided to marry me at once. Right there, out in

the wild, behind our family's back. No witnesses –
what for, if the trees and the air swarmed with little
birds who could serve as our entourage. Wait until we
get old? No, dear cousin, I won't have any of that.
The only thing we're missing is the garland of *uvitos*.
Without a garland there can be no wedding. Should
I confess that at some point during the ceremony I
experienced a bout of anxiety? I might have been on
the edge of crying. Memory tends to trick us, creating
false images in our minds, fabricating episodes that
never took place. I cannot recall Helena consulting
me about the betrothal, which – all things considered
– was slightly premature. And even if she did ask,
what was I supposed to say? Yes, yes and yes, my
beloved cousin. I had thought of Helena of Escurufiní
every day and every night but not even in my wildest
dreams had it occurred to me to ask her to marry me.
And now, it turns out, she's the one who… No, it can't
be. Truth be told, I wouldn't have known what it was
I wanted to do with my cousin even if she had ever
found out about my infatuation. I guessed, therefore,
that given her sudden decision to hold our wedding
under the trees, right then and there, I could simply
change my mind the following day. I was somewhat
confused.

Perhaps my memory has cloaked the details of
our marriage with a merciful and providential shroud
of forgetting, allowing me to escape the sort of
suffering that leaves an indelible wound in the soul.
But the sight of Cousin Helena, radiant in the sunset,
the garland of *uvitos* wreathing her head, the blood

orange light of the sun shining on her before it hid behind the mountains of Guirigay – that, I will never forget. Who knows, perhaps this will be the last image I think of on my deathbed.

I suppose, although this no longer has any significance, that the following day – and unrelated to the wedding on the hill – my father came to my rescue.

2

Two or three years went by and I heard no more of Cousin Helena. Did I forget her? I would be lying if I said that I cherished her memory. But one night she suddenly burst into our home. And here a little detail of time and place is necessary to understand the sudden reappearance of that charming creature whom I could swear I'd forgotten. My father had been appointed as the judge of a tiny village called Burbusay, up on a dry and windy hillside. We had been living in that paradise – the kingdom of the wind – for five or six months. My Cousin Helena's father, a rough man with something of the ogre about him (in sharp contrast to the delicate and refined demeanour of his wife, Aunt Berta, my mother's sister), had lost everything to his weakness for gambling. Lands, houses and cattle, all gone in a game of cards. When he found himself destitute he loaded his family and few remaining possessions onto a wagon pulled by two mules and embarked upon a slow escape towards

Maracaibo. 'Black gold is abundant over there, and I'll have the chance to get even,' said my troubled uncle, meaning every word. Halfway through the long and shameful journey they stopped in Burbusay, presumably to say goodbye to my mother or perhaps to scrounge off the gentle judge, who was said to be wealthy. For a moment the wagon, which to me seemed identical to the one I'd seen recently in a film about Gypsies, stood – the mules unhitched – in a corner of Plaza Bolívar, shaded by a gigantic *cují* tree, the crown of which resembled a witch's hat. Pewter pots, pans, wooden ladles, mirrors, handsaws, an old farmer's almanac, a stringless violin, a Roman steelyard balance for weighing wheat with some garments hung from it, all stored under a canvas, as if it were the caravan of one of those travelling Turkish merchants who ventured along the mountain paths. The fleeing wagon might have stayed in Burbusay for a day, maybe two at the most. Hence, my recollection of Helena on that brief occasion remains incomplete and foggy, steeped in the thickest darkness. I don't think we spoke at all, the two of us. But I clearly remember the conversation my mother had with Aunt Berta in the drawing room, under the watchful eyes of the image of the Sacred Heart I was so struck by, since it depicted our Lord with his heart before his chest, as if a beast had ripped it out with its teeth. My mother, whom I adored and whose charming voice I loved, told her sister that this lass – meaning Cousin Helena – had become a sylph. It was the first time I had heard the word sylph, and obviously I didn't know what it meant. And, of course, I was too shy to ask.

That same night, as fate would have it, I was given the chance to learn what a sylph was. When my bedtime came, I was met with a colossal surprise: in my bed, under the warm covers, lay Cousin Helena. Ever the spoilt child, I was used to having my own bedroom and had slept on my own ever since I could remember. I guess Helena's parents stayed with us for the night, as it would have been unkind to let them sleep in the wagon, practically out in the open. The early morning wind would have swept them away. And since we had no spare rooms, they must have slept on an improvised mattress, while I was entrusted – given my age – with Helena's care. I soon realised that my cousin was fast asleep with an angelic smile on her face – she must have gone out like a light as her head hit the pillow after ten long hours in that rattling carriage making its way along hellish roads. I was surprised that my mother had not warned me about the sweet company awaiting me in my chambers, but then it occurred to me that in the world of adults many things are often taken for granted. Whatever the little ones might think counts for nothing. For a moment I wondered whether I should enter that jumble of white sheets and woollen covers, thinking that if my cousin woke up she would scream. And when I had decided to take my place next to her, a new doubt hit me: should I wear my pyjamas or not? I put on my pyjamas, and as soon as I got under the covers it was me who almost let out a shriek of horror. My cousin was completely naked, she wasn't even wearing knickers, and was hot as a stove.

At school – I was in third grade – I had heard older students talking about women. Some boasted of having had 'intercourse' with bad girls, with an older woman and even with their own sisters but I knew they were all shameless liars. As for me, and despite my voracious curiosity for all things feminine, I was completely ignorant of the details of such mysterious matters. It's hard to believe from the perspective of the wicked adult I became, but right then, in the flesh, had I been presented with the opportunity I wouldn't have known if I should enter from the front or from behind. I still didn't know many years later.

And there I was, at the age of ten, wanting to seem twelve, pretending to be a little man, though I still dressed and combed my hair like a choirboy, shaking with fear next to a naked woman. Well, the woman bit is an exaggeration. In any case, my friends, it was not just any woman. In one of my past lives she had been the object of my desire, and now she was there, like a newly picked flower, radiant and scorching like the sun: unique and in unison, exclusively for me. This was my golden opportunity, my wildest dream, and not for anything in the world should I let it slip by. I assume that my thoughts during that tempestuous night were not so fully formed yet. I switched off the light and a single ray entered the room from above the shutter, which always remained open. Outside, the wind shook the trees and threatened to rip the roofs from the houses. Sensitive to weather conditions due to some millenary legacy, I took that lightning as a sign. Go on, little man, don't stop, even the devil himself can't stop you from fulfilling your desires. Giddy up, horsie!

I stripped naked, and blind as a mole I made my way through the thick and burning darkness. I started to feel my first cousin's exquisite skin, touching it with my hands, lips and feet, stroking her bony shoulders, her round belly and her little buttocks made of silk, clay and silicate. I plunged my wandering-Jew's nose into her mane, which smelled of a river in flood, I clung to her back like a monkey to a branch in the height of a storm, and I hugged her sylph's waist with so much joy that I almost started to cry. Oh, how exciting, dear me, now I know what a sylph is. I struggled with my cousin as if I were trying to pull a drowned body out of a well, and although I might have become a little forceful or violent, at no point did she show signs of waking. A thousand years later I would learn from my own experience that it is harder to deal with a sleeping woman than with a dead one.

Now, I would be lying shamelessly if I were to say that I had intercourse with my first cousin on that night of misery and splendour. The thought of it might have crossed my mind, I can't really remember. But as my dad used to say: easier said than done. And even if I had dared, I bet I would still have been mired in a sea of confusion. Was I conscious of my virility? That's a trick question, my friend. I guess I was, but what was I supposed to do with such a little accessory?

When I woke up a shaft of light kept me from opening my eyes. A ray of sunlight brightened a corner of my room. Damn! I didn't know when I'd fallen asleep but the sun had been up for some time now. And the sylph was no longer by my side. I felt some relief at finding myself on my own in my bedroom, as I wasn't certain I would be able to look my first cousin in the eye. But at the same time I yearned for her madly. And given that I was still dazed and sleepy I thought perhaps it had all been a dream – a beautiful dream, but a dream nonetheless. However, that theory was belied by my memory of the sylph – that recently discovered word which in the darkness had turned into a delightful and violently real being. Her absence was also a product of the fallacious tyranny of reality: Helena had been fetched very early in the morning, for her ruined family was ready to continue the journey in the wretched Gypsy vardo. Did my cousin know we'd spent the entire night together, naked? What had she thought when she awoke and found me there by her side? How would she react if she found out I had spent hours and hours fondling her? Did she even remember me? Whatever happened to that garland of *uvitos*? And, if some day, by some twist of fate, we met again, what would I tell her then? Stop asking questions no one will ever answer. And simply remember that among the white sheets of your bed in Burbusay – those your mother used to starch and iron with so much care – lodged the delicate scent of your first cousin: bay leaf and cinnamon sticks, mixed with a trace of musk. With that formula one could make a fragrance called: 'Promise of a Woman'.

3

When I realised they were approaching down the hall I became a bundle of nerves and ran to hide in my room on the top floor. There was no logical explanation for the paralysing fear that suddenly gripped me, but back when this final event in the romance with my first cousin took place my everyday life wasn't exactly ruled by logic or reason. Just to give you an example, at my advanced age – I had just turned fifteen – a pernicious idea had taken hold of my mind: I wanted to become a writer. I was convinced that a trade full of surprises, adventures, insomnia and strong emotions such as this was my fate. My marks at school had plummeted during my final year, and my reputation as the school's star student, the master of the three Marias – maths, physics and chemistry – was reduced to nothing, trampled on like the filthy swab used by the janitors to mop the floors. Fortunately the summer holidays had arrived, and I had crossed the plains, foothills and a good piece of the mountain range to seek shelter at my father's house. His appointment as a judge had only lasted two years, after which – and against the will of my mother, who put up an obstinate resistance to the very last minute – the couple returned to their rural home. 'To the winter quarters,' Dad used to say, sending his wife into a fit of anger. I completed my secondary education in a small town down on the warm plains, living with some of my father's close relatives who – for some reason I could never understand – treated me as if I were an orphan or foundling. Years later, organising my recently deceased father's correspondence, I learned that during that interregnum in my education – for my stay at my father's house stretched into a full year – my relatives, conspiring with a phony doctor, had determined that I was mentally unwell, and told my father so in a letter that I delivered to him myself.

I must have been a quiet madman – I can't recall dressing like Napoleon, attacking or even intimidating anyone. My father granted me my every wish, though that wasn't particularly telling, since he had always treated me that way. And my mother hardly said a word, because the little time we shared in my father's house – on a meadow surrounded by cornfields in the Visún heights – she spent arguing the terms of the divorce with my father. I still adored her, but the word divorce on her lips besmirched her, don't ask me why. Oh, and in terms of my intentions of becoming a writer, I had already filled three spiral-bound notebooks with my surgeon's handwriting and had started on my fourth. Every line contained the exact same sentence: 'The alchemists are reaching the hallway,' repeated once and again like a damned litany or a desperate plea to I-don't-know-who.

In that not particularly suitable – actually rather damaged – environment, I found out that Cousin Helena was on her way. What could she be after in these godforsaken latitudes? The night prior to her arrival I heard my parents promise each other they would call a truce from their marital disputes during my aunt and uncle's visit. All ominous signs and warnings to the contrary, my uncle, the ogre, had prospered in the infernal reaches of Maracaibo and had made arrangements to pay his buddy Federico – my dad – a friendly visit. Besides, though this could not be discussed in the presence of their dearly loved and slightly unhinged son, the visit from Aunt Berta – what a fine and delicate woman! – and her husband also served a greater purpose: repaying the loan my father had extended to them that time they stopped in Burbusay when they were fleeing as if from the plague. Oh, that child must have grown into a full woman by now. Without prior warning my mother dropped that seemingly casual comment like a bomb. I knew she was talking about Cousin Helena, and the thought of facing her for a third time sent a cold shiver up my spine.

I might thus be forgiven for my state of excitement when I heard the dogs barking, as horsemen approached the entrance to the front yard of my father's house. Hidden in the ample chambers of the upper floor, which served as both a bedroom and a studio, I took long strides, like a surveyor. I stopped by the edge of the small cedar table I used as a desk, and wrote again in my complicated handwriting in the notebook, open like a bird with its wings unfurled, the usual sentence: 'The alchemists are reaching the hallway'. I knew there was no way out of the reunion with my first cousin, and if someone had questioned me with the barrel of a gun to my temple, I would have confessed, with my heart in my hands – like that image of the Lord that used to scare me so much – that my one and only wish, and I could die then and there if only that wish came true, was to throw myself at Cousin Helena's neck, to inhale the perfume of her hair and to drink in her breath, the breath of a woman made for my pleasure. What might she smell like, now that she had ceased being a sylph and been transformed into a woman? Hot amber with a pinch of sandalwood and mandarin. What might the name of that fragrance be? I longed for it like a beast, I went to a deep, freezing pool at the break of day and took the sort of bath fit only for a madman, still dressed in my best clothes – shirt and loose linen trousers – just for her. And then I hid in my rooms where I felt safe from all evil, perhaps to prolong the joy of waiting.

The wait turned out to be short. The door swung open and my cousin burst in like a storm. As she approached like the winds of vengeance, her face radiant and her mane the colour of burned wheat waving like a flag, I could see the tip of her pearly nipples jutting out, sending off violent ripples before me. Yes, my first cousin was a fully grown woman, and if any doubt remained it was enough to watch her luscious breasts bouncing beneath her transparent-blue silk blouse, like two gelatin-filled water balloons about to burst. 'Cousin, how you've grown!' she said, as she threw herself into my arms and I held her, almost unable to breathe.

I don't know exactly how it happened. Did we kiss? Did we hug? We felt one another's bodies with urgency and fury, like two blind people trying to recognise each other after a shipwreck. During that fumbling I suddenly felt her hands – with their

delicate fingers and nails sharp as a hawk's claw –
grasp my penis fervently, devotedly, gripping it as
hard as could be, dear cousin, blood of my blood,
blood calling like a blaze, and that little goat's horn,
that piece of my flesh, started swelling and grew
larger and larger. I closed my eyes and surrendered
to my fate, I saw yellow suns whirling in a sky of
fermented milk, I saw my mother looking into a pool
of murky waters, I saw myself running from a forest
in flames, and as I embarked on my journey back to
instinctive desire, to the centre of an ecstasy I might
never experience again, I kept telling myself that this
wasn't happening. Only now, I murmured to myself,
are the alchemists reaching the hallway. I must have
fallen asleep after lunch, and the imminent arrival of
my cousin had gifted me that exquisite dream. Any
minute now my mother would knock on the door and
I would have to face a bitter awakening. Far, very far
away, as if carried by the lush wind of Burbusay, I
could hear Helena's melodious voice: 'Cousin, how
you've grown!'

I opened my eyes and filtering through my cousin's
tangled caramel hair I could see crimson threads –
like strings of blood – dancing, entwining, gleaming.
It was the red sunset nestling on Helena's little head,
while she dragged me slowly, still holding my raccoon
penis, as if leading me by a halter to the wide window
that faced westward. I posed no resistance, sensed a
perfume in the air hitherto unknown to me – like the
fragrance distilled by those carnivorous flowers that
grow in Death Valley – and I remained suspended,

a hand's span above the ground, contemplating the blood-orange disc of the sun dipping behind the mountains of Guirigay.

PASSION

GISELA KOZAK
Translated by Montague Kobbé

We surfaced from love as if from a plane crash.
Cristina Peri-Rossi

Persuaded and defeated, moist and longing, I watch
you sleep after opening the bedroom door in a mutual
friend's home – a mutual friend who refuses to take
sides in the civil war. You and I are on different sides
and that is why we split up a year ago. There's been
a truce and I have to write a piece about this grey
area between the void and oblivion, but the truth is
I'm here because I still love you. You must be really
tired, since you didn't even switch off the weak
and yellowish light on the bedside table. Your army
uniform lies creased on a chair: a chemist turned
warrior. It's cold but you sleep untroubled under the
thick blankets that cover you and that only reveal a
comely calf, a subtly muscular arm, your neck. I bask
in your profile, your nose emerging from between
your eyebrows, tracing a severe, straight line. I step
inside, shut the door, remove my leather jacket, place
it on the lone chair. I lean over you tenderly, adjust the
blankets around your body.

I want to be those blankets, to encompass all your
skin in a single caress. I lie beside you. You agree to

my presence. You're asleep. Are you awake? I barely touch you with my nose as it travels along your neck, from the nape to the ear; this is the unmistakable smell of you. I can feel you shivering and I wrap my left arm around you. You make yourself comfortable; you know it's me embracing you. My breasts test their firmness on your back. My other hand supports my head. You open your eyes but don't look at me straight away. I let my fingers explore your groin, then travel upwards. You become apprehensive, seek to avoid it; I don't insist, I kiss your neck, I've never stopped loving you, not a single day, I whisper. I long for the pleasure of touching your left breast, of filling my hand with it again, of enticing your nipple to harden. You stir anxiously; we've been on our sides and you turn to face me. You stumble upon my mouth, waiting for you. I hold it over yours, barely tilting my face sideways, putting my right arm around your neck and shoulders. My lips move softly between yours, open partway in a coy gesture. I take your lips in mine, I am the one driving this kiss, the intensity, the length, the wetness, the exact movement of the tongue: just the tip. It is a long kiss – a kiss of recognition, of reunion. I came here to concede defeat, I know.

You try to stop me. I watch your black eyes saying yes and your lips saying no. You sit down, I press you against me. I'm the one who leans in with her mouth, who holds you by the neck, who awaits the relenting embrace, who whispers in your ear, make me yours, do whatever you want to me, I'll grant you any wish. You embrace me. I'm still half dressed – that bothers you, it humiliates you. The fact that I'm still wearing clothes emphasises your nakedness. You've always slept naked, but it's too cold. Or did you know I would come to see you? I pull you away from me for a moment, I look at you, I see fragility, I hug you, I rock you, I tell you what I came to tell you: I give in. You don't answer. The minutes pass while we embrace, we exchange kisses of varying intensity, we stroke each other's backs, each other's hair. I remove my T-shirt right before your eyes, you fondle my breasts, softly at first, then more intensely; my neck curls back (I missed you so much), I furrow my brow (I longed for you so much), my lips part, I moan. The precision, the speed of your tongue, the way you open your mouth and cover my nipple, I've always loved it. We change positions. You let me lean you back, reach down to your breasts. I treat them gently, my closed mouth exploring them before I taste them. I kiss them patiently, I squeeze your nipples between two fingers, stroke them with the tip of my index finger, you start to arch your back, to moan, to lose control. You open your thighs, you want me between them. I abide, careful not to place too much weight on your body. We move slowly, softly, at the exact same rhythm, touching each other's faces, each other's hair, in a single caress that encompasses our entire bodies, focused, looking at each other at times, hiding my face in your neck, holding on to one another with feverish tenderness because in the midst of all this danger we are the life that's left to us.

A long kiss heralds the storm that lies ahead; I return to your breasts empowered and with abandon, I taste them, take them in my mouth. My hand caresses your vulva, you open unhurriedly, I contain myself, barely brushing your clitoris. Your hand in mine tells me you want more. My finger presses softly from top to bottom and then back up. I climb to your mouth and while I kiss you I move down to the gates of your vagina, resting my fingers on the threshold. You stop me, push me back, remove what's left of my clothes and our bodies emulsify in a dance that lasts long minutes; you're on top of me, riding me patiently, knowingly, taming my restlessness while I hold you by the shoulders and ask you to carry on. My body accepts your rhythm, your weight, the way you sink your teeth into my ears, the haughty kiss of your lips against mine, your triumphant tongue, a bite that lands on the mark, triggering a tiny pain healed by the tenderness of your next kiss. The rhythm changes, the kisses become sweeter, our movement becomes more regular. Penetrate me, I beg, and for a moment you hold me on your lap. You search between my thighs, you rub my clitoris with the perfect degree of friction, moments later you carefully push two fingers inside. You take your time to drive me mad.

I asked for a break – wait, I said, so kindly that you let go without protesting. In no time my face was down at your crotch. Your pearl peeked out, round and full. The tip of my tongue ran from the gates of your vagina to your erect clitoris, then it stopped: to start, just a touch… quivering… then another. Press, lick lightly at first and then – given your moaning, your 'Faster' – quickly, I wrap your pearl in my lips and suck it, smell your vanilla scent, feel your carefully trimmed pubes, all prim and proper. Your vulva is beautiful – its flesh rosy, its outer lips as finely shaped as the inner ones. My tongue hits your clit right on the button, eliciting moans of pleasure. Then you tell me, 'Like that, fuck me.' I penetrate your vagina and anus with my fingers and within a minute you start shaking: I feel the first tremor in my tongue and the contractions around my fingers, rhythmic, tighter at first, then looser. Your moans are irregular until they become progressively longer and sustained. You come. You cast me aside, tired, sweet, moaning, shaking. Then, when you sense my face next to yours, you stroke it without opening your eyes.

You don't forgive me for your surrender. You turn me around unhurriedly. I know what you want, I pull myself onto my hands and knees. I arch my back and moan, does it hurt you, no, perhaps it's hurting a little, you kneel, you lean against me, yes, it does hurt a bit, I pant as I feel the shiver in my womb from the orgasm. I rest my face against the bed, fully invaded. After the lesser orgasms already experienced would come greater quakes. Your fingers wrest a deep and visceral moan from me, a full, convulsive orgasm. We are tired but a few minutes later you are in front of me. I hold you down by the neck, I kiss you, my finger caresses your most secret orifice mercifully and tenderly, your thighs are open, you touch your clit with your right middle finger. I want to watch you come again. I lay you back down on the bed, I penetrate you with my right hand and I follow the path to your groin, moving my fingers upwards, applying some pressure. My left hand on your neck is pulling you down, your black eyes shine, your face flushes red; do you take the pleasure I give you because you're lonely? Because you need to? Because of the past? Because of love? The moisture that allows my hand to move inside you with so much ease is your gift to me. I stroke your clitoris with my thumb: your black eyes open even wider, your pupils dilate, you blink, you knit your brow; it's the slightly pained face of extreme pleasure; I can see your teeth, your pink tongue. You look at me as if surprised, secretly rebelling, you let out a breathless scream, you come.

Later your sharp and quick tongue extracts a final orgasm from me, almost on the verge of fainting.

In the morning I wake up in your embrace, your forehead resting on the nape of my neck.

I ask you: what are we going to do now? You don't answer.

Are you really asleep?

CHRISTINA CRIES AT THREE O'CLOCK

MIGUEL GOMES
Translated by Ruth Clarke

All the time now. At three it's louder, because she doesn't bother to hide it; it's the middle of the afternoon and she can really let rip, let her tears drop into the sink as she washes the dishes from lunch or last night's dinner. I pretend I can't tell. It's not like I don't care, it's not like it doesn't break my heart to hear her like that, I just don't know what to do. I've also realised that any attempt to console her only makes things worse. I can picture her giving me that angry glare, like she did last time, and the times before, then she'd bark out some kind of insult – Don't just stand there like an idiot – or she'd close the flowery curtain that separates the kitchen from the lounge, not gently, but with a sharp flick of the wrist, like the many (too many) other flicks of the wrist that have left the curtain in tatters, its rail hanging off – Stop staring at me, dickhead – or she'd decide to repeat what she always tells me when I try to say anything or make the slightest effort to chip into what would otherwise be a monologue on her part – You don't get me, man, you just don't understand. I can't talk to you, it's a waste of time – and me – Christina, you don't let me get a word in – and her – No, of course I don't, you wouldn't understand, you can't – I have to leave it at that, with a lump in my throat like a walnut. I can feel its coarse skin working its way down to my chest.

She cries at three, at two in the afternoon. Once, at ten in the morning, she sobbed until her face was swollen from crying so hard. The other day, I found her cleaning the patio with fat teardrops dripping onto the bucket and brush. I asked her if she wanted me to take over – You have a rest, melove, let me do that – and her – Get lost, stop bothering me. The truth is I don't understand her: that porcupine is not the woman I married. I barely even recognise her.

I stood and watched her for a while; she had her back to me, in the old dress she wears to do the cleaning; I could make out the shape of her breasts, half-visible, because she'd never wear a bra to do the chores. Her neck glistened with sweat and the edges of her dress were damp. Her bushy hair was pulled back into an untidy bun. Strong calves, that they say make her Galician (as far as I know, Christina hasn't got a trace of Galician in her, although I wouldn't rule it out, because folks from Maracaibo have a bit of everything in them, except discretion). My eyes settle on her sturdy calves; the knot of hair; the wisps of grey that suit her so perfectly they could have been dyed to look like that; the sweat stains; her breasts, moving as she works. Then my eyes settle on her wide hips, wider than the rest of her. I feel an erection that quickly droops; another nutshell in my throat; and I feel like crying, too, because I can't imagine life without that woman, it doesn't matter whether I understand her. Maybe it's just a phase. But still.

It's like the whole thing's a con: up until a few months ago, if anyone had asked me who was the most sensible person I knew, I would have said Christina. I always tell my friends she's the one with the common sense in this house. The dog doesn't have any. The kids don't have any (they're intelligent, bright, both well respected in their respective trades, but that's not common sense). I sometimes have it, but nowhere near as much as her. And I do incomprehensible things like selling my share in the law firm to that dick Gonzalo, and for a ridiculous price (I can never regret that enough), so I could dedicate my time to the pizzeria. Because in this crazy country there's no money to be made in intellectual property; you're better off managing singers, and they're soon gone, and you start getting involved with actors and theatre folk, and from there it's a slippery slope. Incomprehensible things like opening a pizzeria in Altamira, in the middle of Plaza Francia, right at the start of the protests, just a few days before the massacre (hours before that, sales were better than ever); totally incomprehensible, like getting rid of the pizzeria, which was making a loss, and setting up my law firm again, now under the name Talent Centre, but this time from home so I wasn't paying for a shop front or staff. I got a messenger, and that's it (even that expense I tend to save, when I feel like driving). I let Raquel go, so no more receptionists: they're like some form of divine punishment. I told Gonzalo to go to hell, because he was useless and did nothing but line his pockets on the back of my work (I've heard he's selling the office because he went bust – of course he went bust, I was the one who did everything). I'm the incomprehensible one, not Christina, she was always so calm, and whenever I was in despair, she was ready to give me advice, and a good dressing down, if necessary. And it usually was. But now she's like this; it's been a year, and I'm running out of ideas. It's a total con: somebody tricked me, pulled the wool over my eyes, switched my wife. It's not Christina's fault, poor thing, she just can't take it. I can hear her now: she's shut herself in her room, crying, convinced I won't notice.

Some days, the worst of them, she shuts herself away with the blinds down, in complete darkness, and doesn't get out of bed; she pulls the covers up to her ears, regardless of how hot it is. At best she'll turn on the TV and find some soap operas, although I don't think she pays any attention; she looks at them, but she's not watching. It worries me if I have to go into the room to get something; I don't know whether she's going to ignore me; I don't know whether she's going to bark out – What are you looking at, man? – or if she's angry – What are you looking at, moron? – I never know how it's going to be, whether they're tears of sadness or tears of anger. The last time I tried to console her or cheer her up, which involved putting my hand on her head with all the care in the world, she turned into an animal, growling at me, she almost attacked me. Who do you think you're petting? I'm not Simon, you know – and me – No, Christina, it's not like that. I love you. I hate seeing you like this, melove – and her – You're so corny. And that's why, to this day, I don't touch her, I don't do anything corny; to be honest, I don't do anything at all, or I don't understand what I am doing, I don't even want to think about what I'm thinking, just to let her be completely right. I don't understand anything. My wife, myself, my dog: the holy trinity that dwells in this house.

Simon isn't well; he wags his tail but it's heartbreaking to look at him and realise he hasn't got long left. It was Christina's idea to call him Simon, she said that when she was little her family had a dog called Tony, which meant it was okay to christen this one Simon. And Simon stuck. To wind her up, I laughed – You Maracaibo folk give your pets normal people's names, and normal people get something completely over the top, like your mother: Esplendidaluz Palacios de Durango. Such a big name for such a tiny woman! At that time, Christina still hadn't lost her sense of humour, she even liked a joke; it was always a joy to talk to her, she roared with laughter and came back with – If you're spoiling for a fight, man, may I remind you of what they say about you folk from Valencia since Boves showed you what for. That shut me up, obviously. We found Simon in the street one day; you could see he was just a puppy. Then he grew up and now his heart's just not in it; his eyes have those strange blue blobs that must be cataracts, I assume. He's going blind and sometimes I get the impression he's going deaf, too, because you call him and he looks the other way; you call him again, and again he gets it wrong; only on the third or fourth try does he look the right way. He's been with us for nineteen years: he's the canine Methuselah. Lately he can't hold it in anymore and he shits everywhere; the patio reeks, so we had to stop him coming in the house. It's a shame. The mess is creamy and sticks to the fur on his paws. It's like he's dissolving, fading away like a stream between the bushes, dying a little bit at a time; and to think of the strength and joy he had when he was young; it was great to see him when you came home from work; or when the kids came back from school and went to play with him. He's a bag of bones now; you can count his ribs, no matter how much he eats. The idea of sacrificing him has crossed my mind two or three times, to put an end to his suffering. Because that's what he's doing: you only have to listen to him howling, especially at night. It's painful. One clean shot in the skull, with that pistol I bought from my brother-in-law in March of '89, when we were all nervous about the looting. The pistol was like something out of a western; it had a long barrel and that was all you needed to look intimidating. I've never used it, and to tell the truth I haven't seen it for years; I hid it so well that, despite how dangerous Caracas has become, I can't even remember where I put it. But it would be worth looking for it to put the animal out of his misery; it's the most humane thing to do. Of course, it's not that easy; as soon as I contemplate the idea of expediting his death, I start putting myself in his place, asking myself whether my kids will be wondering the same when the time comes, when I, too, have lost control of my bodily functions and I'm deaf and blind and so old I can't go on anymore, which is like being dead but without having taken your final breath. Simon even seems to have asthma.

We're coming up to a year of this. At first, we'd sit down to eat and I'd notice she was quiet, with those gnawing silences. I'd try to start a conversation and she'd respond, tell me what she'd got done or not got done during the day, or what she'd found out about one of the neighbours, or some news she'd heard on the radio. Then, as soon as I shifted my attention, either to chew my food properly or to cast an eye at the television, Christina would switch off again, as though her batteries had run out. One week, I was having problems with clients and I got distracted; when I took stock, I realised that she and I hadn't exchanged any words beyond the absolute essentials for at least a fortnight.

After the silence, she moved on to crying. We'd be having breakfast and I'd notice her face was puffier than normal for that time; she'd pour me a coffee, or I'd pour her one, and suddenly tears would start rolling down her face, in a perfectly straight line, as though they weren't real. At first I was shocked – What's wrong, melove, what is it? – and her – Nothing – and me – What do you mean nothing, you're crying – I've got a cold – or it'd be – It's my allergies – But you don't have allergies – and that's when she hit me with it, out of the blue – What do you know about me, what do you know about anyone? You've never been bothered about me, who are you to say whether

I have allergies or not? Somebody switched my wife, I thought, but of course I didn't say that. Don't stare at me like a retard – who was this monster? But I didn't say that either, obviously. Retard, cretin. I can't remember what gibes she took at me. Okay, calm down, melove, I need to go and see some clients in Cumbres de Curumo; if you don't feel well, let me know – Get lost, leave me alone, that was her response. I finished getting ready and left, because they really were waiting for me, and I couldn't afford losing any clients at the time, but when I left it felt like I was embedding myself in a wall, lodging myself further in between the bricks with every step. Not just any wall: one of the walls from my own house, chipped, like it had leprosy, because a coat of paint costs an arm and a leg. Taking the Fiat and pressing the accelerator made things more complicated, it meant I got held up and thought fucking hell, what's wrong with the woman now. I'd never seen her like that: narky would be putting it mildly. And I'd never seen myself look so pale in a rear view mirror. Christina was infecting me with what she had. We'd never been anything like this; not me, not her.

Maybe I'm wrong; sometimes strange things used to happen to her. For example, she'd be listening to the news about a visit from the Pope and she'd be moved to tears (even though we hadn't been to mass since we got married, and even though the visit wasn't actually to Venezuela, but to Guatemala or who knows where). For example, she'd read in the paper that that was the day the first Europeans had arrived in Japan and bam, her nose would start running. For example, Simon catches a mouse on the patio and she starts wailing because – Poor little creature, what did the big nasty dog do to you? (Which poor little creature are you talking about, woman? You're the first to scream whenever he brings a mouse into the house – and her – It didn't do anything wrong, why does he have to chew on it like that? – What are you talking about, Christina? He's a washed up German shepherd, not St Francis of Assisi.) She would say that Simon had no compassion, that neither did I – And don't start picking on me, man – on those days I couldn't say or do anything right: Christina had turned into a Martian. Except that, back then, I'd make up with her after a few hours or, in extreme cases, after a week. At the table, talking to the kids, or in bed, more or less in the dark, because she always preferred the lights off, we'd make peace. But now it's different. Before, when she had those episodes, she'd let me touch her: a moment of affection here and there, a kiss good morning or goodbye. Later, between the sheets, with one foot placed purposefully or accidentally on one of those fleshy Galician calves – Baby, I want you so much – I'd take hold of her hips and move towards her, she didn't seem to mind, in fact she'd shift over a little bit, warming my belly with her trusty behind – that arse could have raised Lazarus. Then I'd draw my own conclusions: of course she'd been acting strange the day before yesterday, or the day before that, because she was on her period, there's a hormonal explanation. A disturbance, the papers call it.

The disturbance that really sticks in my memory is from the months after the birth. The euphoria of finding out we were expecting twins had been gradually wearing off until the point when we actually became parents. Once at home, I simply recall the general exhaustion combined with the torture of having to live with my mother-in-law, Esplendidaluz Palacios de Durango, as a circle of hell that cancelled out any of the joys of being a father, a married man, or a man at all. Christina cried when her mother wasn't there, she said I wasn't helping her, I asked her how she wanted me to help, she said she needed to sleep, I said okay, okay melove, and we took it in turns, and we stuck to it, but after a week – You're not helping me – and me – How do you want me to help you now? We're taking turns: you do one night and I do the next – and she started to cry. I can't bear to see her cry like that, it drives me crazy, and to top it off I had to go to work; it wasn't easy with people constantly coming and going, deals falling through, sleepless nights, and Gonzalo with all the beer to celebrate the kids being born – You know, the office accounts are funny – What do you mean, funny, partner? – Funny funny; how much are you paying Raquel? What? Since when is that her salary? What? But when did we talk about giving her a rise? What? When was it you told me that? What? The day after the kids were born? What what what? I had no recollection of that… but you know, I gave him the benefit of the doubt, because with the insomnia, the irritation of living with Christina when she was being so bristly, the almighty pain in the arse my mother-in-law could be when she wanted to be (But you can see you're not helping round the house, can't you? If you ask me, that's why my daughter has to keep digging her heels in, isn't it, poor girl). (I knew it: it's all the old witch's fault, who knows what kind of rubbish she's putting into Christina's head). I had no recollection. I had to give him the benefit of the doubt, because I was so sleep-deprived I couldn't remember my own first name, was seriously hazy about my surname, and even mixed up my identity card number. I wasn't myself, Christina wasn't herself, my mother-in-law was all too much herself, and that was a problem; another problem on top of two children wailing at once, with their poo and their pee and their hunger and their crazy hours that would be enough to drive anyone mad. But the weeks went by, Señora Esplendidaluz went back to her beloved Maracaibo and the disturbance was over. After five or six months, Christina went back to being the woman I knew.

We're coming up to a year of this new chapter and she isn't pulling herself together. That postpartum hell was unbearable, but it lasted as long as the sleep deprivation. Whereas this, this has been clinging on like a limpit for eleven, nearly twelve months, and there's no end in sight. I want to know why it's happening. It's not like I haven't sat down and thought about it, it's not like I haven't chewed over every possible scenario while I'm walking along, or waiting for a client, or stuck in traffic. The other day, I'd just parked the car outside the Atías Clinic and I was mugged. Some kid, fifteen or sixteen years old, with a knife; he put it to my throat and said, Give me your wallet or I'll cut you. Fortunately, I'd learnt not to keep anything important in my wallet. He said, Your watch. I gave it to him. He said, Drop the briefcase. There's only work papers in there, okay. Drop it or I'll cut you. I gave it to him. Fortunately, I wasn't carrying anything essential, photocopies and such like. I dropped it and he didn't cut me. He darted off. As I watched him disappear from view, I was thinking: Why do you cry all day, Christina? Why are you like this, if we're alright? All things considered, we're alright, you and me. It's all going to shit, this city, this country, that little fucker with my briefcase (luckily it was the old green one with the scuffed corners, not the fancy black one the kids gave me for my birthday), all down the drain, but we're alright, Christina, so why are you shutting yourself in the dark with the covers pulled up to your ears if the two of us are alright, melove?

'For fuck's sake!' I remember screaming like a madman, there, in the middle of the street. And I assume the lady from the news stand correctly attributed it to rage, rather than the fact that I actually was a lunatic (she looked worried, but not overly concerned: I'm sure she'd witnessed the knife-wielding child's antics before, probably two or three times a day. It's impossible, she told me, there's nothing you can do about it, because the little punk's uncle is a policeman. Enough said: I was just another loser who'd wandered into his territory). I straightened myself out as best I could, put a hand down my trousers to make completely sure I still had my cash and cards safely stored in the little bags I kept on my belt – I'm no idiot – and kept on walking, thinking about Christina, of course. I'd gone over possible causes: the kids had left home, and maybe that had depressed her; but Ernesto had a good job in Porlamar, whereas here in Caracas, with everything that's going on, despite his IT degree and his terrific marks, who knows when he would have found a job. And Enrique couldn't have been any luckier; when they kicked him out of PDVSA his godfather had given him another helping hand in the United States, and there he put himself up for a job and he got it; how could he not get it, Enrique's a whizz at that stuff, and gas pipeline engineers aren't ten a penny. Perhaps it was because the boys had left, but I think to myself, No, that can't be it, Christina's happy they've both got jobs, considering the way things are going here – she must be upset because the house is falling apart, and Los Rosales is a cesspit, when you think about how pretty it was when we bought the house, it's like there's been a war; or perhaps it's because, after all these years, she's having terrible regrets about giving up her job at the ministry. One day, around a year and half ago, we were talking about that, it was one of the last real conversations we had, I think; I said, Imagine, sweetheart, what it would be like if you were in the ministry now, working for some Chavista who insisted on you joining the party, that place must be hell, the whole centre of Caracas must be unbearable, imagine working in the Torres del Silencio the way things are going. It would be really depressing, I think she said, and now I remember, or I think I remember, and it makes me feel bad; I'm afraid she's having regrets, these things are irrational, and she remembers the resignation process, it's not like she can blame me, it was nothing to do with me, actually if anything I told her we had options, if she wanted to carry on, she should carry on, if she wanted to quit, she should quit, we weren't rich but we could get by quite respectably; it was her mad cow of a mother who put the idea in her head of staying at home with the children, when she had a degree in architecture no less. Now, Christina my girl, if you ask me, my grandchildren need looking after properly. Without a firm hand these little creatures will end up getting corrupted, won't they? (What was she insinuating with that firm hand? I know she never forgave me for convincing her daughter to stay in Caracas after she graduated, but those Maracaibo folk wind themselves up, they're like hard-talking spinning tops, and Señora Esplendidaluz was insistent). Then the rest is history. Christina didn't get on with her colleague who was a member of Acción Democrática and who hassled her because Christina didn't take sides, she didn't believe in Acción Democrática or Copei or political parties in general or even St Jude the Apostle, and look where that got us. That's right. It must be because every once in a while they'd send her inland to gather data and do site visits, and sometimes she had to make those trips with colleagues she found utterly tedious.

That's what she used to say. One day, I have to confess, I called the office to check a contact number with them, because she still hadn't called me like we'd agreed, and this was back in the days before everyone had mobile phones, I called the office and the secretary, the one Christina said she couldn't stand, told me that the architect was with Mr Rondón, the engineer, in Ciudad Bolívar – What do you mean she's with Mr Rondón? (I thought she'd told me she was going with Dr Escolana, Mireya, Christina called her when they were on good terms) – With Mr Rondón the engineer, yes sir, and the number is such and such – Is it a hotel? – I don't know, sir, that's the number the engineer left us. I was flabbergasted, lost for words, thoughts, feelings or any inclination to speak. I didn't call, obviously, I waited until she deigned to call me. When she did, the first thing she said was, Sorry I didn't call earlier, but I couldn't get a hotel, and the office assured us they'd made a reservation – Assured who? You and Dr Escolano?, I asked, making out like I didn't know – and her – No, actually, at the last minute they told us there'd been a change and they were sending Rondón, imagine (Christina whispered that, there must have been people nearby), fortunately Rondón's mum still lives here and they offered me somewhere to stay, so I'm staying with them. I don't really remember what I said, or how I said it. I felt like all my organs were being dislodged. But I didn't have any reason not to believe Christina. She never gave me cause. Besides, the next day, I called that number and, sure enough, it was answered by a lady with a croaky voice; she must have been old. Why wouldn't I believe her? I hung up without saying anything. The one with the real problem was that tramp of a secretary, Yadira, Yarelis, You-know-who, the one with the secretary's name, who according to Christina did nothing but stir up trouble between her and the bosses, and now she wanted to do the same with me, the bitch. I told Christina when she got back and at first she went pale, then she said she'd rip out the miserable wretch's eyelashes, gouge her eyes out with a compass. Calm down, I said, don't get riled up; but do be careful with that one, she's obviously a nasty piece of work – and Christina – Me and Rondón... Rondón! The man's intolerable, just imagine! I didn't want to imagine. There was something strange and affected in the voice she used to express her disgust for said engineer, but at the same time, I had no reason to think any more about the incident. There were other trips inland, three or four, but it would seem Rondón wasn't there, she was with other architects, doctors, or engineers from the Infrastructure Department, all women, and Christina gave me their numbers or called me straight away, with chronological precision, motorway traffic jams and flight schedules permitting. She left work because her mother suggested it, and because she got tired of all the fuss with the Acción Democrática and Copei supporters and the secretaries swanning around like something out of a soap opera because that was all they watched. She also got tired of Mr Rondón, the engineer (I never heard her talk so badly about anyone, every time she mentioned him she was describing the lowest possible echelons of humanity at the ministry), Mr Rondón and the other scum like him whom she'd had to rub shoulders with in public administration. At that time, work was going well for me, so Christina could look after the children full time, if she wanted; stay at home, if she wanted; keep the dust, dirt and grime at bay, if she wanted. Los Rosales was still a nice area then, although a lot of people we knew had started moving to places like Caurimare or El Cafetal or San Luis. A few of our neighbours did it and we wondered whether we should too, but the house is big, and it was in good condition, not like now; who would have guessed that the streets would get so dangerous (knives were the least of our worries), that there would be looting, or that the grocer's brains would end up splattered across the pavement right in front of Christina and another woman out doing their shopping. For a while we put the house on the market to see what would happen, and nothing happened, so we put any ideas we had on the back burner and stayed where we were. That was decades ago now. My mother-in-law died: that could be another reason Christina is crying now, she sobs it all out, even the name (I keep quiet, bow my head, lower my eyes, trying not to let Simon's howling distract me, and I listen).

I look up and see the poor animal, shitting next to the potted ferns, if my wife sees him she'll cry even more, without trying to hide it, like she still does when she knows I'm around. That is, if she decides to come out of her room; but tonight she's shut away in there and there's no way she's coming out. Sometimes I make food and take it to her, and I ask if she wants an aspirin, but as I know I'm running the risk of having her yell at me again, I need to give it some thought. Poor Simon is breaking my heart, his tail and hind legs tremble as he scours everywhere, by the bushes, a liquid like sugarloaf-sweetened lemonade, but thick and putrid. I don't find it disgusting now, how could I, when this old dog has been our lifelong companion: the kids used to play with him and he barked at all the scroungers who tried to get into the house, and once I think one of them came off quite badly, because we found blood on the patio and it wasn't the dog's and it wasn't the kids' and it wasn't ours. Well done, Simon, attaboy; we gave him some great meals. Now he eats an enormous plateful of leftovers or things that are about to go off, because there's no family around anymore, but we're still in the habit of buying enough to feed four rather than two. Lately it's been mostly flour-based stuff, which is one of the few things you can get at the grocery. I'm going to clean up the mess Simon's made, because if Christina sees it things are only going to get worse.

I once asked why she didn't go and see a doctor or a psychologist or something (thank god I didn't say psychiatrist) and she almost scratched my eyes out the way she'd joked she would with the secretary. She never touched me, but the will was there: you could see it in her face, her teeth bared like an animal – Get out and leave me alone. Do you think you're helping me, telling me I'm crazy? I'm like this because I live with you and you're so boring, look at our life, just look at it, we could be somewhere else, we could – but she didn't finish what she was saying, she was hammering at the door, and I'd already moved out of the way because I couldn't stand these tantrums. I didn't rest for several nights after that, but a couple of months later I'm not losing so much sleep over it. Hormones explain everything, I read encyclopaedias and started to work out what was wrong: the menopause, a late menopause; all her life Christina had been a nervous bundle of hormones, and, inwardly making the sign of the cross, I broached the subject again one lunchtime when she seemed calmer – I meant to say gynaecologist, melove, not psychologist, because I think this could be the menopause couldn't it? They say it can sometimes be quite bad. She yelled at me – 'Faggot!'

And I never did it again. I stood up, I even raised my hand and was on the point of bringing it back down across her face, that'll teach you to insult me. I didn't, it didn't reach that point and my hand didn't reach her face, but she went back into the bedroom. For me, the faggot thing was like fangs piercing my jugular (I also had an image of laying into Rondón with my bare fists, I don't know why) but gradually I calmed down, thinking about what she must have meant by the fact that we still lived there when it was her (I remember clearly) who chose to move to Los Rosales and it was her (I also remember clearly) who was first to throw in the towel when we considered moving to San Luis, El Cafetal, Caurimare or any of those places. It was her. One morning, before I went to see a client, I told her – When I come back I'm going to renew the advert in the paper, do you want me to put it in for a week or a fortnight? – and her, clearly – No, leave it, man, it's a waste of time and money. After all, we're okay here, aren't we? – and me – Yes, we're okay. We both said we're okay, and we both thought so, I realise, because at that point we did still think and say the same things, we were together. Not now. Now I don't know what's up with her. And she doesn't know what's up with me. And I don't know what's up with me either, what gets into my head and buzzes like the flies that follow in Simon's tracks. I just know that someone needs to clean up this foul-smelling shit. He starts shaking again, trembling. All over the flowers, the crown of thorns plant. That's just too much. And he's crying; I think those howls are the sound of a dog who doesn't even have the strength to cry. Somebody should help him end it.

Christina is whining in her room; I can hear her. Anyone would lose hope in this country, with their mother dead, and – We could have moved in to my mother's house, she told me one day at breakfast as I was fastening my tie, about to set off to see an actor who wanted me to sort out his papers because Radio Caracas, now on cable, wanted to take him on. Your mother's house, Christina? You told me it was practically a shack, I thought what you really wanted was for her to come to us, because what was she going to do all alone in Maracaibo after we buried your brother? – You just don't get me, man, it's obvious; there's no talking to you. And she went off to the bedroom to cry. I stood there with my hand on the knot, tempted to take off the tie and cancel the meeting, but I told myself – No, I have to carry on, I can't put myself at the mercy of these crazy outbursts, she'll get over this. That house was a lot worse than this one, and I couldn't see myself living in Maracaibo, 'The Beloved Land of the Sun', you need a serious tan to move into that open-air oven. My God, when I left Valencia I was sick of the heat and the lack of opportunities, I wasn't about to go to Maracaibo, who would think of such a thing? The Menopause, I told myself. I imagined The Menopause to be a one-eyed witch with a wig made of vipers, boas, scorpions, anything that bites and stings. But I wouldn't utter that word again, because my own wife would brand me a faggot, that name she'd hit me with like someone christening a ship with a magnum of champagne; it hurt as much as if I'd been hit smack on the head with a bottle. I can still feel it now, with Christina still crying and poor Simon spilling his guts everywhere, and that stench, God that stench. I bend down to wipe it up with a cloth and start to retch so badly I have to go over to what's left of the orchids I once gave Christina to look after and spill my own guts, throwing up more than I can possibly have eaten, it's disgusting; Christina cries and cries, while I'm dying from one, two, three retches; there was a time when we were so happy, but I can't even remember when that time was, it must have been before we got the news that my brother-in-law had been killed in a car crash, just as he got back to Zulia from visiting us in Caracas; it must have been after the funeral that everything fell apart because Christina sank into a monumental depression; it must be since then that she's been like this – But no – I tell myself, careful not to speak it out loud in case someone, especially her, should think I've lost my marbles – But no, Christina pulled herself together after that, it only lasted a couple of months, the kind of thing you resign yourself to.

A good hosing is getting rid of it all – the dog's, mine. That 'faggot' can't be erased because I've never insulted her. I think she never did it with the engineers at the ministry, and now she's getting her own back on me. Maybe with Ernesto here things would be different, maybe I should call him so he can help me work out what to do with his mother, because, frankly, I'm starting to get desperate, I say starting, I am desperate: she's crying and I don't even know if she is crying, I just think she's shut herself in that room and doesn't want to come out, and I keep thinking what more can I do. Ernesto comes sometimes, in the holidays, but it's still a while until Easter week. As for Enrique, I wouldn't dream of telling him any of this, because he's abroad and the shock of it would be too much. Besides, there's always been something like this going on in this house and I've never had to turn to the boys for help, why should I start now? I'm not that selfish, it wouldn't do anything but worry them and they're working hard to earn a living, make their own lives, I don't need to go dragging them into this marital silliness. It must be because of the country, it must be because Señora Esplendidaluz died too, from what we later learned was an intestinal infection or a series of infections; while I agreed that Christina should offer to bring her here, to Caracas, the old woman was as stubborn as a mule and didn't want to leave; she kept her symptoms quiet enough to stop her daughter from insisting on the move; and now Christina has nobody but me, look how much she misses something like the pseudo-shack in Maracaibo, it's crazy but that's what this is about isn't it? Christina is crazy is what it is.

No sooner have I turned off the tap on the hose and thought that's it for the day, than I realise Simon is shitting again, in the middle of the patio. The creature needs help, he needs somebody to take him from this world once and for all no matter how difficult or painful or simply how very very very hard you find it to gather up the courage to kill a dog. We got married very young I had good career prospects and the firm was going pretty well, it looked good, so who would sell it for a pizzeria, but it was better that way because nobody in their right mind would want a scoundrel like Gonzalo for a partner I wasn't in my right mind the shameless crook did everything he could to fatten the fortnightly pay packet we gave Raquel who turned out to be his lover I was so stupid not to work out from the beginning that Raquel was a pure whore and you could tell, she made a pass at me once asking me to do up her zip because she couldn't reach over her shoulder and she was in her bra and the truth is it made me want to touch her she had really nice shoulders, but I was in love with my wife, I almost always was, except when it was her time of the month and it made me want to kill her – you're corny, you're a faggot – she'd snap, and people are capable of doing things like that when they haven't slept and there are kids screaming and her – don't you touch me – imagine, a healthy, virile man, a faggot, where did she get that from? Six months of nothing at all because your wife is pissed off and what's a man to do? I once thought about going to prostitutes, but I haven't got the balls (maybe Christina's right) I haven't got the balls and they disgust me as much as this turd the dog has left here somebody needs to finish him off the poor thing a mass of fruit flies and mosquitoes because it's painful like the hole drilled into my skull by the sound of my wife crying in a dark room that no one can get her to leave.

I haven't even touched her in over six months, since I tried to console her and she went wild, she howled at me, the office shut down, damn it, and it was the best thing all round firing that vixen Raquel and as for you Gonzalo I don't want anything more to do with you we're splitting up getting a lawyers' divorce let's see how you get by now and for all I know he failed whereas I with no secretaries with no office working from home only occasionally assisted by the messenger I kept all my clients and I think I could even give up work at this point because I've got a bit saved up (abroad, of course) but I can't risk twiddling my thumbs because that's how you really do end up getting old

getting rid of my partner's secretary at the pizzeria bloody flies because she was genuinely crazy bloody flies and struggling along with individual cases actors singers my own Talent Centre not some shack in Maracaibo where did she dream that one up she's crazy bloody flies when I say the name of the engineer Rondón-Rondón I feel something like hatred but it's just that hatred husbands sometimes feel when they don't understand their wives it's a normal part of life like children growing up moving out writing every once in a while calling sending postcards

diarrhoea like that can only be cleaned up with bleach lye whatever you find first; dog shit; I remember there was a bottle of bleach in the kitchen cupboard but I can't see it, it's probably in the cupboard by the patio where I put the tools Christina cries buzzing flies Criestina's cries

the tiny key shakes in my hand like the dog's protruding stomach innards that linger for hours no days when they come out and take over the patio until I manage to open the lock and the first thing I see amongst bottles that do not contain bleach and old rags screws hammers and awls is a box I don't recognise at first and only at first because then I realise I do know what the mysterious red and blue object in the cupboard is, then I see another parcel, a plastic bag, and I think to myself – There's the pistol, out of sight for all these years. I pick up the bundle of paper and plastic, playing the guessing game, solving the puzzle as I shoo away flies, peeling it open like a ripe fruit, rather than the nut caught in my throat, and I study the barrel, the grip, the trigger. It's still new, I say, even out loud I think. Shiny, like the ones you see in films.

My brother-in-law sold it to me in case there was looting.

HALFWAY THERE

MIGUEL HIDALGO PRINCE
Translated by Montague Kobbé

After we lost our jobs we became TV junkies. We had time to spare and rather than leave the house and spend money, we stayed glued to the box as if we couldn't conceive of life without it.

One day the phone rang. We were watching one of those black-and-white westerns where cowboys fight Cherokees. I was cheering for the natives because some members of my family are Guajiro Indians.

'You answer it,' I told Mariana. I was absorbed in the scene.

She raised an eyebrow and looked at me as if she were staring at a polynomial equation. For some time now, we hadn't really seen eye to eye. Any little thing could turn into a time bomb. When Mariana's wires were crossed like that, it was best to tread carefully. I kept my eyes fixed on the screen and acted naturally. She got up without saying a word. She had the rare talent of externalising all our miseries with those little gestures. Come to think of it, I put her through the same thing when I was in that mood. I heard her pick up the phone and say hello. Then some sort of silence.

When she came back she said it was her dad. Her mum had just passed away. Fatal cardiac arrest. She was sixty-three years old.

She began to cry. I held her in my arms, but at the same time I kept watching the cowboys shooting at the Indians. The chief with the feather in his headband was hit and collapsed on his galloping horse. The Indians lost the battle. And the war too.

We bought the tickets the following day. Mariana was from Curarigua – a godforsaken town somewhere in Lara, so she said. First we'd need to go to Barquisimeto and then we'd have to board another bus that would leave us near Carora. Then we'd have to walk or wait, depending on the hour – because there was often no service at all in that direction. There was dust and there were goats. That's how she described it to me the first time I met her. It was at the fifteenth birthday party of a colleague's daughter. Back then she was a nurse at the Clínico Universitario. I worked as a night watchman in a cold store. My shift started at half past ten in the evening and finished at six in the morning. I used to like that job because I could spend the whole night reading. I made myself as comfortable as I could, picked up a book and entered that solitary world known only to those who guard warehouses until the first light of day the following morning. Mariana also worked the nights. At some point we were bound to share lives led during unsociable hours.

Until they sacked us.

In my case it was the union's fault. They refused to honour the collective agreement and we called a strike. We went for months without pay but in the end the corporation opted to wind everything down and leave us unemployed rather than pay up.

In Mariana's case it was due to a nervous breakdown. One night, a full moon, the police brought a reprobate they'd left looking like a sieve and left him agonising on a stretcher. She was preparing to admit him into A&E when he suddenly grabbed her wrist firmly and began to convulse. He was suffering cardiac arrest, which is normal enough in that kind of situation, but what really affected Mariana was that one of his eyes popped out, slopped down his face and was left hanging from a thin thread, like a zombie. Then he started vomiting blood clots until he choked to death. Mariana was a delicate creature and from that point onwards everything came tumbling down. She couldn't even hit a vein for an IV because she would start shaking in complete panic. Once it became obvious that she was no longer of use at the unit, she was sent a letter of recommendation for other jobs. Reading between the lines was simple.

We left La Bandera coach station very early in the morning. Mariana hadn't slept well. Her face was swollen from crying. Some people stared at us. Maybe they thought I had hit her or at the very least that I was the beast who had caused her suffering. I hadn't got that much rest myself. I'd kept my eyes shut, listening to Mariana's sobbing in the dark. Once in a while I let my hand rest on her back and moved it up and down softly. She seemed not to realise I was beside her. At some point I stopped hearing her, but I knew she was still there, crying in silence.

Inside the coach, it was freezing. Apart from Mariana and me, there was an old toothless man tucked under a towel printed with a Mexican sunset and the word Cancún. I tried to read a detective story but music was blasting through the speakers and I couldn't concentrate. Mariana had taken a 6mg dose of Lexotanil and was practically in a coma. I was going to kiss her on the lips but I decided to kiss her on the forehead instead. I hid my arms under my shirt and sat perfectly still, looking at the screen without paying any attention, trying to clear my head of all the nonsense. I shut my eyes and willed myself to sleep, but to no avail.

Hours later we hit something. First a screeching of the breaks and then a dry, almost muffled, thump. The toothless old man opened the curtain and a shaft of light seeped in, blinding me. I frowned and pulled an arm out to cover my face. Mariana had barely woken up. She asked what had happened. Precisely at that point the door to the driver's compartment opened, he came in and explained that a cow had cut across us. Mariana grumbled under her breath. I asked how long it would take. The driver made a gesture that could be interpreted as 'a while' or 'quite a while' or anything else, really. The toothless old man stepped down from the bus. Mariana was starting to fall asleep again when I decided to climb down and stretch my legs.

Outside, the glare of the sun felt like I was looking through the keyhole of the door to hell. I walked to the front of the bus and saw the cow. She lay on her side and mooed in agony. One horn had been ripped off from the root and could be seen a few yards away, in the middle of the road. A purple and slimy tongue hung from her mouth, shaking like jelly. The toothless old man stood by my side.

'Poor thing, huh?' he said.

I turned to face him. I turned back towards the cow.

'Although if you think about it, it was always going to end like this, wasn't it? This is what awaits us all,' the old man added.

The driver was talking on his mobile phone. The fare collector was crouching, checking the bumper. I approached him and asked when we could expect to get back on our way.

'We have to wait until they come get the victim.'

'The victim?' I asked.

The fare collector rose to his feet. He spat on the ground and spread the phlegm with the sole of his shoe. He pulled a handkerchief from his back pocket, dried the sweat on his neck.

'The beef, mate. Can't you see?' he said.

The cow let out a low and faint sound, like an oboe, shook briefly and then remained completely still. The toothless old man said we should end her suffering. The fare collector looked at the cow. He gave her a little kick on the nose. The cow writhed and mooed again. The fare collector shook his head, like a very tired man.

'Do what you can,' he thought out loud.

I cupped my hand over my eyebrows and looked down the dual carriageway. On one side a ploughed field and a girl on a bicycle herding goats.

On the other was a town. While I looked at it the fare collector explained that people would soon come to dismember the cow and take away the meat. It wasn't the first time they had gone through this.

'Is the driver talking to head office?' I asked.

'What head office? He's talking to his wife,' the fare collector answered.

I went back to the coach. Mariana was still fast asleep. I shook her by the shoulder to wake her. She half-opened her eyes and murmured something. I told her that the cow was still more or less alive, that we would need to wait some time yet, and that I would walk to the town to buy something to eat.

'Good idea,' she said, and leaned her head against the window.

I reached the town and walked up the high street. Little more than a few houses and grocery stores that looked as if they'd been shut since the Stone Age. I reached the town's central square, trying to find someone who might tell me where to buy some juice and provisions. I saw Bolívar's bust and read the name of the town on a plaque. San Carlos de Palmira, founded in 1889 by Bartolomé del Suplicio, a Franciscan monk born in Guadalajara, Spain. I looked beyond the bust and spotted a church's belfry. I walked towards the front door. It was locked. I knocked twice and waited for thirty seconds. I knocked one more time and waited another thirty seconds. I pressed my ear against the door and couldn't hear a thing. I retraced my steps across the square and turned left into a cul-de-sac I hadn't seen previously. I walked almost to the end of the street before finding an open window. There was a small radio on the frame, blaring out. I tried to make out something inside but it was too dark.

'Hello,' I said in the direction of the house.

I looked around. Nothing was open. The radio only gave out white noise and a voice that delivered a sermon of sorts, though I couldn't understand a thing.

'Hello,' I shouted.

I heard the unmistakable sound of plastic flip-flops scraping the cement floor and from the shadows – slowly, very slowly – a woman emerged. You could tell that time had played some dirty trick on her for she appeared to be a lot older than she really was. She wore a long, shabby T-shirt with the AD logo of Acción Democrática, a leading political party from a different era. I pictured her as a young woman. Her eyes looked like a tiger's and her nose was dotted with round ant-coloured freckles. She looked at me as if she knew me.

'Hello,' I said again.

'Yes?' she answered, and turned down the radio.

I looked towards the end of the street. I swallowed but my mouth was dry.

'Sorry,' I said, 'I was just wondering whether I could buy something to eat around here.'

The woman scrutinised me. Her patience was of the genetic kind. She scratched an armpit, and the movement made one of her breasts – the one next to the A – bounce a little under the T-shirt.

'Nothing's open today,' she said.

I gave her a helpless look.

'Nothing?'

She shook her head and came closer to the window. I could make her out better now. She was starting to go grey and she had a thin little moustache, like fuzz. She held the bars on the window with both hands. A black line of muck was lodged under her nails.

'I could fix you something, if you'd like.'

'You don't have to,' I answered.

'There's nothing open here today. I won't charge you much.'

I checked the time on my phone.

'It's getting late,' I explained. 'The coach I was travelling in hit a cow and pulled over by the side of the road.'

'Are you from the capital?'

I nodded yes.

'My dad was from Urica, where Boves died,' I added.

'Where are you going?' she asked, in a way that made me feel comfortable.

'To Curarigua. My mother-in-law passed away.'

'Hmm,' the woman said, 'is your wife in the coach?'

'U-huh,' I answered, pointing towards the dual carriageway.

'Hang on, I'll give you two *bollitos*,' she said, and went back into the house.

I checked the time on my phone again. It was mid-morning. I heard a dog bark (or howl) inside. The lady hurried back, her flip-flops squeaking. She held a bundle wrapped in aluminium foil and guava juice in a plastic container with a lid on from a Chinese takeaway.

'Here,' she said, 'the leftovers from breakfast.'

I didn't know what to do. Evidently, turning down her gift wasn't an option. I took the bundle and the Chinese takeaway container.

'Are you going to the processions?' the lady asked.

My face told her I didn't know what she was talking about.

'The ones they have in Curarigua. My husband was born there, you see. Today is the procession for the dead.'

'I've never been. This'll be my first time,' I said.

'Since you said your mother-in-law had died, I thought you...'

She didn't finish the sentence, just flicked a lock of hair from her forehead, dried the sweat on her face with the collar of her T-shirt. Her democratic breasts bounced again.

'I don't know anything about these processions,' I remarked.

The lady turned up the radio once again. She tried to tune into something different on the dial. There was only static.

'Well, they're today,' she said. 'My husband told me that every year on this day the locals walk in procession from the church to the cemetery. At the end of the line you find the elderly, because they have more faith than the young. The dead are right behind them and they whisper things to them, but they can't turn round because if they were to be reunited with a loved one the distress could kill them.'

The lady crossed herself. She had gone round the dial only to end up with the same incomprehensible sermon. I'd stood there, trying to picture the scene she'd described. I think I smiled and told her I didn't believe in ghosts. She looked at me as if we were tempting fate.

'They must have cut up that cow by now, you know.'

That was the signal I was waiting for. I held the food and the juice in one hand, fished around with the other one, pulled out a twenty-bolivar note and handed it to the lady. She rolled it and hid it somewhere under her T-shirt.

'May God Almighty lead your way,' she said.

I thanked her and made my way down the high street. I saw part of the dual carriageway ahead. From the distance I made out the Pájaros de Lara logo on the side of the coach and some people riding their bicycles, carrying pieces of meat on their backs.

It made no sense. The coach was in motion. At first I thought it was some sort of optical illusion but soon I realised what was going on. It was pulling away. Mariana, the driver, the fare collector, the toothless old man, they all knew I was coming. Was it too much to ask for them to wait for me? I looked frantically for my mobile phone. I called Mariana. It went straight to answerphone. Something wasn't right: she never switched her phone off. I started running. I reached the road and was on my last legs as I went past the people who had cut up the cow. They all watched me follow the trail of smoke and dust left by the coach.

I really tried. I can say in all honesty that I really tried. I was very close. So close that I could have reached out to her and kept her from leaving without me. The driver accelerated and that was that. As they drove away I went from running to walking until I finally stopped. My legs hurt and my lungs were crying for oxygen. I inhaled the warm air. I coughed. My face, neck and chest were covered in sweat. My hands too, but all this time I'd held on to the juice and the *bollitos*.

I turned back, headed to the juncture where Mariana and I had gone our separate ways: the exact point where the end of everything began. Motionless by the roadside, standing or sitting on their bicycles, people looked at me the way you look at the wind blowing. They resembled a photograph. I forced myself to seem calm. I tried to control my breathing. I stuck out my chin, tried to greet them as if I were some sort of fugitive, and went to where the cow had lain. All I found was a large puddle of blood, a swarm of flies circling above it. I stood there as if any minute another coach might pull over and I could continue my journey on my own. I called Mariana one more time. I heard her voice on the answering machine, then the beep. I understood there was nothing left to say. My words would be no better than silence. I hung up. I recalled the tale the lady had told me from the other side of that window. Life has a strange and twisted sense of humour. A fly tried to land on the corner of my eye. I blew it away with a single puff. I squinted and looked at both ends of the carriageway. In one direction the ground we had already covered disappeared into the distance. In the other, the coach sank slowly beneath the dividing line between heaven and earth. I was thirsty. I removed the lid of the Chinese takeaway container and drank the guava juice in a single gulp. It was so sweet.

DEATH
&
TRANSFIGURATION

LITERARY SOLUTIONS TO THE DEATH OF MY MOTHER-IN-LAW

SLAVKO ZUPCIC
Translated by Katie Brown

THE PAIN OF LOSING HER

My mother-in-law was – undoubtedly – a simple woman. She only raised her voice once in my presence. She asked us to let her sleep. Although she cooked very little, her pasta *stufata* and her potato *gateau* were world class. She watched detective series, read Agatha Christie novels and was always prepared for a celebration. Weddings, birthdays, baptisms, saints' days and deaths: there she was, or a present from her, or at least a phone call. In monosyllables, she taught me to speak Italian and every time we met each other we would renew our tacit alliance. I don't quite know why, but from the first day we got along. It was a matter of coincidences, or perhaps she just wanted to get rid of Eleonora. We were even able to live together. While I was writing my thesis, she'd open the office door mid-morning with a cup of tea. She liked me to work, to keep working. She'd never have given me a chamomile. She might then play dumb and leave me to do the dishes, but we had a good time. After lunch, I'd sit with her. She'd watch *La Signora in Giallo* and I'd read the paper or a book. We kept each other company while we waited for Eleonora. She was so modest. She was born in Buenos Aires, lived from the age of four in Salerno and died in Valencia. Even so, she was a *salernitana* through and through. My mother-in-law, so special. She recognised me in the days when she didn't recognise anyone, and smiled when I sang the songs I've never really known. Just before she died I could hear her breathing, but my little girl wanted to be fed, and when I returned, simple as always, she had gone.

THE REALITY OF HAVING NOTHING

It was then – first embracing, then each on our own – glued to the telephone, communicating the news to friends, it was then that Eleonora and I realised that, financially speaking, we weren't in the best place. My mother-in-law had squeezed us dry during her long and agonising illness. She had eaten up all my savings and all of her daughter's. She had even eaten up the few assets she had, and faced with her dead body, Eleonora and I knew, without having to say anything, that we had very little left. Just the pain of losing her, the reality of having nothing, the corpse, a Longines watch from the seventies, the silverware, a bison coat, and the need to carry on.

THE CORPSE 1

For that reason we had to resort to the cheapest undertaker's. The representatives were very kind and, I have to say, the service offered at all times seemed no different to me from that offered by other undertakers. With this type of thing, as with everything, there are always categories, but as we prepared to cremate her not a single detail was amiss. A friend had told me to be careful, that the most vulnerable always get screwed over and in a cheap undertaker's it was much more likely that they'd try to take me for a ride.

I paid constant attention and what I saw rather surprised me, the neatness and care with which the staff did everything. When the body had to be removed from the house, they used disposable gloves and masks. When we needed to choose a coffin, they let us choose one that was out of our initial budget. The room they assigned us was quite comfortable: it had four sofas, adjustable air-con, a book of condolences with a CD of Gregorian music inside the cover, a coffee maker and a water cooler. It seemed nice, welcoming even. The flowers were natural and there was no objective reason to think they were recycled. As Eleonora couldn't stop crying, they gave us a book about mourning written by the woman who owned the place. The writing was impeccable, at least to my eyes, and the most frequently used words were gravity and ethics. They accepted that I could only pay 40 per cent upfront and the rest three days later.

There were times when I felt more supported by them than by the friends who came to accompany us.

Towards the end, the owner came up to me, the one who'd written the book, and asked if we wanted a prayer for the dead or a mass. I said mass because my mother-in-law was always very devout, and if in life she went to mass every afternoon, it only seemed fitting that in death she had a complete mass.

The woman accepted.

'If you want a mass, it will be a mass.'

I don't know why but at that moment I remembered that the night before one of the staff had told me that priests always caused a fuss about coming to the undertaker's because they preferred the ceremony to take place in a parish church, but they had now solved that problem.

I forgot about the matter immediately, as Eleonora called me to give her something to calm her down and a while later (the moment of the cremation was approaching and we were all starting to feel worse) I saw the men from the undertaker's heading towards the main hall.

'It's starting,' Eleonora said.

'Don't worry,' I tried to calm her and left the room, hoping to find the staff and remind them that we would need an international death certificate later. They were, as I'd guessed, in the main hall. Together with an obese and wheezy man, they were changing the position of the furniture so that it faced the crucifix instead of the window of the crematory. The scruffiness of the sweaty obese man with a haematoma on his face jarred with the chapel and even with the undertaker's staff who were wearing suits as always.

I stayed watching them from the door and they – engrossed in their work – didn't see me or didn't care that I was watching. One of the staff asked the fat man something and he responded rudely, 'What do you want me to say? I'm an employee here, same as you.'

Could he be the priest? That's what I wondered as I discreetly backed away, and although I told myself it was impossible, when they made us go through to the main hall I had to take it back: there he was, still sweaty, fat, huge, wearing a cassock and behind a small altar.

Don't think the worst, for fuck's sake, I told myself, knowing that that's what I always do. Don't think the worst. Only in that way could I concentrate on my pain and, even though I hadn't gone to mass in many years, remember the ceremony and respond to the prayers (I was the only one who did).

The obese man stared at me and finally we (him, me and the owner, who was acting as altar boy) could concentrate on giving my mother-in-law a decent mass.

Two days later, the woman from the undertaker's came to collect the rest of the payment and I couldn't help asking after him.

'He died, you know? Just yesterday, of a heart attack. It seems he had a blood disorder.'

'I'm very sorry.' The news didn't surprise me: I'd glimpsed something of that death in his shortness of breath, his haematoma and his obesity. 'But, was he a priest?'

The woman gave me a strange look and found somewhere to sit. 'Well no, not really. He was once in the seminary and now we're in dire need of another like him,' she said, not looking at me, before making her real offer. 'Do you want the job?'

LONGINES WATCH

Selling fine Longines watch bought in Italy in the seventies. For women. Authentic. Gold casing, leather strap, wind-up. Works perfectly. Only 250 euros. *We are writing to you because Javier has seen your advert and wants to get in contact with you. Javier's message: 'Hi, could I see more pictures of the watch? Is it solid gold or plated? Weight and diameter? Thanks and regards.'* Good afternoon, Javier. The total weight of the watch is 15 grams (strap included) and the diameter of the face is 22mm. I'll send you some photos in a separate email. If you're interested write to me or ring me. Regards.

Selling fine Longines watch bought in Italy in the seventies. For women. Authentic. Gold casing, leather strap, manual wind-up. Works perfectly. Only 220 euros. *We are writing to you because Roberto has seen your advert and wants to get in contact with you. Roberto's message: 'I'll give you 150.'* Roberto, good afternoon. I'm writing about the Longines watch. If you're interested I can sell it to you for 200 euros.

Selling fine Longines watch bought in Italy in the seventies. For women. Authentic. Gold casing, leather strap, wind-up. Works perfectly. Only 200 euros. *Message from Javier but from a different email address: 'What model is it exactly? Is it 18-carat solid gold?'* Yes, Javier, it is 18-carat solid gold. Forgive the late reply, I've only just seen your message. *We are writing to you because Rafael has seen your advert and wants to get in contact with you. Rafael's message: 'This watch, is it manual or automatic?'* Good morning, Rafael. The watch is manual, wind-up. *'Good afternoon. What condition is the watch in? I mean, scratches, dents, things like that. Thanks.'* Rafael, the watch is in good condition, as you can see in the photographs. I think that the price is attractive but if you're interested, as we're now in clearance sales, I'll give it to you for 20 euros less than advertised. *'Good morning. Yes, I would be interested. I'm in Alicante, where are you?'* Rafael, I live in Castellón. Do you want to buy in person, in Valencia or Castellón, or would you prefer me to post it to you and you pay the same way? *'Hi, the only problem is I'd like to see it before I buy and I can't think how.'* Rafael, as far as I know, it's possible to send it through Correos or MRW and ask for the recipient to open the parcel to check the contents. *'Hi, Correos doesn't allow it, definitely. MRW, I don't know. You wouldn't have any reason to come down to Alicante, would you? It's a lovely city.'* I would like to go, but work won't let me in the next few weeks. I know that SEUR lets you check the contents before paying, but they're a bit more expensive. *'Valencia is a beautiful city, I go there every year, I love strolling through the old town. It's a city with character, obviously. Castellón, the city, I don't know, but last year I spent a few days in Morella. I like the mountains a lot. As for the watch, let's do this: you keep it listed and if it sells, go ahead. But we can wait, for example, for you to come to Alicante one day or for me to go to Valencia. If I manage to get a few days together, perhaps in February I'll come to Valencia. Does that sound good? Now, you'd have to give it to me for 150 euros, please. My number is 699169435. If you agree, give me yours so we can stay in touch. Thanks.'* That seems like a great idea, Rafael. The watch will stay listed until it sells. Were it to go to you, it would be for 150 euros. Let's hope Alicante or Valencia turn out to be possible, for me or for you. Let's keep in touch. My number is 626514362. Thanks for the pleasant exchange.

SILVERWARE 1

'Tired of cleaning and counting them every day, I'm selling my grandmother's silverware.' That was what the message I published on the ad page said, but it wasn't really my grandmother's silverware. It was my mother-in-law's silver cutlery sets. That wasn't the only lie in the message. I said I was tired of cleaning them. Another lie, I'd never done it in my life. In fact we'd never used them in the house and even though silver can tarnish, we'd never done anything to prevent it. We didn't count them either, because as we didn't use them, it's enough to see that nobody had opened the drawer where they're kept to know that they were there, that they should be complete.

I'm a bit obsessive about some things but I think I did a good job on the advert. First I took the photos and classified the pieces by size and weight. The idea wasn't to sell just one set of cutlery, but two. Also, five trays. Pure silver, at least as pure as Italian silver can be. Then I bought a cheap phone: so that I don't get annoyed by calls to the one I always use. They offered me a contract, but I refused: 'Prepaid card,' I said firmly, not letting myself be seduced by the shop assistant's pouts.

I also made an email address, grandmassilver, on gmail. For a password I reversed my usual one, and when gmail asked for a name and surname I gave my second name and second surname. Then I made a blog: grandmassilver. On it, I posted all of the photos and the details of the pieces I was ready to sell. So the cutlery was offered on the ad page, but with a link to the blog.

When I'd finished with the whole thing, I was happy, very happy. It was as if I'd started a business and I only had to sit and wait.

I'll admit it. I'm selling my mother-in-law's silverware out of necessity, but also because I've never liked silver, not that silver. It reminds me of my mother-in-law's family, which isn't my wife's anymore, because they haven't spoken in many years, but it reminds me even more of Grazia, the seller. That woman sold María all of her silverware in instalments. All of her silverware except the first box of cutlery, which was a wedding present.

So, at the time when I lived at my mother-in-law's house, every Friday I saw that woman, Grazia, come to collect her money.

'María, what are you doing? With what you've paid her for that tray, you could have bought a whole jeweller's,' I told her when I found out that she'd been paying 10 euros a week for two years for a silver tray.

'You don't know what you're talking about. Anyway, I pay so little and she visits me every week.'

That was true. When it came down to it, Grazia wasn't charging for the object that she had sold but the visits she bestowed and the kindness she displayed throughout.

'In all likelihood this isn't even silver,' I insisted. 'Have you ever tried taking them to a jeweller to get an expert valuation?'

'You don't know what you're talking about. How am I going to take it to a jeweller? What do you want? For Grazia to find out and get angry with me?'

'Well, I'm sure I'll have to do it when you die. You'll see.'

'When I'm dead, that's a different matter, but never blame Grazia for anything,' said the good woman, without realising that she'd fallen into my trap.

'You see? You also suspect that these things aren't silver.'

THE CORPSE 2

I accepted the job, of course I accepted. As I said, at that moment, financially speaking, we weren't in the best place.

From then on, I became the mortuary priest. I put all my effort into making sure that my administration was the total opposite to my predecessor's, and so, when I had a service, I arrived at the funeral parlour already dressed in a cassock and tried to maintain a friendly but distant manner with the other staff.

'But you're an employee just like the rest of us,' one of the staff criticised my attitude at the end of the first week.

'You are mistaken, my good man,' I replied. 'I am the priest of this funeral parlour.'

Life, you see, is a matter of attitude and that small gesture was enough to mark our difference.

It was then that I really started to work comfortably. Two or three services a day. On the whole, the families only wanted a prayer for the dead, but on occasion I had to celebrate mass, Eucharist included. I had no problems, the whole religion thing had always suited me. I even bought myself a top-notch toaster and made the Host myself next to the crematory.

I made such an effort that the grief-stricken relatives (I can say sincerely) always found relief in my words. And although they left with one less family member, they went away with a friend, the priest who had given the service, and his words of hope.

Through this route, my administration diversified. One of those relatives rang me and asked me to perform his wedding ceremony. As he asked me, I thought about how to say no: I feared that his offer would lead me to a church where the parish priest would unmask me. But, luckily, I then realised that it was a church without a priest in the outskirts of the town, and there would be no problem officiating there in my funeral parlour attire.

So I started to perform marriages which, at first, was an activity that I didn't enjoy much more than funerals. But which was necessary, because thanks to it I doubled my earnings.

I didn't just perform marriages in that church, but also in a function room more or less nearby, whose owner, Eugenio, was an acquaintance of the owner of the undertaker's and when he found out that I also officiated weddings, he asked me almost as a favour.

'It's just that there are so few priests, you know?' was what he told me when I spoke to him about my fees. 'For that reason, and only that reason, I accept.'

Something similar, the shortage of priests I mean, was what a cleric in a neighbouring town told me one day when I went to confession. We (Eleonora, our little girl, and I) were approximately 150 kilometres from the town. I spotted that the church next to the main square was open and I instinctively went in, approached the confessional, joined the respective queue, and when my turn came, through the wicker screen, after a Hail Mary, I let fly at the confessor:

'Father, I'm very sorry, but I sometimes pretend to be a priest.'

I was prepared for any response. I even imagined that after listening to me the man would rise from his seat, push open the door of the confessional, and hurtle himself at my body kneeling by the little window. Sometimes I even think I did it hoping for that, for the priest to unmask me and ban me from officiating, or report my case to the police, or the diocese. But the priest, to my disbelief, only asked me why.

'Why what?' It was difficult for me to grasp the simple nature of his question.

'Why do you pretend to be a priest?' the man insisted calmly.

I was sincere. Absolutely sincere.

'It was offered to me at a very difficult time when we had no money at home and we had to pay for my mother-in-law's funeral.'

'If it's for that reason, I'm sure that God will forgive you,' the priest promised me and immediately asked me how much I charged.

'Thirty for a funeral and 40 for a wedding.'

'I charge twice that,' he admitted. 'The problem is that there are so few of us priests. That's why you can work.'

Then he gave me ten Our Fathers and fifteen Hail Marys as penitence, which I didn't pray immediately, but saved to pray that night, because as soon as I got back I had a memorial service to do.

In some way my sincerity was rewarded because the next day the function room asked me to perform marriages.

'Isn't that what I always do? I perform marriages.'

'No,' Eugenio told me, 'we also need you to perform them dressed as a layperson, as if you were a judge or a mayor.'

'I have no problem with that,' I told him and started to act like a judge. That role, I must admit, was even easier than a priest, because even though the speech was longer, the rites were simple, and if that wasn't enough, I could wear civilian clothes, no cassock or trinkets.

All of this was, without a doubt, a grave error. Nowadays you can dress up as a priest, an archbishop or a cardinal without a problem. But a priest isn't the same thing as a lawyer nor, by any means, a bishop the same as a judge. After two months the Civil Guard summoned me and handed me the complaint filed by one of the guests (I knew him, he was an old friend of Eleonora's) at the second wedding I officiated as a judge. 'Unqualified practice', 'wrongful appropriation', 'fraudulent use': there you have it, just three of the expressions contained in that statement.

When I was due to attend trial, I bumped into a client who believed, perhaps, that I was going to work. Obviously, I didn't say anything. Neither did I speak a word when the judge gave his verdict, the only consequence of which, given that I had no priors, was removing myself from my usual work.

I held out for six weeks on the savings I had gathered, and to distract myself, I started hiking. I was getting fitter, but also more in need of work: for the money, basically.

Luckily I received another visit from the owner of the undertaker's. Realising how badly the lack of work was affecting me, she laid out the problem faced by the crematorium: relatives weren't coming back to collect their ashes, and the storeroom was full to the brim. They needed to empty it and didn't know how.

'I can take care of it,' I told her and from that day on incorporated a small backpack into my hiking kit, in which I would carry one or two urns.

I did everything in an orderly fashion. Thanks to the wonders of the smartphone, I linked people's names to the coordinates of the place where I'd left their ashes and, when I got home, I'd use the urn as a flowerpot and almost always planted daisies. When the plants began to flower, I occasionally brought daisies from their own urns to the people I had met. There was no additional cost, as this was my thing, something spontaneous, that came from my heart. The cost of the service was more or less the same as a ceremony.

So I made almost four hundred journeys and practically emptied the storeroom.

When I took the last urn, although the boss didn't say anything, I knew it was my mother-in-law's ashes.

'I'll come back later for my pay and we can talk for a while,' I said.

With my mother-in-law's urn in my hands I understood that I had come full circle and there was no point trying to continue.

'I think I might have an alternative,' I said as a goodbye.

THE BISON COAT

It was a spectacular coat. My mother-in-law only wore it twice. One mass and one wedding. I remember the latter well. It was her sister's daughter's second marriage. That sister reminded her both times that she saw her in it how expensive it was. Eleonora and I rather held a grudge against that poor coat because, on the occasion of that bloody wedding, my mother-in-law, already sick, sent it for last minute repairs which ultimately I had to pay for.

'I'll sell it, you'll see,' I told Eleonora when we were caught up in getting money.

I thought about advertising it online and believed that offers would pour in straight away, but nothing like that happened. Even though I kept lowering the price, nobody called or wrote. The bison coat didn't seem to interest anyone.

'I knew it,' Eleonora limited herself to saying, 'nothing good could come from something like that.'

'Don't you want to give it to your aunt?' I suggested without much conviction.

'To her, never.'

I didn't reply. I already knew what I had to do. I waited a few more weeks and when I saw there was no other solution I took it to the funeral parlour:

'Could you do me a favour and burn this please?' I asked the boss.

She might have wanted to keep it for herself, but I was watching closely and saw them put it in the oven and even saw when it was removed.

It looked like just another dead person, that fucking bison coat.

SILVERWARE 2

In any case I never said anything to Grazia. Not out of fear (we had already left the city, the country even, and she wouldn't have noticed) but out of annoyance. I didn't want to waste more time. I preferred to sell them, sell them once and for all. That's why I had advertised them at such a good price. That's why I was waiting for the first client to appear, for somebody to write to my gmail account: grandmassilver.

I was waiting for an email, but it never came. We talk so much about the internet and in the end what came was a call to the prepaid telephone.

When the phone rang, I was helping my little girl with her maths homework and while she worked out five plus five plus seven, I listened to what seemed like the sounds of a shop. After thirty seconds the call was cut off and the same number immediately appeared on the screen once more as the phone began to ring again.

'Good afternoon. Did you publish an advert offering cutlery?'

'Yes, that was me.'

It was a strange moment, but I experienced it with apparent normality. With my left hand I indicated to little Eleonora that fourteen wasn't the correct answer, while my right ear listened to the potential buyer.

'Is it silver?'

'Yes, silver, 800.'

'How many pieces are there?'

'Thirty-six, as it says in the advert: twelve spoons, twelve forks, and twelve knifes. Weight as specified in the advert.'

It could have carried on like that, but the man asked the difficult question of the evening.

'And the hallmark? Can you see the hallmark?'

At first I didn't know how to respond, or perhaps I responded with the question the man had asked me.

'The hallmark?'

Then I thought about the silverware in my mother's house and I remembered that there was always a small square with a number or a word stamped on them.

'Yes of course, you can see the hallmark.'

As I said it I cursed myself: how could I have published an advert offering to sell Grazia's silver without first checking whether it had the blessed hallmark? It was the most important thing and I hadn't done it. I had surely failed in my efforts to become a silver salesman because it was highly unlikely that the hallmark would be tattooed on the cutlery I was offering.

Either way, I kept talking to the man.

'Are you interested?'

'Yes, but 800 seems overpriced to me.'

'I can give you them for 600,' I said mainly to gain practice.

'If that's so, I'll call you tomorrow.'

'I'll be waiting,' I replied and, as I was about to hang up, I realised that I hadn't asked his name. 'Sorry, what's your name?'

'I'm Jesús.'

'What a coincidence, me to.'

'Well there you go,' the man said, and without adding anything else simply hung up.

As soon as the call was over, I started to get nervous. It seemed improbable that the man was called Jesús. He could well be a thief, or the police. But I was more worried by my ignorance. I immediately opened a search engine and typed in the words silver and hallmark. Straight away pawn shops came up explaining it. Sure enough, it meant a stamp on pieces of silver that state the purity of the metal in the product. On cutlery, it's usually a small box on the back.

I then went to look for the case of cutlery. I opened it, picked up a spoon, and even though I'd put on glasses for my long-sightedness, I couldn't see anything. I started to curse Grazia and, when I got fed up, I went to the kitchen and found a magnifying glass with a torch from Lidl. I sat with the case of cutlery and my magnifying glass at the table which was once María's, and which is now found at the centre of our living room. There I began to scrutinise the cutlery piece by piece hoping to find a number or a letter that would prove its authenticity.

So yes, it was authentic silver. The three digits, 800, were tattooed at the base of the stem of the spoons and forks and on the handle of the knives.

Then I went back online to look up the real price of 800 silver. It wasn't too bad. Three hundred per kilogram. I was offering a little over 2 kilograms. It was fair to ask for 600. I just needed to wait.

That's what I was doing, waiting, just waiting, because I'd given up the undertaker's thing by then. At least Eleonora had posted an advert online offering the downstairs bedroom as a sort of bed and breakfast. Nobody replied for the first few weeks but then an American started writing to us and two weeks later we had her and her son in the house, eating our biscuits and slowing down the internet connection. So it was no longer Eleonora, our little girl and me, but also Susan and Pierce. The latter was fourteen and his quirk, other than hiding in the pantry eating crisps, was that he didn't speak, didn't even say hello, and when he sat at the table he rested his elbows on it.

It was a difficult situation, but I decided not to say anything to Eleonora. I resolved the problem myself, I became rude and stopped seeing them. He and his mother continued living in the house, but I acted as if they didn't exist: I didn't see them, I didn't greet them, I didn't respond to their greetings, and I didn't share a table with them. I had become a businessman. I was sole operator of grandmassilver and I could afford it.

The hallmark man never rang back. I think it seemed too expensive to him, but two weeks later (Pierce and his mother were still with us) an antiques dealer from Madrid called. At first, he questioned whether the cutlery was really silver.

'It's impossible for it not to be,' I told him with admirable certainty given that I was talking about objects bought from Grazia. 'Besides, they still have their hallmarks.'

The hallmark thing seemed to be important as the man gave in:

'And can you send them to me in Madrid?' he asked in a voice damaged by tobacco and a lexicon that had probably been improved by his profession and by alcohol.

'If that's what you would prefer, why not?'

But the man suddenly changed his mind. I still don't know what, but I must have done something wrong.

'No, best not. It would be better if you sent me a fork as a sample, to check whether it's silver or not.'

I defended myself as best I could:

'I would be risking the integrity of the set.'

'Listen, I am a serious man, an antiquarian. My name is Jacobo Estopiñán. Do not be in the slightest doubt that I will return the fork to you.'

I couldn't argue with that and, before an hour had passed, I was in the nearest branch of MRW sending my fork to Madrid.

They charged me 12 euros to send it, but the next day Jacobo called to ask me to send him all of the silverware.

'The only detail is the price. I'll give you 480 euros and I'll pay the postage.'

I didn't haggle. I could no longer afford to.

'Should I send it to the same address?'

'Yes, the same.'

'Okay.'

The money arrived, and two days later, so did a call from Jacobo.

'Did you get the money?'

As it happened, at that moment I was talking to a friend who buys and sells gold for a living, but who I hadn't told about grandmassilver.

'I'll call you in five minutes. Everything's okay.'

When I finished with my friend, I called him.

'Sorry, I was working.'

'Did you get the money?'

'Yes I did.'

'And do you have anything else to sell me?'

'Of course.'

'Why didn't you say anything before?'

'I've been having a problem at home, with some tourists we're hosting.'

'What's the problem?'

'The boy, the tourist's son, he's an insolent little shit.'

'You just send me what you have and don't worry.' Although remote, I could hear a promise in his words.

'But these things will run out sooner or later,' I replied sceptically to his promise.

'Of course, but then you'll keep working for me. I need you to look for things around your area and send them to me in Madrid.'

'I will do, don't you worry,' I told him and left the house. I had to tell Eleonora to give the Americans a date to move out. From then on, the household costs would be covered by the owner of grandmassilver.

'What are these cottons?' I asked Eleonora pointing to a box full of yellowing old Styrofoam balls at the bottom of a chest.

'I don't know,' was her response.

'Do you think I can put an advert on grandmassilver? "Selling yellow cottons."'

'Stop talking nonsense and look properly, there must be something inside,' she said, and following her own suggestion she stretched her right arm and picked up the outermost ball.

'Wow,' was all I could say upon seeing five or six small gems: two yellow, a green, two blue and one completely clear. 'What are they? Tourmalines, turquoises, sapphires?'

'Uncle Guiseppe brought them back from Brazil every time he came to visit Grandma.'

Two days later I mentioned it to a colleague who made jewellery in her spare time.

'I can make some rings with them and you can give them to your wife as a present.'

I obviously accepted and I don't regret it as at least one ring came out beautiful, spectacular.

When I gave it to Eleonora, she was wearing the bison coat and the Longines watch. That day was the first anniversary of María's death and we had been to visit her at the cemetery.

'We'll eat with the silver cutlery today.'

'Okay.'

'By the way, what was that about Grandma's silver you mentioned the other day?'

'A story that I'm writing.'

'You're writing stories?'

'Yes, literary solutions.'

THE TENT

FEDERICO VEGAS
Translated by Ollie Brock

At the age of sixteen a boy can, and should, be present at the death of his grandfather.

My father left me in front of his house while he went in with my uncles to take care of a few formalities. Before climbing up to his room I went into the library and wandered along the shelves. I still dream that I'm stealing back in there and I can take all the books I want. I start desperately taking them down from the shelves, surrounding myself with heaps of them until I realise that the possibilities are endless. My eagerness turns into anxiety and I wake up.

My grandfather's room smelled of medicine and cologne. He was dying of emphysema inside a plastic tent ventilated with oxygen. That afternoon he was dozing, surrounded by aunts who had come up from Ciudad Bolívar. Installed in their row of chairs, they were drifting between grief and gossip. At first they would be recounting some prank or other of my grandfather's; the next moment they would be remembering his kindnesses, wailing in unison and gorging themselves on cookies and passion fruit juice.

I left the room and on the stairs I ran into Berlides, who was going up with another tray of steaming cookies. When I saw her walk, I thought all the women in the family would discover our secret.

This phase of vigilance, of high expectation, of initiations and of constant tension had begun some months before. First I would lie for hours on a cold granite floor with the sleeve of a Sarita Montiel record; I would bend it, trying to overcome the unyielding resistance of the cardboard, and every now and then, for a moment, I would be accorded the miracle of a giant chasm appearing – and her cleavage would open very slightly. It was a trick that stretched the extremes of pleasure and insatiable indulgence to the point of pain.

During long Sunday mornings I conducted strenuous investigations in my grandfather's anatomy books. I encountered heaving, hanging bums covered with rashes and mild scabies; some tits that were saggy and asymmetrical, others utterly deflated or else twisted like thick pieces of rope. Some looked cheerful, like avocadoes on their branches, or had the joyful abandon of a toboggan on the snow, or the rustic charm of saddlebags. I contemplated nipples like parrots' tongues, or stiff as cast-iron screws; some were wide and spherical, too, like planets replete with their rings, moons and satellites. I came to know fannies with beards of long, lank Asiatic hair, or that seemed to have been stood on end by an electric shock, or looked like bulldogs' mouths, or were cut in Mohawks; others were hairless and almost invisible. There were stomachs with two-toned marks on them, shy and half-hidden behind mossy green dressing gowns. And even that cornucopia of protrusions and pain could have me captivated. A giant, archetypal woman was beginning to arise, incrementally, formed of talcum powder and of girls, of films, paintings, fleeting contact with other skin, of suspender belts. Desire was slowly tipping towards action.

My neighbour on Calle Glorieta was Skinny Ortiz. Skinny was capable of all manner of schemes, tricks and sacrifices. He offered treatments for blackheads, promised classes in piano, hypnotism, judo and chess. He would say that he was secretary of the artists' union, or a cloth smuggler. He used to cut fringes, make braids, read palms, repair sinks and give out creams and skirts that he would steal off his mum. He would sing and profess his love in English, or pass for an ex-seminarian virgin, a deaf-mute, or anything else that might take his victims unawares or collapse their already shaky defences. He needed merely to look a little sleepy and women would be snuggling up to him. With the subtlest of shifts, his half-closed eyelids would move from disinterest to passion, provoking anxiety and submission. He was the scourge of his neighbourhood. His territory began at the petrol station on Chuao and stretched to a block beyond the supermarket.

There was a military attaché living on Avenida Río de Janeiro who was away on a trip. Albina looked after the house and did the cleaning. Skinny had found her before anyone else. Skinny was about three years older than me, which back then was more than a fifth of a lifetime; but he liked me – I knew how to lend a serious ear to his theories and tall tales.

Because he thought of me as a disciple, one afternoon in the holidays he took me to Albina's house to help out with a deep clean. Albina had invited a friend of hers called Anuncia, who worked in the Cunaviche building.

Skinny was an organised guy: the type who doesn't rush into anything, who proceeds steadily and directly towards his goal. With him there were no doubts, no lulls; the operation was smooth and orderly, free of misunderstandings and secondary motives. We started in the living room and dining room. We took out all the furniture, covered the floors in soapy water and took turns launching Anuncia and Albina out from the edges of the room so that they slid and spun towards the centre like dodgems. Right from that first stunt I was open-mouthed at the scale of the bedlam, and I thought that something was about to explode, but Skinny had the gift of restraint, and knew how to keep a situation within the bounds of pleasure, not letting it spill over into anything more than wet uniforms and a good laugh. He had his sequence, his timetable, all planned out.

Albina was ticklish all over her body, not just in the traditional zones of the floating ribs and armpits. You only needed to approach her, threatening with outstretched fingers, for her to burst out in fits of giggles and squealing. Skinny made her laugh until she let out a stream of urine like a jet from a turbine, its foam mixing with the soap suds, then he shouted at her that she was a pig and sprayed her all over with the hose, and I started to realise my appalling innocence, and surveyed the scene as if from afar. I hadn't known that debauchery could be pushed to such limits. I was losing the strength of an actor, and starting to feel instead like a spectator and apprentice.

Anuncia was so tame and so ugly that she made my detached attitude all the easier. From between her nose and the back of her neck came a satisfied gurgling that sounded digestive and dignified, like the murmur of an old lady drinking coffee with very hot milk.

Skinny Ortiz would invent laws of love and solemnly obey them. That was how he drew out the event. His tactic consisted in treating Albina cruelly when he wanted her most and affectionately when he got bored. He knew that passion is perennial, and apathy fleeting.

When dusk fell he went with Albina into the general's bedroom and shut the door. He deported himself like a true gentleman. They would have a hot bath; he would put on a dressing gown and get Albina to try on the soldier's wife's collection of knickers, bras and perfumes. Anyone else would have thrown himself head-first into the soapy water in the living room at the beginning of the afternoon and finished up there drained and exhausted. Ortiz, on the other hand, would arrive calmly at the bed in the main bedroom, having enjoyed all the facilities, all the delights the house had to offer.

I stayed with a wet, sneezing Anuncia on the sofa of the living room. I kissed her skin and it tasted of paper and vinaigrette. I took one of her hands. Her little finger was colder than the rest. She told me that she had cut the nerve opening a can of soda and that the finger was dead. The whole hand started to grow cold, and to change colour with that light that appears at the beginning of the night. That early dusk, combined with her pensive, dark, bovine eyes, filled me with fear and guilt. I ran back home having committed no sin other than not having done something because I didn't dare.

De Armas, a pimple-faced friend of Skinny's, was my successor in the general's house. Then a little crew of sixth-form students started joining in, and they hosted their functions there for two months or so, until some puritan reported them to the school chaplain, and then the famous 'Purge of the Servants' Masters' began at school, spearheaded with implacable viciousness and cunning by the rector. I was spared thanks to Anuncia's chilly finger.

Around that time, Skinny Ortiz charmed a supermarket promo girl who was selling little pots of condensed milk. He had already forgotten about Albina, who adored him, and who by way of retaliation drank a slug of bathroom bleach which burned her throat. But she recovered quickly and wasn't on her own for long. She was already becoming a legend. The Avenida Río de Janeiro began to teem with knife grinders, Turks with suitcases full of clothes, plumbers, foremen from neighbouring building sites and ice-cream sellers; even Teodosio would slow his pace as he passed by with his horses for hire. Albina put on evening shows for them. She would leap around like Isadora Duncan in the window that looked on to the street, without warning, without a plan, without charge and without discernible logic. It was useless pleading with her or threatening to throw stones – the impetuous prancings of Albina, naked except for a pillow case, were only ever brief and unannounced. Later she fell in love with a teacher from the Rossini driving school and her performances came to an end.

I never heard another word about her. My family moved out beyond El Hatillo and the streets of Chuao became nothing more than an unrequited string of memories.

My grandfather always sat at the head of the dining room table, and from there held court over his children, his sons- and daughters-in-law and his grandchildren. He had an impressive collection of pumpkin, papaya, and cocoa plum compotes, chilli sauces brought from Guanajuato down to Guayaquil, a blender for his confections and an electric knife-sharpener. He used to sit me down by his side so that he could correct my manners with raps of a ladle. One day, as he sharpened an enormous knife to carve up a leg of pork, the sparks started falling into my plate of beans. When my grandmother alerted him to the fiery shower, he carried straight on, explaining that an extra dose of iron would do me good.

He was an alchemist, a veritable Merlin of the kitchen. To avoid being spattered by his creations, he would cover himself with a great napkin, wrapping it around himself like he was getting a shave at the barber's. He was the happiest man I ever saw in a dining room, and the best eater too. My grandmother knew that between a table and a bed the only difference is one of height, and she let him follow his inspirations and fill himself with a vitality, with a sense of indulgence and pleasure that would be coming her way within a few hours. They were a very happy and beautiful couple. They liked travelling alone. She had a complexion and a smile like you see in the best of the old fairy tales. When I arrived at their house she would be waiting for me with that smile. I can still see in her eyes how she loved to see me run and jump up to hug her.

When Grandma died, without warning or complaint, my grandfather moved to a house in Las Mercedes and devoted himself to cigarettes and crosswords. Never again have I seen old women so attractive as the ones that pursued him and fell in love with him, but he would dismiss them all with the same gentle, sad smile. In the afternoons he would go out in his underwear with a baseball bat and thrash away at some bougainvillea bushes that had been planted in the borders around the house. According to him, it was the best way of pruning them; and sure enough, the stems seemed to enjoy his ferocious beatings, and within a few days sprays of grateful flowers would spring up where each blow had fallen.

At first he was looked after by an old Spanish woman who made him paellas and tripe, but she had to go because she fell in love with my grandfather too. She would stand looking at him until he got nervous, or cry for no apparent reason the moment my grandfather opened his mouth to speak to her.

I was afraid of him. He seemed to me a hero who had backed out of a deal with fate before it was time. His untold strength, capable of great feats, was suddenly being brought to bear on ordinary things and everyday situations. People feared and adored him without understanding his solitary intensity.

In his new house in Las Mercedes, lunchtime would no longer be the same; it lacked the flair, the colour, the dishes and surprises that my grandmother would bring to them. By and by the table was covered with medicines and books, with pliers, hats and tobacco tins. Soon there was no space for anyone but him.

My father had moved, as always, as far out of the city as he could, and the only way of going to a party in Caracas was to stay over at my grandfather's house. It was impossible for me to get back home late at night. I needed to make a friend out of my grandfather, to gain free entry into a world that he was in the process of closing everybody out of.

I decided to win him over. I planned a series of conversations about the history of Venezuela, and I really did my homework. I knew that for him to enjoy the subject it had to be pre-Gómez, so, when I was well prepared, I sat down at his table to discourse on Guzmán Blanco. It was like luring a genie out of his magic lamp. He looked at me with such tenderness and wisdom that I couldn't finish my little speech.

With a single glance he had discovered my childhood fears, my ulterior motives, and of course he had all the answers. Something in the tone of his words suggested that many other men, including some heroes, were there with us in the dining room. His voice seemed to be coming from several mouths, and falling on more ears than mine. From that first session onwards, I would think more about the Sunday morning at my grandfather's side than the party on the Saturday night.

Two weeks in I started to read him my poems. They were about the old house in La Castellana, when my grandmother was still alive, about the little moments, the nooks and crannies that only he and I remembered: the enormous sink; the little cave that was formed under the creeper that covered the garage roof; the loose tiles in the bathroom; the patio drain that always got blocked with the mangoes that had been too many to pick up; the lost turtle that had reappeared to greet my grandmother on her saint's day.

While I was looking for the bit of paper with my sixth poem on it, I glanced up at his face and noticed he was captivated. He was looking at his abandoned garden and gently shaking his head. I squeezed my hands between my knees thinking that my grandfather was moved, and I read with increased verve and volume, but it wasn't the greenery that held his attention.

Berlides had started working in his house that same week. When she passed in front of us I only noticed the plastic bucket full of water and her bare feet. She wasn't beautiful, but when I saw her with my grandfather's penetrating eyes, watering the ferns and sprucing them up by passing her open hands between the branches, I fell into an embarrassed hush. My grandfather asked me to carry on; he needed my words and the light of the morning to keep his yearnings afloat. I didn't need to read – they were my own poems and I could recite them from memory while I accompanied his unhurried, nourishing gaze. My words became less important than the sound of my voice; I could have talked about anything as long as I carried on in the same tone, and my grandfather would still be at the other end of the table, and Berlides would still have clean water in her bucket.

When she turned towards us the spell was broken. I lowered my eyes to my poems, pretended to put them in order. My grandfather stayed still and continued his gentle rocking, looking at the birds and big leaves of the garden while she fled to the kitchen via the patio where the sink was. From that moment on we were as good a pair of friends as two men can be. Now we could only grow apart.

Once Berlides had become part of that concentrically growing, idealised woman who will lead me to the end of time, all my quivering organs seemed to be in tune with her, as well as with the Saturday night party, my grandfather's house, my poems, the little garden, Anuncia's finger, Skinny's words of wisdom, the purges and the confessions.

After watching her on Sunday mornings and then thinking about her all week, I knew by heart the way she walked around the house, the way she dried her hands by shaking them in the air; the way she folded sheets and ironed my grandfather's shirts, or hid behind the door as she opened it for me; the way she poured me water without letting the ice cubes splash in the glass, and held on to the banister with both hands when we passed on the staircase; the way she avoided my gaze. When I imagined going down to her room in the middle of the night, I felt as nervous as I used to before a fight at school, although I knew well that once the first punch has been thrown, fights aren't so bad.

One Saturday afternoon, after a game of football, I arrived at my grandfather's house to change for a party. At five o'clock I went to the kitchen to get something to eat and I heard a shower running. I dashed into the garden and clambered up the wall. On my way to the little skylight of Berlides's bathroom I had to get through the bougainvilleas, which were in rude health. My progress was like that of the prince cutting through the undergrowth towards the enchanted castle to kiss Sleeping Beauty – only I was wearing shorts and lacked a sword. I made my way stealthily so as not to shake the branches, frightening cats and large black ants as I went. The thorns cut my arms, cheeks and thighs, but the clear water sounded ever closer. I was glad of the scratches – I felt they would make me worthy of some boundless new pleasure. When I arrived at the window, Berlides was behind the shower curtain. I waited. The location was favourable, and the mosquitoes hadn't arrived yet. Standing on top of the shed for the gas canisters I would be able to see if my grandfather's car arrived. The window pane was opaque with steam and I didn't have much time to clean it, to clear a path for my contemplation. I decided to clean the whole pane so that it looked even and my interference wouldn't be noticed. Then the shower was turned off.

The apparition was at first angelic, producing in me more devotion than desire; then in my mouth and legs I started to feel an urge to touch her, to press her against the wall with my whole body. She stood still, waiting for her skin to dry in the heat. She merely rubbed her hands down her legs as though she were getting out of a river, and shook her head, letting her hair flop against her back. Then she turned a few circles on the same foot, and came to rest in front of the little mirror. She took a little cloth – from my vantage point it looked no bigger or redder than my own lips – and used it to dry just her neck and hands. Perhaps she liked the cool and damp to linger, refreshing the rest of her skin. She went to the door to see if there was anyone in the laundry room, then ran naked to her bedroom, where I could no longer look at her.

My return was slower and more wounding. Night had already fallen.

The scratches did me proud at the party. I gave the explanation closest to the truth: I had had to rescue a cat trapped in a creeper. But I didn't have any bright ideas about what to tell my grandfather on the Sunday morning, so I managed to get a friend who had a car to take me home.

I decided that the Saturday after I would go into Berlides's room. I wouldn't mind if she screamed, and I already knew what it was to be scratched and it was worth it. It was better to have my grandfather kick me out of the house than to feel like a coward. I would go in quietly, my movements slow, and give her all the time she wanted to say yes or no. I would let the night show me the way from shame to love.

The next Saturday arrived. It was late and it took her some time to answer the door. I went in and then stood still, watching her as she closed the door and turned the key. She went to her room without speaking to me. I thought about following her, but it seemed wise to let my grandfather hear some sounds coming from my room first. I went upstairs and sat down on my bed, fully clothed, to wait. I wanted to grow accustomed to the sounds of the night. I could hear my grandfather's fan and his breathing. I heard the walls of the house groan and the roof expand in the heat. The whole house yawned. Then I heard the sound of a bare foot lifting off from a stair. At first the steps were hesitant and the intervals between them long, but then they decided on speed over secrecy and I heard the high-pitched shuffle of feet skipping quickly over the recently polished floor.

I, the attacker with a premeditated plan, waited fearfully for her to arrive in my hideout. I was unnerved, and while I was trying to make out her silhouette in the doorway of my room, I sensed that it was another door that was closing, softly and far away.

Now there was a second wait. Still dressed and sitting on the bed, I waited for my body to sense the next developments. I walked in my socks to my grandfather's room and waited to hear a signal, some explanation, but the only thing I heard was my own shyness and respect palpitating against the wood of the door. Standing there motionless, I had to accept the truth. I understood that all that wisdom, pain, strength and loneliness deserved some recompense. But I needed somebody to talk to about my upended desires, to transform that dignified defeat into a useful nugget of knowledge.

The next day my grandfather woke me up early and asked me to go with him to a friend's funeral. He didn't allow time for Berlides to make us breakfast; we ate at a bakery on the way. We didn't talk during the journey, and he asked me to wait in the car while he went to express his condolences. He looked half absent, half irritated as I watched him greet and listen to his old friends. When we were back at his house he explained that he was getting old and that he found it very difficult to get back to sleep when I woke him up coming back late. He asked me not to stay the night at his house any more.

I knew we would have just the same problem during the day as we did at night. I wanted to talk to him man-to-man, to tell him I understood and accepted the weight of his real motives, the reasons that whirled around his head at night until they soothed his insomnia, that calmed him down and allowed him to catch some sleep, that shielded him from the sunlight in the morning. Just at that moment I had to contain a strange delight, a euphoric urge to laugh. Rarely have so many things come together in my heart: I was proud of my romantic grandfather and fed up with looking without touching; I wanted to continue our friendship but also to protect his little adventure. The second option won out. No rite, no hierarchy can triumph over love, and the only way to help him was to play the slighted, bitter grandson. Only then could he enjoy his last nights secure and uninterrupted. My mother's father didn't have the strength, or the time, for rivals or accomplices.

Intense feelings are stronger when we deny them than when they are expressed. My mother thought the two of us had fought. When my grandfather's emphysema flared up, she demanded, with a mixture of pleading and rebuke, that I help her look after him. She explained how much he had always loved me, but he was unsociable, and since my grandmother's death had only thought of destroying himself so that he could join her as soon as possible. I was the oldest grandchild, and I should be by his side like a younger son.

That afternoon I sat down behind the tent – that way I was protected from my aunts' visits and kisses. My grandfather and I had never been alone again. The few times we crossed paths, he hadn't done more than ask about my studies and when I would cut my hair.

A prisoner in his tent now, he spoke very little; the slightest phrase cost him some asphyxiation. He was a different man; he was no longer the old gent of noble, strong, solemn bearing. He was gaunt, his skin had a pearly glint, he had discarded his dentures, and his mouth was more often open than closed. Sometimes even his eyes lost their vigour; he would stare at me and they would seem devoid of any brightness or authority, and full of a gentle gratitude.

My mother waited on him hand and foot. She knew that he ruminated for hours on every order he gave while he mustered the strength to speak. When he reached a hand out between the plastic curtains and called her, she put her head inside the transparent tent and tried to press her ear to his mouth, waiting for some secret to come out, but my grandfather gave the order with a blasting shout.

'Tell that bunch of old biddies to clear out.'

My aunts obliged. They enjoyed a bit of his usual rudeness, and anyway, that command was the customary preamble to some awkward tasks with which only my mother and I could help him.

He reached his hand out again and my mother put her head back in the tent.

'I'm scared… Tell Berlides to come.'

My mother didn't hesitate, she thought quickly. She called Berlides and asked her to bring an empty tray. No sooner had she walked in than my mother locked the door behind her.

Berlides left the tray on a chair and let herself be led to the tent. My grandfather didn't even look at her, he was concentrating on breathing and on patting the sheets with the palm of his hand while he tried to shuffle over and make room for her. It was with that same gesture that, when I was a child, he used to motion to me to join him to read the Sunday morning supplements.

Berlides took off her sandals and went into the tent without bending down. She lay down beside my grandfather, allowing her full, firm breasts to push up against his chest while she caressed the top of his head, keeping the tips of her fingers a few millimetres from his scalp. The few hairs on my grandfather's head seemed to stand up as though wanting to be brushed. The gentle tickling made him smile. He felt understood by his daughter, by his grandson and by the woman who had loved him to the end of his life.

My mother didn't know that I was still sitting motionless in the room. Everything had happened so quickly. Like Berlides, her only thought was of looking after my grandfather, and it was only once she saw him grow calm that she noticed my presence. We looked at each other through the tent, two ghosts blurred by the plastic curtains. She spent a while taking on board the fact that a child of sixteen can already know the mysterious fullness of love. When she looked at her father, as frail as he was loved, death no longer seemed so terrible or so definitive, nor I such an innocent child.

My grandfather was unconscious for three days before he died, and Berlides cried for him along with my aunts. My virginity would persist for another interminable year, and my eventual initiation would be no more suitable or romantic than that of the rest of my generation, but at least I had a future ahead of me. I still aspire to having a loyal grandson and a girl who'll tickle my head when I start approaching the field of my own tent.

ONE OF MANY POTENTIAL SHORTCUTS

JESÚS MIGUEL SOTO
Translated by Montague Kobbé

Fifteen years have gone by and I'm still living in that same apartment, surrounded by the same furniture, bar a piece or two, by the same smells and textures that remain despite the coats of paint, dust and grime covering the walls, like how the stories – however few or many of them – pile up, comprising what we have become and what we have left behind. In terms of the building you could say it's looking tired, covered in cracks that – like wrinkles – etch its surface, and I could almost venture – though it's best not to – that a little hump is beginning to form on its concrete back. The garden, once populated by invisible crickets and slow-moving spiders is nothing more than a small piece of land peppered with discoloured beer bottles and the burnt carcasses of barbecue coals.

Despite the time that's lapsed, I still can't bring myself to put the rubbish down the chute in the corridor. I'd rather let it pile up, sometimes for as much as three weeks, until I have five full large bin liners and only then do I carry them down the stairs and drop them by the containers on the road. Though Dayana knows the story, or part of the story, or the version of the story I told her, she always complains about my bad habit of storing the rubbish in the flat instead of using the chute like everyone else.

Sometimes, though less and less, I wake up to the voice of Julio calling us; he doesn't call a specific name but we know he's calling us. It's neither a scream nor a whisper, but rather his peaceful voice, as if he were asking a stranger for the time.

What I remember about Julio is that his parents were always fighting for any old reason; the most common one was that his dad spent most of his salary on 'cows'. At the time I didn't understand what cows were, even though Gustavo, the oldest of us all, would explain that cows were the sort of whores you could find in some of the buildings on the Avenida Urdaneta; and though Julio's mum called them cows alluding to their large udders and their four stomachs, Gustavo assured us that they weren't all like that.

I have this image of Julio's mum as the most beautiful woman in the building, so we didn't understand why Julio's dad would prefer to go for a ride with some flabby cow. She wasn't like the other adult women (the ones from the parish committee, the ones from the neighbourhood watch or the group of friends from church); she was twenty-five at the time and to us, children between nine and eleven years old, she seemed unapproachable. What I remember most distinctly is her mouth, painted bright red, and her curly hair, almost always damp. She smoked so much that I can't but recall her shrouded in a thin grey cloud. I loved to see her wearing sandals, although I don't know what it was that I liked so much about her feet, or if I even liked them; perhaps it was the fulfilled desire of eyeing some more of her naked flesh. Once, in her home, I secretly stole the butt of a cigarette she'd smoked. It was drenched in red from her lipstick and it gave off this strange scent, halfway between air freshener and sour beans. I hid the cigarette butt under my mattress and every night, for several months, I would search for it and press it lightly, smell it, pretend I was smoking it, and contemplate how lucky Julio was, or rather, how lucky Julio's father was; I would again fail to understand why he would visit the cows, which remained a mystery even years later, when I started to spend my own first few pay-packets on the busy Avenida Urdaneta, without ever finding a woman who could compare to Julio's mother.

I could not attest to him being physically abused, but he (and once or twice even the rest of us) would sometimes suffer collateral damage. His parents would throw things at each other during these heated fights, and Julio was caught in the crossfire of some disputes, as various kitchen tools and appliances flew from side to side. The most memorable of these battles was when the TV got broken right at the end of the baseball season, which for Julio was worth several months of mourning.

The fights got to be so violent that we stopped meeting in his apartment. Somehow we felt, although not in so many words, of course, that we had violated his intimacy, or rather, that his intimacy had violated us. So we only got together to play outside his home. To me, the worst aspect of this was no longer being able to see, at least in close proximity, the sandalled feet of Julio's mum.

Julio was the fastest, most skilful and most daring member of our gang. In all likelihood I secretly hated him a little, especially because I was angered by the fact that, although a few months younger than me, he kept beating me and most of the other boys at almost every game. Nevertheless, I never openly displayed the least sign of antagonism towards him. When he won, I played the role of admirer unreservedly and with the distance that befits a good loser.

Sometimes I told myself that he had made the play facing away from the basket or lined the walk-off hit simply by luck; but one day I understood it was more than luck, or maybe that word simply stopped meaning what it had meant for me up to that point and blended with other more powerful terms, like magic or miracle.

That day we had climbed to the flat rooftop. Although the barred gate that led to it on the top floor was padlocked, we were so small that we were able to squeeze between the bars and thwart the concierge's efforts to keep us out of there. While I wasn't too fond of the place, and just the sound of the wind made me dizzy, I used to pretend I liked it; what's more, I used to propose an excursion to the rooftop when I knew the rest were too tired, in the knowledge that my idea wouldn't be seconded. Except when Julio was around, because no matter the time of day he was always up for climbing up there.

Our building is only a scant few metres from the next, such that all you need to do is take a little big leap from one rooftop to reach the one on the other side. The idea was Marlon's, but Julio was the only one who put it into practice. Without even thinking whether or not the rest of us would follow him, he simply said: 'I'll go first.' He rolled up the bottom of his trousers, undid the laces of his shoes and tied them again, real tight; he flipped his cap backwards, adjusting it as if he were looking for some sort of aerodynamic effect, and crouched into the position of a sprinter about to start a 100m race. To me it seemed (it still does) like an impossible leap, not so much because of the distance between the two buildings but because of the ledge on either side, which meant you had to climb a small step before taking the leap, thus neutralising whatever momentum you had been able to gain in the run-up. But no one said anything, not even a single word of support. Except for Omar, who to disguise his fear mumbled optimistically: 'The wind is blowing in that direction, that's good.'

I later learnt that I wasn't the only one gripped by fear, and that as a matter of fact, the others forced themselves to hold it together, not to dissolve into tears or pee themselves, as they longed for an adult to walk in through the gate and call off this circus act before sentencing us to eternal punishment in our respective bedrooms.

But none of that happened. What took place after Omar's intervention was Julio's speedy run-up, not in slow motion but rather in fast-forward, so much so that I can only recall it like that, taking three to five seconds at the most, I'd say. He took fifteen steps before reaching the ledge and then he took one more long jump, so strong that his cap flew from his head and tumbled through the sky in freefall while his feet landed on the other building, before he fell on his palms and knees on the rooftop.

Although we claimed (and today I'm ashamed of it) that it wasn't as far as we'd thought before his jump, no one even thought about emulating him. We simply cheered and congratulated him as we peered from the edge of the rooftop. Oscar, the tallest of us, reached out with his arm and managed to brush the tip of Julio's fingers. The rest of us were reduced to publicly acknowledging that we wouldn't be able to do it, that it was so fucking amazing that no one would believe it. At that moment I thought that no game would ever make sense again, that unless we played Russian roulette or something similar no game would ever prove anything at all.

I felt stupid for having attributed Julio's past achievements to luck: in other words, I acknowledged that everything about him was above us, a thousand times above, as far above as bright red lipstick on a pair of lips shrouded in smoke. I thought about all this – in a different order and using other words – as Julio walked towards the gate into the other building and tried to force it open. It seemed to be locked from the inside with a padlock, Julio explained, as he pulled the handle, pushing one of his legs against the wall. Once he realised all his efforts were in vain, he

139

headed back towards the edge of the rooftop, where we waited for him with increased anxiety and fear.

It didn't occur to any of us that the most logical course of action would have been to climb down to the ground floor, to look for the concierge of the other building and to explain the situation to her: that a boy was locked out on the rooftop terrace of her building and that he couldn't get back in because the door was locked with a padlock, and if the concierge didn't believe us we would make her come out and look up and we'd tell Julio to wave his hand, but since the sun was out and made it difficult to see eight floors up into the sky we would have to convince the concierge to climb with us onto the rooftop of our building so that she could see that there really was a boy trapped on her building, but that would have meant asking the concierge of our building to open the gate through which we could easily squeeze but which the other concierge would be unable to get past, unless it were open already, etc.

In any case, the fact is that we decided not to go fetch anyone, and the solution I came up with, and I voiced, and no one found ridiculous, was that the fire department or the military would have to come get Julio in a helicopter and that they would deploy a rope ladder in order to take him from the rooftop of the other building back to ours.

Another idea which was equally lauded and even put to the test was Marlon's. He proposed using a wooden board to bridge the space between the two rooftops and have Julio come back that way. His idea was discarded, however, once we were able to place two narrow strips of wood between the two buildings, only to see them tumble down and disappear as soon as we tried to make certain they were sturdy enough.

It was Julio who took the simplest and most logical decision: he'd get back in the same way he'd gone, so without giving it too much thought he took a few steps back; this time his run-up wasn't so long, perhaps because he realised he didn't need so much speed as strength when he leaped from the ledge. Someone noted that Julio no longer had his cap. Almost as if responding – though I'm certain Julio didn't hear this comment, because it was spoken in such a soft voice, almost a bashful whisper – Julio crossed himself. He did it wrong, he didn't make a cross, it was more like a triangle or some irregular polygon, not because he didn't care but because his hands must have been experiencing the same vigorous shaking that afflicted our whole bodies, our tongues, our arms, our legs, our sphincters. Quicker than the first time, and even more gracefully, Julio jumped and was already with us. He was greeted by our applause and we lifted him on our shoulders and paraded him around the rooftop, although we stayed well clear of the edge, of course.

Not only had he done it once but twice, and I'm certain he would have done it a hundred times more, a thousand times, had the rest of us not agreed a tacit pact of keeping away from there. As a matter of fact, I never went to that place again, not even years later when wire fences were fitted all around the edge of the rooftop, which was transformed into a washhouse.

There was nothing tacit about our agreement not to tell anyone about what had happened on the rooftop, not least because we would have been punished for a fair few centuries, and Julio would suffer more that the rest of us because the TV in his house wasn't working; although in all likelihood he would have escaped punishment, since his parents were so busy with other matters.

And though we carried on playing the same games as ever, at the same times and with the same rules, nothing was ever really – at least in my view – the way it had been before. The only bonus was that our admiration for Julio grew by one thousand per cent and that he had the final word on everything, from choosing the members of a team to ending a game that had been tied for too long. No one questioned his authority, although, truth be told, he was not pretentious about it at all, nor did he seem to feel superior to the rest of us for having achieved such a heroic deed. The pleasure of the adrenaline rush was the only reward he sought every time he met a challenge. And if he were still with us and still the age he was then, the wire fences would be nothing but another challenge, and he would have climbed them just to jump from one building to the next.

One day Julio's father left the apartment, or rather, one day we heard that Julio's father had left the apartment some days earlier. Perhaps they'd run out of things to break or throw at each other. On the one hand I was happy because I thought we'd go back to meeting at Julio's place and I would again

142

be able to see his mum wearing sandals, smoking one cigarette after the next watching soap operas, oblivious of what we were or weren't doing. But my wish went unfulfilled because a square-faced guy started frequenting Julio's home. We called him The Mechanic, because he always wore blue dungarees covered in grease.

Julio told us that once he spat in The Mechanic's face because he caught him rummaging through his mum's purse. He was ready to take a punch from the guy but instead The Mechanic twisted his face into a grimace that made him look like a hungry hyena to scare him away, Julio dashed out of the apartment, defeated but holding his enemy's stare. I think that Julio had just been crying that day, which was surprising because we had convinced ourselves that he never cried.

Although The Mechanic didn't usually stay overnight at Julio's, bar the odd weekend, there was always trouble brewing between the two; they couldn't stand each other, and Julio's one desire was to run away to his aunt's place, which was far away – but not so far if you took a bus – and then come back in five years' time to smash The Mechanic's face in.

One day the character even had the temerity of trying to play the paternal role. It happened one afternoon when he saw Julio and me playing in the corridor, outside the apartment, with two toy tractors that carried moderate loads of mud and stones.

The Mechanic dragged himself towards us sluggishly, clearly in a mood, and started shouting that we had spattered shit all over, when in fact it had been him who stepped on our play area and spread mud in the living room of the apartment. He threatened Julio, warning him that if he didn't clean up the mess he wouldn't let him go out to play for a full month, assuring him that he would stay at home all that time just to make certain that he received his punishment. Julio stood up to him but The Mechanic, with his blackened hands and nails, stopped him in his tracks by placing his outstretched arm on his chest. Just with that simple gesture, Julio understood he'd been beaten again.

To make sure Julio wasn't breaking the rules, The Mechanic placed his welding equipment at the top of the stairs. He started to repair some spare part from a motorcycle, and while he couldn't see us playing in the corridor from his vantage point he did have all exits covered, both the stairs and the elevator.

Julio said that he had to escape, even if it meant climbing through the window, that he wasn't going to take any more of this; but we were on the seventh floor, and no matter how brave Julio was, trying to evade the prison guard that way was simply too risky.

So I came up with the idea (I did, not the ingenious Omar, or even the courageous Julio) of having him escape through the rubbish chute in the hallway; there was an opening to it on every floor, and The Mechanic wouldn't be able to spot it from where he was. The shaft of the chute was neither too wide nor too narrow, so with a bit of patience Julio would be able to make his way down, sliding his back little by little and helping himself with the soles of his feet.

Julio approved of my idea as if it had been the greatest ever conceived of and his confidence allowed me to partake in a portion of his greatness, which made me feel like I was second-in-command. Since entering the shaft was easier than getting out of it the plan wasn't to climb down to the sixth floor and then to run down the stairs but rather to go all the way down to the ground floor in order to complete the escape though the garbage room, the doors to which we were sure could be opened from the inside since once we had been there spying on the concierge.

That's where the plan ended. Neither of us knew whether his escape had as its final purpose the possibility of him joining us to play in the playground or whether it entailed a journey to a more distant place. The fact is that Julio told me to stay in the hallway pretending to be cleaning up and putting the tractors away in order to keep The Mechanic from suspecting anything unusual was taking place. So I stayed there for about twenty minutes, giving Julio enough time to make it all the way down. After this period had lapsed I made my way to the stairs and when I walked past The Mechanic I told him that Julio was tidying up everything and that he should forgive him, but the guy didn't so much as look up, he just carried on repairing his spare part.

Julio didn't come to the playground all that afternoon nor that evening; I thought that perhaps The Mechanic has figured out our plan and pulled Julio out of the shaft, making his punishment three times worse.

My sleep was disturbed when I heard Julio's voice, which seemed to be saying (not screaming, not whispering, but rather speaking in the same tone you'd use to ask a stranger for the time) my name or that of any one of us, and I thought I could hear some noise coming from inside the walls in the precise moment when the door to my room swung open with a bang. The lights came on, illuminating my mum's face as she asked me if I knew anything about Julio. She told me that his mum had been asking after her son, that she didn't know where he was.

They'd looked for him in the playground, in the car park, on the rooftop and in each of the apartments of the building. Such uproar in the middle of the night filled me with panic but then I was overwhelmed by a sudden joy: I sensed that Julio had once again been a hero, he had escaped and had headed for his aunt's and that he would be back in a few years to exact revenge, with our help of course.

Since in theory I'd been the last person to see him they questioned me time and time again over the following hours. I said a thousand times that I'd left Julio at his place because he'd been punished and wasn't allowed out. In fact, not without maliciousness I insisted that in all likelihood the last person to have seen Julio was The Mechanic, given that he had been the one who had barred Julio from leaving the flat and had stationed himself by the stairs, the only escape route. I won't deny I felt joy when Julio's mother started hitting The Mechanic on the chest while she blamed him for what had happened to her son.

I only confided the secret that Julio had run away to his aunt's to Omar, who had also been woken up by his parents, upon receiving his solemn promise not to tell. I gave him no details of how he had escaped, so he assumed it was through the window, which he didn't find particularly surprising.

The following day, roundabout noon, my conscience started pricking me for not telling Julio's mum the truth. So I knocked on her door and I told her that he had gone to his aunt's, that she should phone her and look for him there; she answered, her sorrow sheltered in a veil of listlessness, that if he were there his sister would already have called her and brought him back, and that, besides, his aunt's home was not nearby at all and that he was too small to make it there on his own. Nevertheless, she obliged, I don't know whether just to please me, though I doubt it, but she called her sister and confirmed that there was no news of her nephew. I approached and hugged her. I wanted to comfort her in some sort of virile way but I ended up sobbing on her shoulder; she hugged me and I guess she closed her eyes and imagined I was her son.

It wasn't until the third day when some of the neighbours started to complain about the rubbish chute being blocked, and the waste that was accumulating between the fourth and eighth floors. At first the concierge tried to clear it up with a broomstick, then came the people from the management company and finally some men in white robes.

As soon as I heard the news I ran to my room, looked under my mattress for the cigarette butt, by now almost in shreds, and flushed it down the toilet. The spiral of water didn't make it disappear until the third flush.

To this day I'd rather let the rubbish pile up in bin liners inside my apartment and then take them down in bunches of five straight to the containers by the road. I do it slowly, drowsily, like just about anything else I've done for quite some time.

THE VILLAGERS

CAROLINA LOZADA
Translated by Katie Brown

Mr Kobe, the blacksmith, was the last to leave. From the window we watched him take the cobbled path leading to the bridge. He carried his heavy tools in his hands, only the minimum of personal belongings fitted into the rucksack on his back. He didn't turn to look at what he was leaving behind, few did. His steps were lost along with his dry cough beyond the fog of that morning. Antonio moved away from the window and asked me to do the same. 'Your eyes will run dry,' he warned me. I stayed by the window a while longer, watching as we were left alone, in limbo.

Antonio returned to his workshop and continued with his daily labour, which he had undertaken for years: carving miniatures out of wood, toys for collectors. He made them and I was in charge of polishing the pieces, that's how we made our living, which is why he resented Mr Kobe's leaving so much, the blacksmith used to put the finishing touches to his works. The night before he left, Antonio asked him to stay, tried to convince him that the three of us could carry on despite whatever might be happening outside. 'Nobody comes to buy your toys anymore,' Kobe reminded him, 'and there's no one left in the village to offer my work to. Worse yet, there aren't enough people left for there to still be a village,' he sentenced, and we all fell silent. Our only neighbour tried to persuade us to go too, surely carpenters and toymakers are needed elsewhere, he insisted, but Antonio had stopped listening and preferred to ask him to just leave already. My husband didn't want to say goodbye, nor did he accept the hand stretched out to wish him luck. A hint of a smile appeared in my watery eyes as I opened the door for him to leave for the last time, our last friend.

San Mateo is a small village; in reality rather than a village it is a hamlet, embedded among the mountains, bordered by a river that becomes a sea when it rains. The days are often rainy, on occasion very cold. Until shortly before the occupation, we lived off tourism. A few villagers had their own livestock, others planted strawberries and vegetables. And the bread made with aromatic herbs and dried fruits had made San Mateo a gastronomic destination. Antonio and I were from the city, but we grew accustomed to the landscape of the village the longer we stayed there. The death of our only son, washed away by the swell of the river, was the defining moment: we would never abandon him, only death would take us from San Mateo.

The fear started to reach us from the city, which people were fleeing to avoid getting caught in the occupation. As we had no idea what was happening, speculation mounted, disturbing the calm of San Mateo, but it wasn't serious enough to completely disrupt our normality. However, all of a sudden, everything was cut off: no one came to visit us anymore. It was as if we were suddenly isolated in the middle of nowhere. Days became languorous, the idle villagers wondered about the occupation: Russians? Terrorists? Yankees? Communists? We had to make do with our suspicions because nothing reached us from the other side, not the slightest information. The last man from the city to pass through San Mateo was so disturbed that he couldn't even speak. He arrived in a car that had run dry, his weary face fell with a thud onto the horn. It was dawn when the noise woke us. Outside our houses we saw the car like a ghost vehicle in the middle of the road. We thought that the driver was dead when we saw his whole body slumped forward, pressing the horn, which didn't stop sounding. He wasn't dead, but he would be a few days later, after we'd taken on his care as if he were an injured bird. We were waiting for him to recover to tell us what was happening in the city, what the occupation was all about, we wanted to know if we were at risk staying in the village. But the visitor didn't speak and one morning we found him dry and as dead as a dodo.

At first we were very patient, trying to take things in our stride; but then something happened which heightened the tension and caused mass hysteria to break out: Despite their parents' pleas, Tom and Duno, young locals, decided to travel to the city to find out what was happening. The boys went and didn't come back – nor did their parents, when they decided to go looking for them. After these disappearances, the calm of San Mateo was shattered and the outrageous conjectures as to what could be happening outside only increased, leavened by the fear of the threat of the unknown.

At some point it occurred to someone to speculate whether the occupation of the city was to do with an epidemic, a mortal illness, and that the man who arrived at the village had been trying to flee from this sickness, but was already contaminated and had surely transmitted it to those around him. Eyes filled with fear by this premonition turned to Herminia and her husband Sacramento, the Samaritans who'd taken charge of the last visitor's care. The fear and hysteria cornered the old couple to the point where they were obliged to flee, lest they be fed to the purifying fire wielded by a mob that dreaded the prospect of collective contagion. They left behind their sheep, the weaving from which they made their living; meat and cloth fed the fire with which we sought to kill the virus carried by their owners as soon as they were gone. Herminia and Sacramento were very old to be crossing the wastelands, they wouldn't be able to escape the steep mountains. We all knew it as we watched them leave along the damp and mossy path. We were certain that the barren vastness would swallow them, yet nobody did anything for them. From that moment we would never be the same again.

To get out of San Mateo you have to go down a zigzagging and stony path with deep chasms on either side, which leads to the A-road, the link to the city. The path is only suitable for off-road vehicles. The other route is more difficult and dangerous: it requires crossing the mountains until you arrive at Pueblo

Hondo, another settlement as isolated as our own. This way demands days of climbing and walking, and is only advisable for young people, experts and adults in peak physical condition, never for the old Millers, who took the path one morning as the rain cleared and who, with a rifle in hand, warned off anyone who tried to halt their hazardous journey.

In the community there are several vehicles used for trips to the city, to carry merchandise or to buy essential supplies, but with the threat of the occupation nobody dared use them. As a result, almost all of the cars had been put away: all but Tobias's. In a fit of courage, or wild desperation, he fired-up his jeep and sped off downhill. Just like Tom and Duno, he never came back, despite assuring us again and again that even if he were dead he'd return as a ghost to inform us about the occupation. After Tobias's disappearance we felt truly trapped and isolated in that bleak upland. However, the real face of the tragedy only began to show itself later, when the tins, packets, livestock, and other food started to run out. Concerned by the shortages, we suddenly descended upon Mr Gómez's little shop to get to the merchandise he had – following his survival instincts – hoarded. Silently, we approached the store to insist he share the hidden goods. The resistance presented by his solitary body served only to fall beneath our indifferent shoving and trampling, until there was nothing left of him but a bruised and broken pulp in the corner of the house. We were too ashamed to bury him, preferring instead to burn both him and the house in a hidden attempt to erase the crime that had been committed. Even so, the ashes of guilt embedded themselves in our memory.

Most of us in San Mateo were over fifty, retired; younger villagers left for the city when they grew up, in search of a more exciting life, far from the bucolic calm they were used to. Tom and Duno were a couple of the few young people who decided to stay with us, but they are no longer here. When the hysteria broke out, not all of the villagers were prepared to leave: people like the Ricoeur family preferred to commit suicide in the groves, very close to their house, leaving a note asking to be buried in the shade of those trees. Their ancestors had escaped war after war, the letter explained, and they did not want to continue wandering: it was time to stay put. The bodies of Adèle, Fréderic and their cousin, Monique, were taken down to fulfil their last wish. Antonio was one of the volunteers to help with the task. He didn't sleep well that night, I felt him fidgeting in bed, murmuring between clenched teeth. I pretended to sleep, I knew that he was thinking about death, about our little one, the day when after a long search we finally found him, wedged between rocks in the river. Held captive by this death, we stayed put; like the Ricoeurs we would never leave San Mateo.

The days passed in a haze of fear and paranoia, no one tried to stop anyone leaving any longer; on the contrary, we organised farewell parties and wished them luck. Those who had family and friends outside took the chance to send them greetings, saying that they were okay so that they wouldn't worry. Those who were leaving took written and spoken messages. It was all a pantomime, each one of us playing our part, knowing full well that the wastelands would swallow whoever tried to cross them, and that if there were people outside, they wouldn't be the same anymore. Our suspicions would be confirmed later, when the most willing, the least frail, of us were charged with searching for meat from the bodies to whom we had wished farewell, meat that would provide desperately needed sustenance.

Naturally, isolation began to disturb us, madness to rear its ugly head. Mercedes, who used to sell woollen hats and scarves, was seized by horrific visions of germs eating her skin. Filthy, rubbery and green, that's how she described her attackers when we tried to protect her from biting herself. Our relief from her insanity came the day when, trapped by her terrible visions, she threw herself off a cliff. There wasn't time to get over the shock. No sooner had Mercedes died than another strange situation began. Emma and Rudolph, the German siblings who made the village's bread, started behaving oddly: they stopped speaking Spanish and would only communicate in their mother tongue. As well as this linguistic turn, which hampered our communication with them, they insisted on dressing and acting like children. The strange siblings (who we presumed maintained an incestuous relationship) ran about the village like little kids, getting up to mischief. They played hide-and-seek and had imaginary friends with whom they flung manure at houses before running away in a happy stampede. Emma stopped wearing her hair in a high bun and opted for two braids and a fringe while Rudolph cut his trousers off at the knees. It was chilling to see the siblings playing on the swings or speaking with a childish inflection, but the macabre content of these infantile games wasn't yet visible. Something truly terrible occurred when Emma, Rudolph and their imaginary friends decided to enter the houses of our elderly neighbours and play with them like dolls. The worst tragedy ensued when they went too far with the weak bodies of Herta and Milos, the Austrian couple who grew strawberries, and ended up killing them. These deaths angered us so much that we cornered the formerly friendly Emma and Rudolph and beat them so fiercely – so that they would learn to respect their elders – that all of a sudden they stopped crying and moving.

These last events had made the neighbours lose trust in one another. We started to live behind closed doors, there was no longer any friendliness in our community. I was immersed in the angst of uncertainty, Antonio worked like a madman not to let himself get trapped. He made hundreds of little wooden dolls, waiting for everything to go back to normal and for tourists, his potential clients, to return. I don't know when the toys stopped fitting in the workshop and started to occupy the house. Soon the little men were sharing every corner with us. They were piled in the pantry, in drawers, on the tables, in the closet, under the bed, lying on the sofa, some even put themselves in our coat pockets. While the house was filling up with these miniature new residents, Gilberto, our immediate neighbour, started to build a wall around his house, which, according to him, would keep out both the virus and outsiders. Raúl, his partner, agreed with his plan, so together they started to build their refuge. Day by day we saw how our old friends' house, the one highest on the hill, disappeared behind a wall of stone and concrete. In their crazed attempt to remain isolated from the encroaching fatality, Raúl and Gilberto weren't content with building a wall the size of their house, but kept going higher, piling stone upon stone in an unending wall which finally blocked them off from any trace of the outside. From our window we watched how, while one toiled at bricklaying, the other guarded the fort, shotgun in hand. We understood that reason had departed – that they had lost their heads, and they were capable of shooting anyone who came near their territory, which is why we didn't try to find out what happened to them once they stopped building. One day the wall stopped growing and there was no more movement from inside.

Communication between me and Antonio broke down. We spoke so little that I wasn't even aware of his project to build an army of soldiers to protect us from whatever was coming from outside, using those little green soldiers, the plastic ones, as models. From the model he would make them life-size, fearsome wooden men over six feet tall. His mood having gone from bad to worse with Mr Kobe's departure, I hadn't been into the workshop for days, trying to avoid his sullen attitude. I preferred to stay in my room, or to wander among the deserted houses in search of a tin of food, or some salt or sugar which the neighbours might have left, forgotten, in their sudden disappearance. This time I found only some coffee grounds and an album of photographs from when we had started to build the village. An album full of the smiling faces of the old visitors who one day decided to establish this village in the middle of the mountains with us. In the photographs, San Mateo was a construction site, the dream of those of us who wanted to get away from the swarm of the city and ensconce ourselves in the calm of the countryside. Antonio was in most of the photos, the ideologue of San Mateo as paradise. Excited by the discovery of happy memories, I ran to show them to my husband, with a newfound love for him.

The first thing I came upon was a piece in the shape of a soldier, grenade in hand, whose position suggested that he was about to throw it at the enemy. At that moment, Antonio was putting the finishing touches to a soldier who held a rifle in one hand and with the opposite signalled others to follow him. To one side was a soldier crouching down, staring into the viewfinder of a weapon about to be fired. 'They're from the infantry,' he responded to my questioning gaze. A beard covered a good part of his face, he looked unkempt – recently he'd been labouring in the workshop until dawn – and I'd been so wrapped up in my own fears that I hadn't noticed the changes in him. 'I will build an army to defend us,' he said, 'no one will take us from San Mateo. If necessary we will die fighting, but never fleeing.' He pronounced every word with the conviction of a madman. 'You have to paint their uniform in camouflage colours,' he requested lovingly, squeezing my cheek. His hand brushing my skin gave me a shock. How long had it been since we'd last touched each other? I thought. When was the last time we'd had sex? Antonio remained focused on his work. He told me that he had to work until he crashed to get the army ready, the rest of the battalions were still missing. He didn't even glance at the album in my hands, although he was happy when I told him that I'd found some coffee and I'd go and prepare it. When I came back with the drinks, I took the chance to show him the album; it was the only way I could get him to stop his maniacal work. He smiled as he looked at our past frozen in images. Some photos brought tears to his eyes. We spent the afternoon remembering stories from the time of the founding. The bittersweet memories hit us in the chest and the silent soldiers witnessed our sobs and our renewed vow: they would never take us from San Mateo.

I promised to help him make the army. Once they were ready, we would put the soldiers in strategic places for defence and attack. That day we came together again, rolling around naked in the sawdust under the silent gaze of the wooden figures.

Everyone left. If it weren't for the soldiers we would have been completely alone. At night, the clouds fall so low that the village is completely hidden – the next morning we reappear like a ghostly ceremony; but there are whole days of rain and fog when San Mateo literally disappears. On those days we worked feverishly, if we wanted to prevent the occupation from taking hold of the village we needed to complete our army as soon as possible. In some way, the clouds were our ally, hiding us from the enemy. As a precaution, we began to place the finished soldiers in their defence and combat positions. The first place we chose was the watchtower built brick by brick by Gilberto and his lover Raúl. When we decided to approach the construction, we didn't know whether the pair were still alive, so we proceeded with great caution. To scale the wall we made use of the climbing gear that – in another time – we had bought to rent to adventurous tourists who liked to scale the mountain cliffs. There was nobody to stop our ascent, our premonitions were fulfilled, the house was uninhabited. Near the exit we found two skeletons, one of their skulls broken, so shattered that it seemed a great weight had crushed it; perhaps the rock next to the body. The other body was very close by and its skull was almost intact, save for a pronounced hole in the right temple, probably caused by the shotgun that lay close to the corpse. What had happened to Raúl and Gilberto? *Post mortem* we're all the same. Who was who? Who smashed whose head in? Who pulled the trigger on himself? Perhaps one of them wanted to flee the fort and his lover stopped him? At first we thought about burying the bodies, but then we decided to do something more practical: take the skeletons apart to place the bones on the wall and scare off the enemy. We put the two heads next to each other, facing the path that leads to the entrance.

Before deciding what to do with the bodies, we prioritised inspecting the house, sure that Gilberto and Raúl must have been very well stocked up if they had planned to survive shut in. We were right, inside there was food, tins and rats. Rats that surely ate Raúl and Gilberto's bodies. Rats and their babies, who we could eat if we ran out of supplies. Antonio and I are prepared to survive at any cost until the occupation ends and everything goes back to how it was before. That's why we did survival training. At this point I'm no longer disgusted by eating worms or any other creepy-crawly, and if it were necessary to boil these rats to kill their germs before eating them, I would do it.

After inspecting the house, we realised that it was in a better condition than our own, so we decided to move in, but we left the workshop where it was because our frail bodies could not handle a complete move. Some of the off-roaders still had petrol, thanks to which we could take the soldiers up to the house to place on the wall. Before each soldier was put in place, we made each swear an oath promising to safeguard the noble land of San Mateo. It was a very emotional act, and would have been even more so if we had had a national anthem, as I hinted to Antonio, but there was no time for composing songs, our boys had to be at the front, pronto.

We felt more protected in the walled house and, further calmed by the stocked cupboard, at times we allowed ourselves moments of relaxation. We even made love, sometimes in front of the soldiers – that really turned us on. Antonio liked to see me bent over before the wooden man's package, which he had intentionally crafted in prominent proportions, in the position of taking it into my mouth. More than once, while Antonio was shut up in the workshop, I went to play with the troops. I liked to rub up against them. The wooden men were undoubtedly a breath of fresh air for our sex life.

When we finished making our army, we set about placing each man in his attack or defence position: on the bridge, on the bank of the river, hidden among the trees, aiming out of a window, keeping watch from the trenches, at the entrances to our rooms. Thanks to our efforts, San Mateo was protected.

The days dragged by monotonously. Nothing came from outside, no kind of threat or information, waiting and lethargy began to niggle at our spirits. I missed the old dynamic of San Mateo, the sense of community. I sometimes thought I could hear the voice of Martín, our little boy. Antonio consoled me, assured me that normality would return to our lives, that one day the occupation would end. But nobody can bring our son back, I sobbed in response, flooded with sadness. Antonio didn't say anything, he observed me silently with pained resignation, suddenly kissed me and embraced me and then left the room to lock himself in the workshop, where the hours became days without me seeing my husband's face. During those days, I didn't even try to pester him, I preferred to wander through the village's solitary streets. I felt too sad and alone, which is why I started to call to the neighbours through the doors, and I sometimes went into their houses and got the idea that they were there and pretended to visit them.

One day, Antonio finally left the workshop. He looked for me everywhere, I can't remember in whose house he finally found me. He was understanding and tender with me, he told me he had a surprise for me and led me to Martín's room. 'What are you playing at?' I asked him. Antonio made me go up to the bed and uncover a bulge beneath the sheets. There he was, a little Martín, body, mind and soul made of wood. Antonio had paid attention to every detail, even the scar on his cheek from when he was playing in the trees. This time I cried with a crazed happiness, our beloved son was returned to us thanks to his father's skilled hands. I kissed him, cuddled him, loved him. The two of us cuddled the little one, we loved him, finally the family was united again. Martín, Antonio and I, the three of us together everywhere, walking through the village, having picnics, celebrating each other's birthdays, going from house to house to inform the neighbours that our boy had returned.

'Antonio, what if we brought the neighbours back too?' I suggested. My husband thought it was a great idea and the three of us got to work. That's how we started to repopulate San Mateo, day by day we crafted each one of our dear former neighbours, guided by memories and photographs, working out the best pose for each one. We placed the siblings

Emma and Rudolph at their bread-kneading table, rosy-cheeked and smiling. Herminia and Sacramento we put in their pen, with life-size replica sheep. Even Sacramento's flat-cap was perfect, tilted a little to the right, as he always wore it. We left the Millers at their window, admiring the scenery as they drank their coffee. We put Herta and Milos in the greenhouse, both tending to the strawberries, while we sat Mercedes in the rocking chair in her house where she would spend hours knitting hats and scarves. Behind his shop counter, the enthusiastic salesman Mr Gomez smiled. The Ricoeur family pronounced their French Rs sat around the table, forever ready to take tea. Mr Kobe can be seen striking metal with his strong arms. We left the couple formed by Raúl and Gilberto peering out from the top of their wall, looking to the other side of the river, with the guards, in charge of watching over the village. We brought back those who had left and never returned: Tom, Duno, their parents and Tobías, making them walk over the bridge towards home. The boys' arms raised in a greeting: 'Hey, we're back, here we are.'

They were days of hard work, especially to get the villagers' features right, to place their soul in their eyes. We were worn out by the end, but it was worth it. Martín gave us the strength, he brought us back to life. All the villagers of San Mateo are here together now, each going about our daily lives, resisting the occupation. Not even death is going to get rid of us, Antonio and I have taken precautions: our faces and bodies have also been sculpted. Mine was captured with a look of maternal devotion towards Martín. Antonio put up resistance when I insisted that his body should have the appearance of a hero because his wooden man had to occupy the podium in the plaza, as founder and saviour of San Mateo, so that when the occupation arrives, they will know that this village and its villagers have a hero, a God who gave them life. Antonio finally understood and the three us got to work on the most delicate piece of all: the hero, founder and saviour of San Mateo, and together with the neighbours we raised him onto his pedestal. No occupation could defeat us, the villagers.

THE BODY

LILIANA LARA
Translated by Katie Brown

The phone rang. It was the ringtone for unknown numbers, a popular ballad that Vladi had programmed in for him so that he would know it was a stranger calling. And precisely because it wasn't one of his limited circle of friends calling, his heart leapt, a sudden gallop, infinite longing for it to be a call about work on that Monday morning. Any work, he was willing to do anything. He reached to the bedside table to grab the phone that was trudging through synth chords, and, still lying down, answered. An androgynous voice asked for him: hearing his name pronounced with an unfamiliar accent and the impossibility of determining whether his interlocutor was a man or a woman gave him a bad feeling. The voice said that this was the only number for a relative of Rodrigo that it had been able to find, that it was frightened to death, didn't know how it had happened, didn't know what to do. It said that Rodrigo's corpse was there, face up, naked. The voice had started to tremble, whatever came next sounded like a muddle of fears. Rubén's jaw also trembled and he couldn't make a sound. It had to be a bad joke, he told himself, and started to grope for the cigarette packet on the bedside table with his free hand. It wasn't there. With the phone still attached to his ear, still mute, he rose from the bed and headed to the bathroom. On top of the toilet tank shone the red Marlboro packet.

The voice cried. From the skein of words, Rubén salvaged some like: fuck, Vicodin, hotel, police. His heart raced so loudly, he couldn't hear his own words. He didn't hear himself say anything, but he saw himself note something on the bathroom wall with Mayra's eyeliner. As if his eyes had detached themselves from his body and perched on the bare bulb of the bathroom light, he saw himself from above: small, his back turned, greying, washed up. He saw himself search for something to write with, saw himself write on the wall, saw himself nod several times, gesticulate, hang up, fall to his knees on the tiles.

He couldn't say how many minutes he spent in that position but when he came to, his knees hurt. When his eyes returned to his body, he could read the address written on the wall. It was the name of a famous motel and a number. He transcribed everything into his notebook and tried to erase the black scrawls he had made. It left a dark stain, a black cloud, a miniscule representation of the bad luck that dogged him. Now this, he said. He got dressed as best he could, his hands shaking. He grabbed the car keys and, feigning normality so as not to arouse suspicions, crossed the room, kissed Mayra, told her that he didn't have time for coffee, that he'd been called for a job interview and that it could be something good, and left the apartment.

Why didn't he tell Mayra?, he asked himself as he left the city behind. At this hour traffic into Maturín was heavy, but somewhat less dense outbound. He covered miles without being able to answer that question. The motorway ended in a roundabout where it split into two small and battered roads. He took the one on the right. The voice on the phone had said Vicodin, he thought as he reached the green countryside on that Monday morning. During the last part of the conversation, the sexless voice had revealed itself to be that of a young man. The last man to have seen his brother alive, face up, naked. If only Rodrigo could prescribe him another batch of Lexotanil or something to get through the shock of seeing him dead. His corpse in a motel in the outskirts of town, 'dead happy' perhaps. Rubén couldn't imagine him like that, he had always seemed so alive, had always been so alive. He who had won himself a scholarship to specialise in psychiatry in Spain and who was the apple of his mother's eye, the yardstick for all the other brothers. No matter what the others did, for their mother only Rodrigo shone, at every medical conference, in every journal article, in every newly decorated office. Thank God she would never know about this scene, lost as she was in the hallways of dementia, nor did the dispersed brothers need be informed of the full details.

The idea not to notify the family about the circumstances of Rodrigo's death entwined itself tightly with the sound of the sexless voice crying out how like his brother he was. Older, yes, added the skinny and still naked boy before he continued to cry, barely covering his genitals with the duvet, but forgetting to cover them most of the time, while he gesticulated and tried to put a story together. A long and flaccid member that swayed with the toing and froing of its owner. Another corpse.

The motel was a bad copy of some Arabian castle. Domes surrounded by minarets, a kind of Taj Mahal made of plaster and steel rods. The decoration of the room followed the same lines. A harem's quarters, badly painted.

'Take something to stop you shaking,' he told him. 'And get dressed.' He seemed to be the same age as Vladi and perhaps because of this he started to treat him like a teenage son. The boy obeyed: he put on frayed jeans, a black T-shirt, pointed boots, and took a pill from the inside pocket of Rodrigo's jacket. The jacket hanging from the back of the chair reminded him of an old family joke. Rodrigo was so ticklish, their mother said, and one of the brothers repeated, that when someone tickled his jacket he would die laughing. It was enough to touch his sleeve and move your fingers to see him explode with giggles. Tickles would have no effect now. While the boy was in the bathroom, Rubén hugged the dead jacket, searched the pockets, found the drugs: powerful painkillers. He took two.

In the bed lay the corpse which he had avoided looking at since he arrived, but which he now had to dress with the help of the puny boy. Its nudity surprised him, a strange body with recognisable scars.

Marks on his knees from childhood falls. On his right foot, the reminder of the beer bottle which exploded next to him at a teenage party. And other new marks which he knew nothing of: accumulated fat, hairs, callouses that he had never seen before. The only body he remembered was that of the preadolescent Rodrigo.

'Brothers', he said, 'are like distant satellites: they're there but we know nothing about them. You reach an age where they get lost.' The boy kept crying while they dressed him and didn't even register the comment. He also knew this body, but in its current form, and knew nothing about those old scars.

'Do we need to call the police?' asked the boy once Rodrigo was impeccably dressed, except for the jacket which Rubén held to him tightly.

'An ambulance, but not from here. We'll take him home,' Rubén mopped the sweat from his brow. He was sweating from nerves or from fear, but put the jacket on nonetheless – he didn't want to let it go. 'Do I have to go? I'm scared,' the boy sounded like a girl.

'Help me to carry him and then you can go.'

They walked towards the car like a trio of drunks. He had parked it to the side of the road under a thick tree at the foot of which hundreds of mangos were being devoured by a cloud of flies. He had thought it better to leave it there, camouflaged by the branches rather than in the motel car park. An old car, it looked abandoned amid the weeds. He now realised his decision had been a mistake, especially because his brother had arrived by taxi and the car park was empty and extremely discrete. No one would have seen them carrying the body. The walk to the mango tree, by contrast, was long and uneven. Exposed to the view of cars passing down the motorway or the motel employees, if any of them were to come outside at that moment.

He had never really noticed how tall his brother was, how solid his chest and legs were, his fine hands. He supposed it was also the weight of death. He looked at Rodrigo's leather shoes during the long walk to the car because he didn't want to, he couldn't, raise his eyes to the non-existent pedestrians or the distracted drivers who traversed the cracked tarmac in the distance. He looked at the shoes so as not to see the swollen face, lolling head, skewed sunglasses. They seemed like three drunks who'd drawn out the weekend's binge into Monday morning. Their walk left a weaving trail in the dirt. Rodrigo's shoes seemed to move at the pace they walked, avoiding potholes, gaps, stones or mounds. Shoes so expensive that they seemed to walk by themselves. Rubén's, by contrast, stumbled, leaving a cloud of dust with each step. They were cheap and plastic and falling apart, and kept an unsteady rhythm. When they reached the car, he couldn't help thinking that he should swap shoes. They sat him in the backseat, panting from exhaustion. The jacket made Rubén sweat twice as much on that humid morning. The boy lay down on the hood of the car, wiped his sweat with his sleeve, looked like he was about to faint.

'Wait there,' he shouted, 'I'm going to make him more comfortable.' He didn't want the boy to see him swap shoes with Rodrigo, he felt like a thief, a grave robber. But the boy didn't even notice the operation, he was dumbstruck, caught up in his own tragedy. Without tying the laces, he closed the door and sat behind the wheel. The boy took his place too. Once in the passenger seat, he started to talk.

'I found him online, you know?' he said, looking into a green nothingness, a black and lonely road. 'Your brother, I mean.'

'How?' he asked for the sake of asking. He assumed that he had found him on some dating site.

'He did online therapy sessions too.'

'For free?'

'No, you had to pay by credit card. My dad got me one,' he said, and to Rubén he seemed so like Vladi. If he hadn't taken part in that oil strike, if they hadn't fired him, he too could have gotten Vladi a credit card. Imagining his son in this boy's situation made him shiver.

'We wrote to each other loads,' continued the boy, 'until I decided to come and see him. Eight hours on the bus every weekend.'

'Since when?'

'Ages ago. Loads of times.'

Rubén didn't want to be there. Not in that car, not shouldered with his brother and his lover, not in that city. Many had left the country. Alberti was in a Saudi oil company and sent back happy photos; his wife, veiled in black and covered from head to toe, with just her sparkling eyes visible through a narrow slit. Happy – Mayra said – because all she did there was shop and shop. Beneath that veil there's Botox, surgery, jewels, she fantasised. But he hadn't been brave enough to leave and now he was stealing the shoes from his brother's corpse. He searched his shirt pockets, but found nothing: the packet of cigarettes remained on the toilet tank.

A dense heat foretold sudden rain. The cicadas chirped in the depths of the plain. A few trees broke the monotony of the grassland. Hurriedly, the car retraced the route travelled that morning. Rubén's foot sank into the accelerator while the corpse stiffened on the backseat, jacketless and in cheap shoes. He needed nicotine or a shot of rum, so he stopped at the service station opposite the roundabout, at the start of the motorway leading into Maturín.

'Do you have cash?' he asked the boy. 'I need cigarettes.' The boy took a note from his wallet and gave it to him.

'Bring me a Gatorade, please,' he said and turned to look at the body on the backseat.

'If anyone asks, he's sleeping, okay?' The boy nodded.

On his way back, before getting into the car, Rubén opened the bottle hidden in a brown bag. With the first swig of cheap rum, a weak light ignited in his heart. With every drag on his cigarette, the light grew. It was a sign, he told himself, that this boy had called him and not another brother. It was a sign, he repeated, that Rodrigo had his number to hand. And now, in his jacket and his shoes, he felt a new strength reborn from where there was nothing left. The boy cried without moving, without looking at him. The body couldn't be seen. He finished the cigarette and got in the car.

'What's the page called?' he asked when they got on the motorway.

'Psychiatrists-online-dot-com' said the boy with a child's face, sucking his Gatorade through a coloured straw.

There was no fear in his heart. He floated along the motorway, as if there weren't a corpse on the backseat, nor a stranger sat next to him. Purposeful, like someone who actually had received a call about work after such a long time. Happy, like someone who had finally discovered their destiny and concluded that every detour had been, in reality, a confirmation of the path to follow. He turned on the radio and quietly sang along.

'Don't you think singing is a bit much?' Traffic on the motorway slowed the car, but not the joy in his heart.

'No. I'm not afraid of this body,' Rubén said.

'You must be high.' It surprised him that the boy suddenly spoke to him in such a familiar manner.

The traffic came to a complete halt, but not his head which buzzed with ideas. Taking on his brother's digital identity required knowing the passwords to access his electronic memory, his email accounts, his virtual surgery. He was sure to find all that looking through his computer. Rubén was an expert.

And psychiatry was, after all, literature: organising the discourse of others, reading the unsaid, making connections. Nothing that he couldn't do. Beside him, a taxi tried to cut into the queue. He let him in, what was one more car?

'The heat is going to melt Rodrigo,' the boy said and began to sob once more. 'Why did you let that car in? We'll never get there.'

'We're nearly there,' Rubén said unperturbed.

'I never went to his house.'

'You always met in that motel?'

'Yeah. And in others,' he said, sniffling.

The traffic was a compact mass of stressed drivers doing the impossible to advance a millimetre. In the distance, the cause of the gridlock could be seen: one of the National Guard's improvised roadblocks. It wasn't uncommon, they would search for contraband, drugs, stolen cars, any motive to negotiate a bribe. Rubén took another swig from his bottle, the boy's sobs intensified. 'Calm down,' he shouted, but in truth he would have liked to slap him.

He looked at the body. It looked like a man sleeping. He had better not arouse suspicions. How would he explain that body on the backseat? Why hadn't he called an ambulance from the motel? Why was he protecting the good name of a man who was already dead? What did it matter if the circumstances of this death became known? What the fuck was he doing in such an unlikely scenario? It was a sign, he repeated to himself. He was protecting the name of his electronic identity. The name of the brother who would be replaced. The only way to have a decent job in this country where everything had already been denied him. Mayra would have Botox and Vladi could have a credit card. And he would become the best psychiatrist online, the apple of their absent-minded mother's eye, the owner of those shoes which were so comfortable and that jacket which didn't suit the weather.

The sea of cars was more like a stagnant lake. The boy cried from fear. He drank his Gatorade slowly. Tears escaped his sunglasses, ran down to his chin, jumped to his neck and shoulders. Rubén wanted to open the window, light a cigarette, but he was scared that the heat and humidity would have an adverse effect on the body on the backseat. I am not afraid of this body, he told himself, and suspected that his bravery was somewhat artificial, didn't belong to him. I am not afraid of this roadblock, he told himself, convinced that something unnatural was operating within him, in the entire scene, in the pain that refused to appear despite the memories awoken here and there by the sight of those old scars on the naked body. I am not afraid of this boy, he told himself, and the sight of him, defenceless, dissipated all doubt that he was underage. He would take him to the bus terminal, send him off forever. He told himself thousands of things as the car inched towards the roadblock.

A uniformed man appeared at the window. He looked at him, looked inside the car, looked at the boy who pretended to be asleep, behind his sunglasses. Looked at the body.

'We're coming back from the beach,' Ruben said. 'My brother and his son are worn out.'

'People get too damned drunk at beach!' he said with an accusatory look, disapproving of the age of the car too, and let them pass. Once they had left the roadblock behind, the traffic diffused rapidly along the motorway. It was the sign I was waiting for, Rubén told himself, and he entered the city like someone entering a new life.

THE EXPEDITION OF THE DOLLS

ISRAEL CENTENO
Translated by Guillermo Parra

People live to find a treasure. Today I'm beyond
the hope of doing so. Now I sink into an easy chair
and I won't let any surprises make me believe in
opportunities. Sick and free of any referents, I have
calmly made the decision, there are no supports, I
simply wait and smoke, drink and go out at night to
pervert myself: these are the only resources I have.

Everything was different at my grandparents'
house – I was fifteen years old and unhinged. Disorder
was the natural state of things. I've always thought
anarchy expressed itself with no filters in that place.
Each person was whoever they wanted to be – at
least that's what we thought. There was a consensus
of sorts, we weren't like other families. Ever since
my grandfather kept us from attending religion class,
we began to feel different. The nuns would arrive and
we'd be excused from their hours full of tall tales and
commandments. I always wanted to go to religion
class and I nearly took communion in secret, but if
anything was clear in those days it was that, even
though we didn't have rules, an anathema ruled over
us: we were under the tyranny of my grandfather's
anti-clerical ideas.

We weren't atheists, as they accused us of being
in class. Not at all, everyone in my house believed

in the soul. We spent our lives thinking about souls, brothers would arrive and gather to talk about their past lives and the twenty-nine missionaries who would transform the world. It was common for us to encounter sessions where great figures expressed themselves through a medium. My grandfather always emphasised he wasn't just some quack spiritualist, his spiritualism, despite the contradictions such an affirmation carries, was rational, scientific, and the sessions took place within the strictest considerations and rules in order to avoid any imposture and folkloric touches. No images of rum, or the mutations through which a portrait of an Indian appears. Just the circle of brothers seated around a medium, as if they were holding a vigil, while she solemnly declaimed. The medium handled her possession with austerity, she seemed to be reciting transcendent statements and she invited us to follow the paths of praise. We always thought the medium never said anything concrete, it was like she had read pages of Positivist authors and on certain occasions she'd take a verse by Rubén Darío and a phrase by Victor Hugo and toss them into the ring in order to call the brothers to fight for a truth and a light that were impossible to confirm. But it was enough for her to say light and truth for those anxious souls to noisily sigh as if following a higher call. Each person would interpret his own light or truth. The tone was always apocalyptic, which led us to agree with the belief that an imminent cataclysm would split Mount Ávila in two. It would be a day of justice, it would be terrible, the sea would come and sweep away all mankind, the universal cataclysm would take place in Caracas which, after being destroyed along with the Church, would be confronted with the restitution it deserved.

Yes, we were communists. My grandparents' house was permanently submerged in a state of agitation. Newspapers against the clergy were printed while at the same time a party cell would hide weapons or camouflage meetings. This is how my aunts got together with a fauna of revolutionaries who filled their wombs with 'new men'; and women, why not. We were raided more than seven times and witnessed several pursuits across the rooftops. There's little sense in seeing a book by Joaquín Trincado on the table next to the philosophical proposals of comrade Mao, as if dialectical materialism had something to do with eternal and continuous life. We'd hear about imprisonment and assassinations, people would always talk about so-and-so being assassinated. My older cousin was punched in the face as an exemplary punishment when he asked if so-and-so hadn't assassinated someone else. The neighbours on our street accused us of being communists, we all got to know the jail cells of the political police, it was natural to think our telephone was bugged and that new men and women would keep coming into the world. And that's how we came to be a numerous family, due to the great pleasure the comrades took in our aunts' bodies – in the end we all had a father in common, a father as abstract as light and truth.

*

It was around this time I met Adela. She was a strange spiritualist sister who came from Coro, her arms always covered in jewels and her hair fixed in a tall bun atop her head. She lived for many years, her face never changed expression, her eyes would leap slightly, she smiled enthusiastically, and her laugh was full and hard, like her face. She would never leave the house, where she stayed with us until she was very old. Her world was truly foreign, on occasion she would whistle to invisible entities and she used to say she communicated directly with the superior brothers from other worlds. She wasn't a communist: that entailed an altogether different anathema. She was terrified of communism, which she said was nothing other than a promiscuous relationship of equality. Why did she stay? Why would she bring treats for my grandmother's dog? Why would she talk with my aunts about the imperious need not to fill the world with new men? Her husband built the upper section of the house – he made it bigger to extend the limits of the commune.

Communists and spiritualists were not the only ones who would show up. Friends of my uncle, who lived on an entirely different wavelength, were already installing their stuff on the upper floors. They were a group of kids exploring the world of psychedelia and leisure. They'd spend their days playing with a rubber ball on the street, making shots in Blanco's billiards hall, would save money to buy a bottle of anisette, had long hair and never listened to *guarachas* or salsa music. They wore pants they'd bought at Carnaby Street and smoked marijuana at will. They were responsible for my sexual initiation in the laundry room. I remember they took the cleaning woman's shirt off and left her tits out in the open, playing with her nipples, licking them, sliding their hands under her skirt and that was when they called me. They told me to smell, to touch the black crown, to feel its warmth, they were all laughing. The woman never stopped scrubbing the clothes in the tub while they moistened her with their tongues. Even now when I love a woman I feel her sexuality is expressed amid the scent of laundry detergent and the acidic brine of tinned sardines. That was who we were, hippie caricatures, revolutionaries who loved our aunts, one or another lunatic who had joined the party, and the embryos of the future; we'd look at each other with suspicion and even with disdain, but we definitely found a way to live together. A few of us would exchange blows, others threats and warnings, while the rest of us tried to overlook scenes of abandonment and hints of sexual abuse.

But in the lower part of the house the spiritualist brothers continued to hold their sessions. Adela persisted and never left. She even stayed when we were forced to move into an apartment.

Our cohabitation was compressed in that apartment, many embryos left with the aunts who stabilised their lives, while others remained. That's when Juan arrived. He had been in the mountains, going up into one of the many guerrilla fronts and he had marched in some direction – his march was always circular and fearful. He wasn't scared of bullets and soldiers, or confrontations with the adversary, the only thing he feared was his comrades.

Juan studied engineering at university. His time at secondary school, despite the political turbulence that was roiling the country, was fortunate; he got good marks and abstained from enlisting in any political organisation. That's how he graduated with honours. He would tell us that his first mistake was moving into student housing. He should have stayed with his parents, because no one in those days escaped being courted by a communist party cell.

He ended up with two roommates who were party activists, people whose job was to maintain the university hallways in a state of agitation. Juan didn't realise this, but they kept an eye on him and would always talk to him about the importance of keeping his mouth shut, since informers weren't treated kindly. He already shared secrets; he began to put his classes aside and attend the study circles. It was understood that *Capital* was a matter learned through practice. Two or three elemental concepts regarding the class struggle were enough. There wasn't much time for theory and there was lots of work to be done.

At first they would plaster the university with flyers time and time again, the slogans changing from day to day. They had to cover up the enemy's propaganda and put up flyers insidiously, helping to shape people's will. Shaping people's will was of utmost importance, which is why they advised him to leave Margarita. Juan loved Margarita, she was a dentistry student. They would often go to the movies, get ice cream at Castellino, and sleep together in halls when there wasn't a meeting going on. He enjoyed himself with Margarita, a thin girl with a long neck and a white smile, short hair and small ears. He would tell his friends he wasn't sure if she was 'the one', if they'd end up getting married, if they'd have children or travel to Europe together. Margarita liked Paris. Who didn't like Paris back then? She wasn't drawn to the dynamics of the student movement, which was something circumstantial, as she told Juan one afternoon while they were having a few beers. 'Cities are beyond circumstances or the historical moment,' she noted. 'For example, an afternoon in Montmartre, a service in Notre Dame or in Sacré-Cœur, autumn in the Louvre.' This was enough for all of Juan's expectations to be defined. He took her by the hand and led her to the women's toilet, where he placed his body between the door and the sink, they struggled for a while until he finally got rid of her panties, with resentment and violence he finished her off and threw her aside.

It was the right thing to do, they applauded him and asked for details. Juan simply smoked and drank rum. You can't have a girlfriend whose expectations are so out of tune. That night they celebrated and called on some female comrades, they played music and filled the room with smoke, transforming the night into an insurgent noise, a delirium. This was how the day would meet them and how the work too would continue, they had responsibilities and the city was no longer enough for them, now that the others were headed up into the mountains.

Juan believed he was capable of finding the treasure. One lazy afternoon we started talking with Sister Adela. She had aged and would make dolls out of cornhusks. Those dolls, according to her, had their own life, she would ask them about their affairs and assured us she would obtain answers from Zebulon, Astrulio, Manasseh or Cistilia. At first our relationship with Sister Adela was a game, we were bored, on occasion we'd carry an air rifle and shoot at the butts of the girls who were playing on the volleyball court facing the apartment balcony, we were willing to pay close attention to the insignificant and diverse matter of life. So we'd play along with the sister regarding the existence of other worlds, we would speak as though we'd been possessed by spiritual masters and create cosmic battles in my room. The sister felt like she was in charge of a legion of fighters who would establish the kingdom of spiritualism throughout the universe.

Everything took place within parameters that, up until then, were quite normal at home, but one afternoon something changed while we were looking at the future in the mirror. We had prepared the mirror very carefully, kept if from the light of the sun by covering it with a black cloth and buried it for three days. When we brought it into the bedroom, we lit a white candle and uncovered the mirror. As expected, neither Juan nor I saw anything, our three faces reflected, all of us wearing bandannas tied around our heads at the medium's requests. 'So what now?' we asked her. Her eyes began to jump around, to lose their colour, they were yellow and green and they were jumping, she was knitting her brow and concentrating. During these moments her face was inscrutable. 'Don't you see it?' she suddenly screamed. 'There it is!' We asked her what she meant, we kept seeing our three heads covered in bandannas. 'Those are General Falcón's three men! Look, they're unloading the trunks, Negro Benito is with them, they're rounding up mules.' She said they had departed from Vela de Coro. General Falcón, before marching on Caracas in the previous century, had ordered a treasure to be buried in Paraguaná. 'It's true, my grandmother told me about it,' the sister said. Before bombarding Vela de Coro and preparing to retake the city, the general decided to bury the treasure of the Federation in a safe place. He sent his second-in-command, Negro Benito, to hide it in El Barbasco, but once a spot was chosen, and after they had dug a basement they lined and covered with a stone wall, one of the three men, having turned his back to Negro Benito, spun round and slit his throat. Negro fell into the depths, with no time to even release his breath. The others brought their hands to their waists and grabbed their swords, but each one of them was hit by a pistol shot that marked their foreheads. 'Ortiz, that was his name, I know it. It's not a memory, I know it,' said Sister Adela. 'Ortiz was the name of the man who robbed General Falcón's treasure. No one knows what happened to him, he fled through the desert amid the scrub bushes, ate with the Indians, and was never seen again among Venezuelans until the day he was found at the foot of a cactus, with six knife wounds in his chest.'

Immediately, Juan and I uncovered our heads. We already suspected this wasn't just another game. There were no indications it was, but Sister Adela was from Paraguaná and she could be manipulating memories. 'Up to what point could it be a joke?' I asked. 'Since we've always played tricks on her, maybe now she's doing the same to us.' That was meant to be the dynamics of our relationship. We decided to have another session, with a reading of a glass of water. We went to find candles and waited for nightfall.

After reading about mediums and their laws, reciting a spiritualist Our Father, handing ourselves over to the guides and protectors, we nearly shouted at the sister to begin. No one in our session was declaiming or talking about cataclysms. Nor did we talk about roads, light or truth. We put on the bandannas and looked at the glass of water, a crystalline glass of water in which the luminous oval of fire was reflected, an undimmed fire with a blue aura. The water was a clear, quiet element, nearly dead, the water was a contained element, with no waves, only minor particles suspended in front of us.

'There they are!' the sister startled us. 'Who?' we asked. 'The men!' 'General Falcón's men?' we asked again. 'No! These are the men of Captain Morgan, the pirate!'

Juan and I looked at each other, thinking the old

lady was taking us for fools. 'Look,' she murmured, 'they're in Punta Macolla, the ship is anchored outside the bay, but here comes Captain Morgan.'

Captain Morgan was making his men row toward the beach, he was coming from Maracaibo, where he had just looted the city. They disembarked and were led by a guide to the mountain in El Barbasco, where there was a cave lined with stone in which they'd hide their treasures, or actually, where the diggers would rest and the treasure would be saved. Morgan came out of the water, one of his trusted men took the rowboat when he got to Punta Macolla, Morgan told him he would keep his secret and that he knew very well that keeping quiet meant staying alive, and this is how he went back out to sea while a straggling sailor from the crew sliced open the guide's belly.

'The treasure is right there in El Barbasco,' the sister said and pointed to it while we kept staring at the contained, dead water.

Juan and I talked. I don't know at what moment we began to take the matter seriously, I don't know why we believed the treasure was buried somewhere between Jadacaquiva, Cape San Román and El Barbasco. Me, because I had grown up in an environment that made it easy to cultivate scepticism, and Juan because he came from a Marxist education. We considered the matter from all angles and came to the conclusion that the treasure existed and the sister was merely transmitting something she'd heard as a child; memories are left trapped in glasses and mirrors. The sister continued talking with her dolls or with Piopiar, a superior master in the form of a bird. She insisted all of it was true, and what caught our attention was her insistence that we had to go and dig up the treasure as soon as possible.

El Barbasco is a difficult mountain, people get lost and go in circles around their tracks, and if they find the place they're looking for, somehow they get lost again, just like in life. We began to study maps, we visited the zone, saw El Barbasco, a tangle of sharp and wounding vegetation where you could easily become disoriented. We asked the locals and they confirmed the legend of a treasure hidden in the mountain. There was nothing else to do, we had to equip ourselves and go after it.

I had my doubts, I had never been in the mountains, Sister Adela kept insisting on coming with us. 'That's impossible,' we told her. 'Only Piopiar can lead the way,' she warned us. The most confident of us was Juan, who could be considered a veteran. While we prepared for the trip, he told me about his experience in the mountains of El Bachiller. The action around the university was over and Juan had taken part in a couple of bank robberies, helped place bombs near the US embassy and had been involved in planning a kidnapping. He had but one option left, the police were after him and it was time to go up into the mountains. Besides, an offensive was imminent. He spent four days finding the camp, along with several others. The mountain was thick and it was always raining. The mood at the camp wasn't great, some international comrades had arrived and were leading the operations, trying to impose discipline on the guerrillas and to avoid their disintegration. Juan had already heard stories about discipline, he knew about a commander's suicide in Lara, after having procured the death by firing squad of a female guerrilla for sleeping with the detachment's political chief. Juan was scared, it was constantly raining and the group was moving at night. They set up an ambush, the army would be passing through, a small convoy, the internationalists stared at the Venezuelan commanders of the guerrilla front who were challenging them, they would show them the bravery of the New Man and they set out on the trail, all of them, internationalists and local guerrillas, and the rattle of the machine guns began, the grenade explosions, one dead, another dead, a jeep burned, the crown of a tree was on fire. The commanders and internationalists failed in the ambush. It's very hard to fail in an ambush if it hasn't been betrayed. Why had they failed? Why had half the group been killed or detained? Juan had always been certain it had been a matter of pride. The commanders had wanted to show the internationalists that the New Man's balls were right there between their own legs, not in theirs, and they turned what should have been an ambush into a battle. According to the classics of guerrilla warfare, confrontations should be avoided at all costs. When they regrouped they kept talking about a failed ambush, about the lack of discipline, the party was already divided back in the city, and likewise in the mountains, among the commanders there were those who tried to blame the failure on

190

ideological problems, on low morale, which is when the firing squads began in El Bachiller. Juan told me he would sleep with his rifle loaded and close to his chest, he wasn't about to let anyone kill him; because if it came to a firing squad he would execute them first. There was nothing to be done anymore, he had no alternative, he would scream during the storms and cover his ears when they came to take the person who had previously been on guard and accused him of falling asleep or robbing a can of condensed milk.

One night he decided to desert. 'That happens in the best of armies,' he told me, 'why wouldn't it happen to us, if I hadn't deserted they would have killed me, I wasn't with the right faction, there were constant purges.' He leaped from his hammock, disappeared into the night and progressively got rid of his equipment, whatever was left of it. The only thing he held on to until the end was his rifle. He spent days eating roots and herbs. 'Now *that* was a labyrinth. Why should I be scared of El Barbasco?' The creeks had grown, the snakes jumped off branches like mosquitoes, and the farmers who saw him would immediately grab their machetes and start yelling. He never thought he would get out of there, he had lost weight, a fever was paralysing him as he fled. It was sensible to flee, to depart from life, to plunge into a fever. Suddenly he was certain, a dream, the caress of an angel's wing made him feel that somehow he would find a way to tell his adventures, but which adventure, the wing or the certainty blanketed him, he passed by a river where he lost his rifle and from that point on he was guided by a single sensation, that of his fever, he thought this was what gold fever must feel like, now that he was being dragged along by a fever for gold – the desire to live can be a fever or it can be gold. He reached a paved road and a truck appeared. Instead of turning him in, the driver gave him food and water, bought him clothes, and gave him enough money for a bus that would take him wherever he needed to go.

'So,' he said, 'what saved me? Gold fever. I've kept myself alive up until now so I can have my gold, life has a buried treasure for each one of us.'

We prepared the expedition very carefully; according to our plans, it wouldn't be too complicated, it was simply a matter of finding a stone-lined tomb in El Barbasco.

Paraguaná is arid, solitary and confusing, it's a nearly round peninsula. We travelled through it and slept in the open air under the most complete, spherical and starry nights anyone might conceive. They looked like nights from a comic book. We descended from Cape San Román and set up camp on the shores of an irrigation canal. Based on the calculations of Sister Adela and the locals, the stone-lined tomb was south of Punta Macolla. So, our search radius was compressed enough for us to explore the area quickly and find it. In principle we would stay together, we carried compasses, every afternoon we would meet at the irrigation canal and return to camp, as we shouldn't sleep anywhere else.

The first day was full of enthusiasm and good

discoveries. We came across two or three stone constructions in heaps, then we found a place with three campfires, later on we discovered a cavern in the perforated ground. We decided to go back and evaluate the excursion. The next day we tried to find the stone mounds, our clothes were filthy, our skin sticky, we spent the entire day looking for them. Instead we just found a single campfire. We couldn't explain where the mounds had gone since we took precautions to ensure we'd find them again. We returned to our campsite, we were saving water and eating twice a day, we barely drank any coffee and would fall into a deep sleep. We went out again without finding either the stone mounds or the campfires, or any other signs. The earth had already formed a layer of clay on our faces, our hands were swollen from the heat and our eyelashes and eyebrows were grey. We weren't drinking too much water, so we returned to the campsite with our lips in shreds. This is how it went for an entire week, finding nothing. We were lost in a sea of cactus, the goats kept us company, they weren't even a reference point, they were all black or white and bleated like demons. I was absolutely dispirited and I said so to Juan, who no longer had a face, it was a piece of red, cracked clay. He answered that we couldn't leave the matter as it was, he had already deserted once before, he was sure, there were signs that proved it, for example, the stone mounds and the campfires, the caves in the ground, all those things that appeared and disappeared even after we'd marked them, none of that was gratuitous. He said he had a theory, that it might seem crazy, but that if the search had no logic we shouldn't be proceeding logically. 'Sister Adela was right, this has something to do with the dead. There are two treasures: that of the pirates and General Falcón's.' The assistants hadn't been buried just to keep a secret – he had dreamt about Ortiz and had seen a beautiful bird fly out of the hole in his chest, he couldn't tell me what type of bird, it was an enormous bird and it flew and flew over El Barbasco, he had felt the flapping of its wings. Ortiz had told him to follow the bird, the bird would show us where to find the two stone-lined tombs with our buried treasures.

'You don't understand, damn it – each man has a treasure on this Earth!'

So we departed before the sun had finished rising. I felt useless, I was repeating a biblical story, walking in circles in the desert, and that was when I realised I would be denied the Promised Land. We were now men of clay, our clothes and skin were covered in a thick, cracked red layer, we embodied the aridity and barrenness of the landscape and moved around that landscape like the stone mounds and campfires. We were landscape. We wandered and lived among lizards and goats, the snakes let their rattles shake on our hands, the thorns avoided our path.

There are no more clouds in the sky, but Juan keeps following a flapping of wings, a strong and absolute sound that makes him lose control amid the thorns. I turn my back to him with no dilemma at all, I don't run as I leave him behind, my steps are calm, the only

thing I can hear in the immensity is Juan's voice:
'Piopiar! Piopiar! Are you here?'

TRAVELS
&
EXILE

Variations on Goodbye

Leonardo Padrón
Translated by Ruth Clarke

This story took place in Petare's Barrio Carpintero in Caracas. Just before midnight, two brothers were making their way home from a party. The road was silent until some private joke had them in fits of laughter. That's when death appeared, accompanied by a local lowlife, empting every last bullet from his pistol in their direction. At the funeral the following day, distraught with anger, their mother let out a curse: 'I swear, every boy on this block is going to die!' Nobody knows who played the part of the executioner, but it's been six years and exactly one week ago today, they killed the area's last remaining young man. That's the word on the street. That's what Elvira told me, as she wept for her murdered cousin. They didn't take anything. No car, no phone, no money. Just his life. Her next-door neighbour made her son go back to Colombia a couple of years ago to make sure his death sentence didn't catch up with him. She was the only one who had the chance to say a proper goodbye to her son. No one else.

*

Traffic lights leave just enough time for a twist of fate. A woman in her forties was driving her SUV through town with all the care of someone who feels like life is smiling on them. She'd just been to the carwash, everything around her was sparkling, and now she was on her way to the gym. It was set to be a great day. She pulled up gently at a red light. To her left she spotted a man in a wheelchair with his hand out and a smile that called for a token gesture of pity and solidarity. She wouldn't, as a rule, but that day she felt like extending some kindness to her fellow man. She looked through her wallet for a ten-bolivar note and rolled down the window, just enough to slip the money to the kindly beggar. In one swift movement, the man launched a frisky live rat through the gap in the window. Startled, the rat ran back and forth around the vehicle. The woman flew into a panic and leapt out of the car. Hysterical, she ran a fair distance, shrieking in a daze of shock and disgust. When her horror allowed her to return, there was no SUV, no beggar and no wheelchair. She found herself in the middle of the road with no wallet, no money and no papers. Just her pounding heart. The traffic light glowed green. A light that seemed to be saying goodbye to her car, and to solidarity with her fellow man.

*

I'm waiting for a takeaway order in a pizzeria in Los Palos Grandes, watching a European football match with the sound down. A man nods to me from the bar and asks the inevitable question: 'What do you make of it all?' We agree on the forecast: very gloomy. Like it needs to be said. There's always a stifling sense of uncertainty in those words. He tells me about a chain email he received. A large organisation sent him a list of certified risk areas in the capital. He reads it out to me and we end up laughing until it hurts. It turns out Caracas is one big booby trap with no way out. He tells me he's thought about leaving the country, but he has five children; the eldest is barely fourteen. Quite a crowd, to be honest – how can you leave like that? He shows me the bag he's carrying from a popular clothes shop. He had to buy some school gear for his copious brood. The place was offering the mandatory 50 per cent discount, but they would only let him have two items per day. So he had to go back the next day to buy trousers for his other two children. And a third day for the shirt the other one needed. It's ridiculous, and he won't stand for it. The country never used to be like this. He wants to get away from the illogical landscape we're in now. But he can't. He doesn't know how. Goodbye is not an option.

*

On a recent trip to Miami, I struck up a conversation with a Venezuelan of Lebanese origin in the immigration queue. He got his troubles off his chest at the first opportunity. After witnessing a violent assault at her son's school gates, his wife was so afraid she ran all the way to Los Angeles, along with her entire wardrobe, the children and an ultimatum. She encouraged her husband to leave with her, or make a new life for himself. He asked her for six months to make the decision. The businessman doesn't want to move abroad. So many years, such a strong attachment, such familiar routines. He's running out of savings as he pays to support his family in California. Meanwhile Venezuela's economy is going down the pan. The fate of his marriage is entirely dependent on measures taken by the president of the republic. I still think about that man and his wife's desperate goodbye. It's not fair on him that the main means of combatting delinquency should be regulating soap operas. It's not fair on his own love story.

*

'I was gone long before I actually left,' writes Israel Centeno in a text included in *Pasajes de ida* [one way tickets]. This book, compiled by Silda Cordoliani, brings together fifteen accounts by writers who make up part of what Silda calls the 'troubled country of emigrants' that Venezuela has become. 'Many of us had already been cast out of the country while we were still within its borders,' Centeno comments. That's the first lashing you get from the communication guerrillas on Twitter: 'Get lost, queer!' They want us to shut up or ship out. Self-imposed silence or exile. They're kicking us off our own land. Every time they insult us, or shame us, they're pushing the suitcases into our hands. And if we make it clear what we think, they – rather cynically – call us toxic.

'It's actually when you're in the country that you experience the worst and most heart-breaking reality of being an outsider,' concludes Blanca Strepponi.

*

In the state of Florida, I discovered a fantastic initiative called Microtheater Miami. The idea started in Madrid; now it's proving a success on Biscayne Boulevard. In a sort of converted garage in the Centro Cultural Español there are six containers, each housing a different production. Each one lasts no longer than fifteen minutes. You can see six plays in a single night. The atmosphere is reminiscent of the heyday of the underground scene around the Caracas International Theatre Festival. Drinks, chats and interesting experiments in a bohemian setting. Plus there's a strong presence from Venezuelan artists. It's true: the new theatre movement in Miami is sustained by the talent and experience of the Venezuelan influx. Actors, writers and directors forced to leave the country due to the crisis. Most succumbed to the fear of crime. You could say they were keen to stay alive. In the gaps between one play and the next, you hear many different ways of saying goodbye to the country. They all encourage you to make up your mind, suggest the right kind of visa, the best lawyer, how to overcome the initial resistance. They get you high on good advice. There's a weight we call nostalgia in their every word, but they make a valiant effort to hide it. They have to fall in love with another country. And they don't want to do it alone.

'Only in fiction do I manage to talk about Venezuela without getting short of breath,' writes Juan Carlos Méndez Guédez, from his other shore, in Spain.

*

In a café on Brickell, a legendary Venezuelan soap star lets me in on her harsh reality. 'It's really tough, after a long career and winning so many awards, to go from casting to casting with a little sticker on your chest that just says your name and how short you are.' On top of that, there's the worry of giving up her accent, as Venezuelan as maize flatbread, Guayanés cheese and lemonade sweetened with sugarloaf. It's like learning to talk at the age of fifty. 'Plus I'm up against thirty Mexicans in each casting, and I have to talk like them, like I was born in Tijuana,' she tells me, her eyes looking cloudy. How do you say goodbye to your own achievements, your history, your past?

*

Juan Gelman says: 'A country that was will be'.

*

We're living through the most miserable period in our recent history. The economy is a black spider crawling across our stomachs. People squander their days in interminable queues for flour, milk and oil.

Print media is in a state of exasperating agony that could lead to its complete extinction: something the world has never seen. Airlines have no choice but to delete us from their list of destinations. We're starting to feel claustrophobic, trapped, suffocated. There is a general sense of anxiety. It seems like we've been relocated without realising it. We are the darkest night in a landscape of Caribbean light. The very shape of the country resembles a gun. Even calls for peace come with threats. Our homes are the setting for more and more nervous conversations. It's decision time. Do we leave? Resist? Fight? Do we say goodbye to our country or our life?

You pour yourself a drink, you take a look at Mount Ávila, you think about your children and the risks inherent in each decision. Like Méndez Guédez you contemplate Bolívar Coronado's definition of a nation: 'A place where you're guaranteed at least twenty-five hugs; a place where you stay in bed when it rains, feeling like you're at home.'

It's all so hard. So unfair.

Where's the immigration queue for the land that all Venezuelans used to call home?

INTRIGUE IN THE CAR WASH

SALVADOR FLEJÁN
Translated by David Swift

Mohamed was only just starting to come to grips with the expression 'easy peasy lemon squeezy' by the time I saw his face on CNN News. It was an old photo (he had a beard and was wearing a turban) that looked like it had been taken with one of those old Polaroid cameras that are impossible to get hold of these days.

I wound up at the car wash through Susana. Before that, I'd been working at the Riverside branch of Don Pan, but walked out over issues with the manager. It was the first job I'd got after arriving in Boca Ratón. Susana was Tony's girlfriend, and the three of us first met when we were fellow students at the Catholic University in Caracas. After graduating, Tony and Susana went to live in the United States and I heard nothing about them until another former student passed on their email address and I dropped them a line.

Initially, our correspondence revolved around the usual nonsense: the situation in the country, friends and the like. Later, in one of his emails, Tony held out the possibility of giving me practical support should I ever decide to emigrate. Truth be told, I didn't seriously consider it at the time. For one thing, I'd never lost any sleep pining for Florida. But things had started to take a turn for the worse in Venezuela and the temptation to leave gradually became a necessity.

One day, I took the plunge and booked myself a flight. I made the mistake of not taking Tony up on his offer straightaway. My dream destination was New York, where I also had friends, who ultimately proved not to be. I barely managed three months there, though that was enough time for 5,000 of the 15,000 dollars I'd brought with me to go up in smoke.

That was when I stopped being so precious and turned to Tony one more time.

Tony and Susana rented a flat in a residential block on the outskirts of Boca Ratón. They'd gone through the usual jobs that all South Americans do when they first arrive in Florida. Now, they were more or less 'comfortable': Tony worked as a delivery driver for a major florist and Susana was the manager of a car wash in the Town Center.

It was Tony who got me the job at Don Pan. He knew the manager so it was easy for him to get them to hire me. But the manager was one of the many Peruvians around here who act as if they're from California and we had our differences from the word go. I stood it for two weeks: one afternoon, while I was wiping down the bar, the guy had a go at me over God-knows-what to do with some order or other and I told him to stick it.

As luck would have it, a few vacancies had opened up at the car wash where Susana worked. Then, I found out that the franchise had changed hands and that Mohamed, the new owner, wanted to start again from scratch. Mohamed was a strange bloke: he spoke English as if he was trying to sell you a pair of panties, and something in his eyes said he would never take no for an answer. No one in the Town Center had any prior knowledge of him. According to Susana, the man turned up one day with a case full of money, spoke to the former owners and, by the following week, was the flamboyant new boss of Rapid Wash.

Purely by chance, I turned out to be the pioneer of what became known as the 'Venezuelan takeover' of the car wash. Mohamed, possibly because he'd been impressed by Susana's efficiency, had a high opinion of Venezuelans in general, a false impression that paved the way for an almost immediate influx of my fellow countrymen. This would obviously have repercussions.

Kiko and Jorge arrived before the week was out. They'd been working in a Chinese restaurant but the immigration authorities and the low wages had combined to drive them out. They'd spent over a year as illegal immigrants and were on the verge of starving to death. Marcelo and Mr Martínez landed shortly after. Mr Martínez was the oldest of the lot of us: he'd survived fifteen years in the US and had originally arrived at a time when Venezuelan emigrants only made it as far as the casinos on the island of Aruba, fifteen miles off the country's north coast.

Marcelo, on the other hand, had just got off the plane. A native of the Caricuao district of Caracas, he looked like he'd been released from jail. With characteristic prison wit, he changed the owner of the car wash's name from Mohamed to 'Ma-homo-d'.

When I got to the car wash, the first thing I asked about was the machines.

'What machines?' asked Susana, with a look of surprise. 'The machines!' I said, urging her to think of gigantic brushes and industrial water sprays. 'We don't use that sort of stuff anymore. These days, it's all "dry" washed,' she said, as if we were suddenly in the business of cleaning clothes. Without further ado, she led me to a depot where a dozen small cars were lined up. They looked like the sort of vehicles Haitian ice cream vendors push around Caracas, except that, design-wise, these were more futuristic and they didn't have any bells.

Susana chose a Mercedes LX to demonstrate her very own version of the 'dry wash'. I would never have imagined that anything as small as that ice cream cart could incorporate so many antiseptic wonders. Susana looked bizarre manipulating the hose, like a baby tangled up in a killer umbilical cord. Added to which, she was waving a yellow cloth around. After ten minutes, I was fully aware of the emphasis Susana placed on the word 'dry'.

'In Florida, cars don't get dirty,' she told me, as if she was imparting some kind of managerial secret. She was right: Florida is a wasteland with no redeeming features that apparently has a Hoover run over it on a daily basis.

Ultimately, the yellow cloth proved to be more effective than the half-hearted dribble of water that spluttered from the hose. 'The less water, the better,' she repeated like a mantra. Susana's crash course included tariffs, other 'tricks of the trade' and even philosophical pronouncements: 'It all hinges on the climate,' she said, scanning the cloudless south Florida sky as though she were presenting the weather.

There were three VIP parking garages in the Town Center. A vague arrangement between the mall and the car wash allowed us to stake out parts of the surrounding area in order to seek out clients. Kiko and Jorge wasted no time in taking over the most profitable pitch, outside the entrance to Fridays. Mr Martínez occupied a vaguely defined spot we christened the 'Twilight Zone' – between the Burdines department store and Sears – where things went exceptionally well for him.

Susana paired me up with Marcelo and our hunting ground was bordered by Fridays on one side and a chemist's where you could buy everything except medicine on the other. 'We're going to have to come up with an "angle", man,' said Lucky Marcelo, after evaluating the economic potential of the unproductive sector we'd been allocated.

The place where my hosts lived was not unlike a Brazilian refugee camp, apart from the strange absence of women in thongs by the swimming pool and samba music at a deafening volume. You could basically tell them by the 'prayer groups' they formed around one of their irritating Sunday barbecues, like a cult worshipping some bovine deity. 'They're a pain,' ventured Tony the first Sunday I picked my way between the smell of grilled ribs and prayers in Portuguese.

In fact, the Brazilians weren't the only annoying thing I came across in Boca Ratón. Tony and Susana were far from being the dynamic duo I'd known at University: after the evening meal, they'd sprawl out on a threadbare sofa to consume loads of ice cream and laugh at unfunny television programmes. At first, I tended to join them in that calorific tedium, but after a few days the routine began to get as depressing as it was fattening. Besides which, the main topic of conversation was almost invariably some bloke called Bill, who, because they always frowned at the mention of his name, I thought must be some particularly irksome neighbour. One day, curiosity got the better of me and I had to ask who the hell Bill was. It was when Tony produced a pile of outdated invoices from a drawer that I first realised that debts in the United States are given the name of an adolescent gunslinger.

One morning, Susana and I arrived earlier than usual at the car wash office. As we approached, we could hear raised voices spitting out Arabic. Then we saw that Mohamed was having a real shouting match with someone who was a dead ringer for Omar Sharif. Susana put her finger to her lips and we waited silently outside the door to see if anything happened. After ten minutes, Sharif's doppelganger put a pink folder on the desk for Mohamed and left. When we finally decided to go in, Mohamed hastily put away the pink folder in a strongbox he kept beneath his desk.

'Some strange things have happened since that guy bought the car wash,' Susana told me almost as soon as we got out of the office. 'Strange in what way?' I asked. 'In the evenings, when you all leave and I stay behind to go over the takings, Mohamed goes online and checks out some really weird websites.' I don't know why I imagined the Arab poring over photos of naked boys, but when I said this to Susana she replied: 'No, if only it *were* that: he's looking at planes,' as if an interest in aeronautics was worse than paedophilia. 'I tell you what: as far as Arabs go, I like their food but that's it,' was her judgmental verdict.

I was just about to ask her what was so strange about someone liking aeroplanes when Kiko and Jorge came in and we had to drop the subject.

I wouldn't have given Susana's suspicions another thought but for a comment that Marcelo came out with while we were wiping the grime off a Mini Cooper: 'You know what, mate, I reckon Ma-ham-head's a bit of a fruit' – it was impressive the amount of variations Marcelo could conjure up from that name – 'he offered me 2,000 dollars to go with him to New York next month. "What's that all about?" I thought. Now, if he gives me 3,000, maybe I'll think about it,' he said, before becoming absorbed once more in the Mini Cooper's wheel rims.

As a rule of thumb, I tend not to trust people who have no respect for money, and while Mohamed didn't exactly throw fistfuls of the stuff around, I couldn't help picking up signs that clearly indicated how little it seemed to matter to him. The invitation to New York was just one example. There was also the Spanish lessons for which he paid Kiko and Jorge a staggering amount. Not to mention the commission we were given, which was the envy of the Town Center. It was all too good to be true. Mr Martínez reckoned that with Mohamed we were living the 'Arabican Dream'. Nevertheless, it all made me feel really uneasy. Something was about to go down, I could sense it. Something heavy.

It didn't take Marcelo long to come up with the 'angle' that would raise the level of our meagre income. The real moneymaker for the franchise wasn't the dry washes but an idiot-trap known as 'full detailing,' the car wash's premium service. Detailing a car could easily cost as much as 200 dollars and included, on top of the wash itself, cleaning the upholstery and general polishing. The idea was to do lots of full detailings in order to see the fruits of our labours. But it was no easy matter: two of these services could take up almost a whole day and left you with arms like a puppet. It was then that Marcelo devised the ruse that would instantly elevate him into the car wash hall of fame. 'If cars in Florida don't get dirty,' he reasoned, 'then there's no need to polish them.' That was how he began to implement what he branded the 'fantasy wax' service.

Susana could not work out how Marcelo and I managed to do up to ten full detailings a day. It was really very simple: we didn't. Gringo ingenuity and the very latest model of vehicles combined to facilitate the miracle. You could only detect the con by running your finger over the bodywork. But that never happened. Or, at least, not before it was too late.

From that moment, our commission rates shot up stratospherically. They say sudden wealth always brings with it pernicious side effects. In Marcelo's case, he simply couldn't handle the extra money. It wasn't just his increasingly flashy clothes that marked him out (he now looked like a villain off *Miami Vice*) but his scooter, hairstyle and penchant for scent also gave him away. I began to get worried about the situation the afternoon he mentioned 'personally tailored rates'. That really was the last straw and I had to say something. He came back with: 'It's a gift from heaven, blood,' rubbing his hands together and exaggerating the pronunciation of the L like a hip-hop singer. My partner had no idea that what would put the kibosh on his corporate delusions would also come out of the blue.

Ultimately, the decisive factor in derailing our economic growth would come courtesy of that deadly, and typically Venezuelan, sin: envy.

Kiko and Jorge were also unable to get their heads round how we managed to deal with so many cars a day without winding up in hospital every evening. They seemed to be losing sleep over it. Every morning, they would show up on our patch in an attempt to unravel the mystery. But Marcelo was convinced that 'the silence of the jealous man speaks volumes' and he'd bribed a Dominican security guard to act as his radar, and to warn us of any potentially hostile activity with a blast of *merengue*-style whistling. It all seemed funny at first but then it became a stressful chore. Even Mr Martínez would occasionally emerge from his fifth dimension on some obscure mission.

With the benefit of hindsight, I now know we should have shared our 'secret' with our compatriots; I don't doubt it would have saved us an interminable amount of hassle. I even went as far as proposing the idea to Marcelo, but his characteristic response was as pitiless as our little scheme: 'Fuck 'em!'

Around that time, Mohamed called me into his office. I have to admit I feared the worst: I didn't know if our rivals had given us away or if the Arab was about to make me 'an offer I couldn't refuse' regarding New York. But it was for another reason entirely that he wanted to see me: he asked me if I could do him a favour.

Every time I do somebody a favour, it all turns out badly – and this time would be no exception. Mohamed took a package out of the strongbox, which I thought would probably be the pink folder containing dirty photos, but the weight of it ruled out that possibility. He gave me 150 dollars and an address in Miami. The parcel had to be delivered that same day to a district in the southwest of the city where it was very easy to get lost. As far as Miami was concerned, I just about knew the airport and the Aventura Mall but I didn't intend to miss out on 150 dollars for such a stupid reason. What's more, I was the only one who hadn't always seen eye to eye with the boss and it was about time that changed.

Susana lent me her car as if she was delivering up her virginity. And there were less tips than threats. In Florida, not only did cars never get dirty, they were never lent to anyone else. To do so was a risky act of faith and she handed me the keys as if she were passing on a sacred object.

The journey along the Turnpike was routine but as soon as I got downtown, I got predictably lost. Every block looked exactly like the one before it and I felt like I was in the middle of some fibreboard maze festooned with neon lights. After a forced city tour lasting an hour and a half, I finally came out into 8th Street, which I recognised from television programmes on the carnival. Seeing it in reality, it looked more like an avenue in the centre of Caracas. Except there was grass. What happened next bordered on the shameful, especially considering it took place on a major thoroughfare in the United States: I ran out of petrol. Susana's tips on using her car did not include making sure the tank was full. Now, as far as gringos are concerned, breaking down through lack of fuel is a crime on a par with running over a little old lady. I was thinking about this at the very moment two motorcycle cops arrived. These guys are only friendly when they're in TV shows. One of them, who sounded like he might be from Havana, asked me for my licence then began to fill up a notebook with sadistic efficiency. When he finished, I expected to be given three consecutive life sentences. The list of infringements was long, and running out of petrol merely served as a pretext for the police to fulfil their entire monthly quota of fines in one go. When they ran a check on the car, Susana's Honda came up as a stubborn recidivist: there were problems with the lights, the insurance, the gas emissions. It seemed to be on the Florida Transit Authority's most wanted list.

Due to an oversight on the part of the police, I was able to slip into a Burger King: I'd left them with a Venezuelan driving licence on which the surname was spelt incorrectly so I felt more relaxed about things. After five minutes, a tow truck turned up and took the car away. Half an hour later, I remembered Mohamed's package.

It made me want to return to Caracas rather than Boca Ratón. It was not going to be easy to deal with what lay ahead. The train I came back on made so many stops I had time to concoct a more or less credible story. Susana didn't even believe the bits that were true. She just kept repeating, 'I told you so!' over and over again as if that in itself would bring her car back. Tony calmed her down a bit and they went off to their room. Then I began to think of what I could possibly say to the Arab, but this was where things got complicated because whatever I said was not going to satisfy him, plus I didn't even have the package. Out of desperation, I called Marcelo. 'Leave it to me,' he said, as though he was talking about settling a score in Sing Sing.

The following day, Susana travelled to Miami to get the car back. My main concern was the package in the boot, which she didn't mention at all. When I got to the car wash, Marcelo greeted me with a surprising bit of news: Mohamed had gone off to New York without saying anything to anyone. My friend was obviously upset by the broken promise of the 2,000 dollars, but as far as I was concerned the news was something of a relief. As long as that blessed package was still in the boot, everything would be sorted.

At midday, Susana arrived with Tony in tow, which was a really bad sign. She didn't say a word to me for the rest of the afternoon but her eyes said things like 'we'll sort this out at home.'

When we finally got back to their place, Susana just told me to get my stuff together. I didn't even get the chance to tell her about the package. I was surprised to discover that my 'stuff' fitted easily into a Gap bag. I rang Marcelo but couldn't get hold of him. Marcelo lived in a tiny room – forty metres square – with six Mexicans so I figured eight people would fit where there used to be seven. To kill time, I decided to go back to the Town Center: I had a copy of the car wash office key so I thought that even if Marcelo didn't turn up, at least I'd have somewhere to spend the night. The small sofa Mohamed had in his office was better than a park bench. Or so I thought until I lay down on it and began to long for the park bench. The sofa smelled of red onion, battery acid and baby gorilla. I called Marcelo again and a Mexican answered. The only words I could make out were 'right on, man!' I left him a message. The stench of the settee was such that I opted for the desk, which was surprisingly big and odour-free.

The sound of the phone ringing dragged me from a dream I'd have been better off not leaving. It was Marcelo and he was drunk. While I was listening to one of his Galician jokes, I struck my foot against the strongbox and could immediately tell for certain it had been left open. Marcelo's joke was a kind of prophetic conundrum: 'How many Galicians does it take to find buried treasure?' 'Two,' I answered, fighting off cramp.

Eighty-five thousand dollars in fifty-dollar notes makes a ridiculously bulky lump. It's something you only become aware of when you're obliged to secrete it about your person. To travel with that amount of money on the back of a scooter demands if not bravery, then a modicum of sang-froid. The thought that every patrol car we passed on the way knew exactly what we were carrying was a constant torment. Over the course of our journey, Marcelo rattled on about car-chases, Steve McQueen films and Mexican friends who'd help us cross over in McAlister. Suddenly, anything beginning with 'Mc' made me really edgy. Nevertheless, the one thing I could not stop thinking about was the pink folder.

Marcelo had taken fifteen minutes to get to the car wash. He had found me in the middle of a startling clutter of banknotes, passports, maps, manuals and an impressive collection of daggers. All in all, it could easily have been Carlos the Jackal's basic survival kit. I actually had the damn folder in my hands at the time and must have looked a bit shocked if Marcelo's comment was anything to go by: 'What's that then, mate? The Gay Book of the Dead?'

Undeniably, the colour of the folder did not do justice to the gravity of its contents, which, unlike the rest of the documents, I don't think is worth the bother of describing in detail. You can still see it on television.

When we had to decide what to do with it all, we ran into trouble. Unsurprisingly. On top of his share of the spoils, Marcelo wanted to keep hold of the daggers and a full-colour map of Manhattan. I said we should just leave everything as it was and get the hell out of there. I think I might even have mentioned the FBI in an attempt to impress upon him the seriousness of the situation. But it was like talking to a brick wall. Marcelo was in a state. With bulging eyes and sweat pouring off him, he just kept repeating: 'We're dead meat, bro.'

As ever, my friend came up with the perfect metaphor to pierce my cardboard morality. After some minutes' deliberation, he proposed a solution that he arbitrarily qualified as 'biblical': 'Let's just torch the whole lot.'

The bedsit Marcelo shared with the Mexicans was a triumph of interior design in an overcrowded environment. I was anticipating something like a cabin in a submarine but it was quite the opposite.

The jugs along the walls (which, as I was to discover later, were there for a practical rather than decorative purpose) served as the perfect complement to the hammocks hanging in a row the entire length of the room. An ancient poster of the wrestler Pipino Cuevas, pilfered from *Ringside* magazine, and another of Lucerito brought some home-country iconography to the space. What I wasn't too happy about was the dogged smell of armpit and grilled tortilla that pervaded the cramped quarters. However, one gets used to anything in this life and soon I was unable to distinguish one smell from another.

Though I didn't want to spoil Marcelo's fun – he was already cracking open a bottle of José Cuervo – it seemed prudent to remind him of the magnitude of the problem we found ourselves in. His reaction was a touch over the top: 'Do they have the electric chair in Florida?'

I patiently explained to him that the methods of execution deployed by the state were gentler than they used to be. That these days things were snappier, less hardcore. I tried an analogy: 'There's no blood – it's a bit like kosher food… see? They give you a few injections and make you fall asleep, like putting down puppies.'

It would have been better not to have said anything at all to him. In a split second his dreams of being a landowner on the Venezuelan plains were transformed into the nightmare of a believer racked with guilt. He even wanted to burn the money. He began desperately pacing round and round, as if he was already in the queue on death row.

Although only two of the Mexicans Marcelo lived with were in the flat at the time, it wouldn't be long before the rest arrived so there wasn't a lot of time to sort things out before the convert dropped to his knees in the middle of the room and started yelling his *mea culpa*s. So I decided to make up a story that had Tony as the owner of a speedboat (Marcelo asked me how powerful the motor was so, for the sake of his peace of mind, I exaggerated) with friends in the Bahamas and a beach hut in St Maarten. If I'd had more time I'd have added locations in Ibiza and Gstaad, but as it was I thought it was quite sufficient that our voyage ended in a ferry heading for Vela de Coro.

My pitch restored some of the adventurous gleam to Marcelo's eyes. He wanted to know more details and I told him I'd fill him in on the way to Tony's. In the meantime, I'd think about my own contingency plan, which, in contrast to the blockbuster I'd outlined for Marcelo, had me on a tedious Greyhound bus journey to San Diego, eating some dreadful meals and paying a coyote 3,000 dollars to do the usual but in the opposite direction.

First, however, I had to find out exactly what had happened to the package I'd left in Susana's Honda, which, judging by the pink folder, more than likely contained uranium. When we got to the block of flats, there was no sign of Tony's van but, by an extreme stroke of good fortune, the Honda was parked outside. Both of its rear tyres had been slashed and there was a green decal on the windscreen. I told Marcelo I needed to get a pair of trainers I'd left in the boot. I also told him that Susana had mislaid the keys and that we'd probably be doing her a favour by opening it up. But my companion was still fantasising about the splendid escape plan I'd come up with half an hour earlier and demanded to know more.

I was obliged to improvise a load of clichés to inspire him: I had him eating lobster and drinking gin fizzes in a catamaran and was about to inject a bit of sex into the mix when he pushed me to one side purposefully. I thought he'd bring out a jemmy, or something similar, to open the boot but instead he surprised me by adopting a fighting stance and then giving the lock a kung fu kick. 'It's all in the technique,' he explained. The way the boot opened up gave me some indication of my pal's former lifestyle. When Marcelo saw the size of the parcel, he asked me if the trainers were Shaquille O'Neal's. It was obviously the time to come clean. Though, knowing him as I did, that was not going to be easy. It would be like saying: 'Look, man, Club Med's fully booked but I managed to get us a couple of reservations on Devil's Island.'

However, in an unexpected turnaround, Marcelo demonstrated a capacity to adapt that I'd dearly like to have myself. He told me again about his 'mates' in McAlister and that really did seem like the keys to heaven. The only problem, as I pointed out to him, was that McAlister was a seven-day drive from Florida. 'So whatcha want, gangsta? Stay here for the Hialeah SWAT team to come use us as target practice?' he retorted, and I suddenly had an image of him with a shiv in his hands.

The lighting in the bus station was as bright as you'd find in a dentist's consultation room and, to my mind, made us really stand out. Added to that, Mohamed's box could hardly be described as unobtrusive. Up to that point, I'd refused to open the parcel despite Marcelo's attempts to persuade me to do so. I feared he'd come up with another of his biblical solutions and turn the lot of us into passable versions of *The English Patient*. Among the endless amount of solutions he proposed, those that stood out were unmistakably Venezuelan in inspiration: 'We'll open it up and, depending on what's in there, we'll wait and see' or 'We've got to sort this shit out,' he'd say, with metaphorical bravura. Unfortunately, it was that 'depending on what's in there' that made me nervous. Being up all night was getting to me by now and I was in no condition to make a level-headed judgement. I said we should decide things later and just concentrate on getting out of Florida first, which was already enough to be dealing with. 'What if we just have a quick look inside…' was the last thing I heard him say before I left him muttering away to himself.

What the package contained could turn out to be one of two things: an unexpected bonus or something really bad. As far as I was concerned, however, it was a dead weight that we had to dispose of extremely carefully. I already had more than enough with the 40,000 dollars I had stashed in my underwear. Maybe it wasn't a fortune but it would do me. What I was definitely sure of was that Marcelo wouldn't be content until he'd hit what he envisaged as the jackpot of the whole thing. That's why I considered burying the parcel in the desert around McAlister and waiting 'to see what happened'. But that, too, seemed pointless: I would be burying it only for Marcelo to return the following day with a spade to dig it up again. I'd have to think of something more elaborate and sophisticated to throw him off the track. The only problem was that nothing sprang to mind.

For now, my main concern was getting on a bus and travelling to Texas. I left Marcelo sitting on a bench and went to buy the tickets. It was while I was standing at the counter that I realised how careless I'd just been. Now I regret not so much the mistake I made in leaving Marcelo with the parcel but everything that I allowed to happen afterwards.

This, more or less, is how things went: when I returned, I found him sitting on the bench where I'd left him waiting for me. Obviously, the parcel was nowhere to be seen. Before I could say a word, he opened up the palm of his hand and showed me two shiny chrome keys. He took one and handed it to me, explaining that he'd put the package in a left luggage locker at the bus station and that we'd leave it there to 'cool down' while we decided what to do. That was the moment I should have reacted more forcefully but the idea seemed so practical, I failed to see the bigger picture. If there was one thing you couldn't accuse Marcelo of, it was of not being consistent. This extended to his cinematic preferences: every heist picture worth its salt features the old luggage locker scam. How could I have fallen for that one! What really annoyed me was that I didn't think of it first.

We went to the bar in the bus station to 'celebrate' our good fortune. That was another mistake. The bar was called Matchstick Men, which spooked me. At this point I should add that I was partially responsible for making things even easier for Marcelo. In other words, I shouldn't have drunk as much as I did. All I can say is it was a combination of stress and stupidity. The bus was due to leave at four in the afternoon and we had a lot of time to kill before then. Marcelo ordered a bottle of whisky as if we were in a club with a really lively night ahead of us. The only detail is it was nine in the morning.

Inside, there were flickering TV screens everywhere but they barely broke the gloom. As if that wasn't enough of an imposition, there was also a small monitor on every table. I meant to point out this aberration to Marcelo but his mind was obviously on other things. He started talking about 'investments' while I watched a documentary about extraterrestrials.

By the fifth shot, I'd already agreed to invest in a prawn farm in Güiria… or was it Paria? We talked about ecolodges, a nightclub in Margarita, a taxi firm. If I hadn't fallen asleep, we might well have bought the Leones del Caracas baseball club.

When I woke up, the only thing still there was the TV screen.

To say that I felt empty inside is not to use a poetic or romantic figure of speech, or at least not in the sense that I mean it: that was exactly what I experienced when I felt my waistband. I looked at my watch and it was almost midday already. A simple calculation indicated that my money was probably somewhere around New Orleans. It was obvious that Marcelo had no intention of sharing anything with anybody; not even the bill that lay on the table as a testament to my naivety.

When bad things happen, they happen all at once. I became aware of that when I focused on the monitor on the table. The CNN logo told me that what I was watching wasn't one of those disaster movies. Rather, it was a video version – with state-of-the-art special effects – of the craziest part of the material contained in the pink folder. Then I saw Mohamed's face and my world fell apart.

I immediately began to see CIA agents everywhere. I expected the barman to bring out an assault rifle at any moment and make an arrest that would go down in history. Miraculously, the pink folder still contained the 150 dollars the Arab had given me for the package business. I paid the bill like I was getting rid of some bloodstained evidence.

When I came out of the bar, I didn't have a clue what I was going to do. For want of anything better, I went through my pockets to find the key to the luggage locker. What I was really looking for, though, wasn't the key – it was a miracle. Along with the key, I found an atrociously handwritten note in which Marcelo thanked me for everything and advised me to check out the locker because 'there might be a little present in there'.

I spent half an hour trying out the key in the hundred or so left luggage lockers in the bus station. Marcelo had taken the ticket with the number on it off the key, presumably to gently hike the piss-take quotient of my humiliation. Together with the derisory 1,000 dollars he'd left me 'as a present,' I found another note in which he wished me the best of luck and signed off with a phrase that demonstrated his wide-ranging cinematic awareness: 'See you in hell,' he said, like some suicidal sergeant striding off into a paddy-field teeming with Vietnamese fighters.

What happened next was the worst September of my life.

The only 'safe' place where I could hide out was the Mexicans' bedsit. I went back there in a taxi that charged me limousine rates. The Mexicans were willing to let me stay as soon as I'd paid off the three months' rent debt my 'cousin' had built up. Over the course of the next few days, I learnt of further financial liabilities my relative had left unpaid. With some justification, the Mexicans ended up calling Marcelo 'the Artful Dodger' and never was a nickname more appropriate. In his wake, 'Hurricane' Marcelo had left a trail of destruction through all the Mexicans' pockets. I've no idea how he managed to convince them to appoint him treasurer of the modest household emergency fund they kept. Nor how he contrived to rip them off without being lynched in the process. And that's without taking into account the odd remittance that never made it to Monterrey, which – coincidentally – Marcelo had been responsible for depositing in

Western Union. I think there were other petty crimes, minor scams that the Mexicans looked back on with more astonishment than anger, but which would be pointless to relate at this juncture. The Mexicans were fair with me, however: they never held me responsible for those particular transgressions and even offered me a job. Though I'd have been better off not accepting the favour.

I had to drag myself home every evening after working an average of fourteen hours a day as part of the Mexicans' demolition gang, which was a sick joke as far as I was concerned. But worse than that was the dose of paranoia the news bulletins gave me on a nightly basis. One day I resolved to stop watching television, and the problem gradually diminished. But I was still going to have to leave the job or it would be the death of me.

That was when the United States government stepped in. By deporting me.

In fact, they deported the lot of us. Though, in the Mexicans' case, that was another joke. The immigration authorities caught us on one of their regular routine raids while we were in the act of demolishing a retail centre. What followed was more or less in line with illegal immigrants' recurrent nightmares: three weeks in an orange jumpsuit, white-walled cells, mug shots, reviews. Then, in full view of everyone, the final ceremonial procession through customs at the airport.

After a couple of months, I'd almost forgotten about the whole affair. But there was one thing still nagging away at me and it was not what had happened to Marcelo: no, what really intrigued me was what had happened to my money. Specifically, what he'd chosen to do with it. But, with time, the memory of that too faded until it was no more than a hazy anecdote my friends were bored of hearing about.

One Sunday, a friend invited me to a restaurant. It was one of those places with art deco Indian huts and annoying waiters. The first clue was the name 'McAlister Grill' written along the back of an image of a large bull in the entrance. I tried to convince myself it was just coincidence, but when I checked out the menu I was confronted by one of those naff photos of a smiling owner flanked by his attentive staff. Marcelo had even taken the liberty of naming one of his sangrias the *Marcelitro*. I got up from the table and went to the bathroom. There was a mahogany door next to the kitchen with a sign on it saying 'office'. I remembered Marcelo's 'dead meat' comment and couldn't help but smile. Then I went in.

LJUBLJANA

EDUARDO SÁNCHEZ RUGELES
Translated by Guillermo Parra

1

'The madman, the madman!' said a child's voice. The little kids on the block came out running. 'Run, run! The madman's coming!' they yelled laughing, shielding themselves behind their frightened mothers. The scene would repeat itself every single day, in the morning, when I'd walk down to get the newspaper. It took me a while to understand.

Madness is asymptomatic. I never realised it. I was convinced I was a normal person... I just wanted to kill God.

2

My childhood was shit. I don't have any memories from the eighties. All I know is I was the youngest child of Nena Mercedes Guerrero and I went to primary school at the Augustinian Cristo Rey School. Beyond that, the past is a blur. Our school was an army of clones. A good education was a privilege we idiots enjoyed. Anyone who showed signs of autonomy and failed to assimilate into the school's dictatorship disappeared, without much fuss, into mediocre institutes in other

Caracas neighbourhoods such as Los Chaguaramos or Bello Monte. Adolescence was a simple procedure too, a friendly match. I belong to a generation that made a virtue of boredom. Inspired by the example of my century I became an ordinary kid, with no excesses or defects. I never had any outrageous expectations. I never had impossible dreams. My main aspiration in life was always to become a common man.

When I say my childhood was shit I'm not trying to insinuate any type of trauma. My story lacks sadistic grandparents or drunken stepfathers. I simply have the impression that, between 1980 and 1992, nothing happened to me. Memory is an urban cartography that draws the streets of Santa Mónica in an imprecise manner. The memories, most of them unstable, evoke places I forgot and that now, due to some whim of my sick heart, insist on revealing themselves. For example, the Aldebarán grocery store emerges, solitary, and insomnia finds the scent of coriander in the wrinkled hands of Mrs Cristalina. The Alcázar bakery and Arcoíris butcher shop also appear, the transparent dough of the pastries mocks my fat-free diet, the shadows on the ceiling delineate the poster of a cheerful cow that exhibits the parts of its tragic destiny: brisket, sirloin, flank, round. This strange sum of fragments is the past. Conquered by arrhythmia, I've tried to seek out my early years but all I've found is a movie on Betamax cassette, a Golty football, and other such meaningless things. My childhood is a hypothesis.

Memories with an actual plot are a matter belonging to adolescence. Conscious memory has the shape of the building where I grew up, the Inírida. Our street was a false hydrographic series in which all the buildings carried the names of rivers lost in Barinas or near Guayana. The Inírida stood between the Orituco and the Caura, facing the entrance to the world's most insignificant mall, the Parsamón. All the people I loved now live together in my memories of that building. Some faces, exiled from memory, include the epithet for their floor in their names, as if those alphanumerical signs were an essential part of their identities: Álvaro from 4B; Alfredo, aka Dandruff, from 13B; Darío, the *goofster* from 6B. For us, the kids who played street football with old chocolate milk or *chicha* cartons for goalposts, the Inírida was the base from which we governed the vast empire of Santa Mónica. The northern border reached as far as Cumbres de Curumo and disappeared into the labyrinth of Las Rutas. Los Próceres, to the south, was part of a prohibited crossroads that led to dangerous El Valle. Behind our building there was a giant mountain and on the other side, to the east, it bordered the Cristo Rey School. From that point and beyond nothing belonged to us. Los Chaguaramos was part of another republic.

'If I'm going to die, I want to die in Ljubljana,' I said to myself. My heart failed. I never imagined that I would have to admit defeat at the age of forty. The pain began in my left arm. Clumsy motor-skills. Blindness. Asphyxia. I felt as though my lungs were filling up with oil. Before the heart attack I was convinced of my inevitable finitude. But I thought I still had plenty of time.

I woke up in a room at the Clínica Metropolitana hospital. Atilio explained the situation to me: my heart had collapsed. The heart attack had also partly affected my memory. A series of amorphous images reinforced the soporific effect of the sedatives. All the voices of the past began to speak. Some scenes appeared in the form of old photo stills, in negatives, with perforated edges: the airbag drenched with blood / Alejandro's serene face / the prettiest girl in the world standing on my shoes / the Dragon Bridge / Mariana's opened lips / the cursed song / Vivanco's green estate car / the façade of the Inírida / the years of madness.

I was thirty-two when I went crazy. I spent ten months as a patient in the psychiatric unit of the Instituto Profesional Caracas. That experience, in its own way, healed my ill-fated reason. I was able to be a man again after my therapy. I grew accustomed to living with the awareness of failure, with a fear of the past, with a horror of dogs, with the vain hope that the prettiest girl in the world would kick open the door to my house. I was so committed to regaining my reason that I neglected other aspects of my health. When the heart attack came I had accomplished my objective: I had become an ordinary and invisible man.

Atilio was rigorous: if I wanted to live, I had to get used to absolute rest. Fatso even spoke of the possibility of a delicate operation. *Forty years old!* I never thought the end would come when I was forty. My medical leave of absence turned into weariness, an essential boredom. One particularly hot night I dreamed of an old bridge. I awoke humming the cursed song; after a cup of forbidden coffee I felt better. The prettiest girl in the world once again sang in my ear. Without thinking about it too much, I made the decision. I opened the laptop. Iberia.com. Destination: Brnik Airport, Slovenia. 'If I'm going to die, I want to die in Ljubljana,' I thought, right before the hiccups, right before the coughing fit.

CHASING RABBITS

FREDDY GONÇALVES DA SILVA
Translated by Lucy Foster

*To my grandfather's cap, which held
his memories close to his hairline.*

Agustina knew the order of her days. She got up, ate cereal and toasted sesame seeds for breakfast, fed the dog and drank some coffee, while her husband got himself ready to go out for his walk. At eighty, my grandfather was still a big walker and, though twenty years her senior, he was an ideal match for Agustina.

Granddad came over from Portugal in the sixties. The Salazar regime and the war with Africa continued to generate its monthly consignment of mutilated youngsters and official notifications of the death of some neighbour or other, until one night, tormented by nightmares of black man killing white, Granddad gathered up his daughters and his sick wife and bundled them into a boat. The air at sea was different and, breathing it in, he began to accept that *obrigado* was giving way permanently to *gracias* in his mental dictionary. So he filed it there, under G, in its place.

Bom dia, eu sou da Madeira. Granddad felt Madeirense as he stood on the quayside, suitcase in hand, surrounded by his neighbours from Ponta do Sol, thinking of the rabbits hiding in the fields at home.

He had often hunted rabbits among the mulberry trees. Rabbits all around him, jumping, as if on their way down Alice's rabbit hole into Wonderland. All he could feel was his chest puffing, his eyes narrowing, and – as though a single intake of this new air might finish him off – he let out all of his *saudade* in one long breath.

Granddad's first wife, Celeste, put her face close to his and whispered, *Voltaremos* – we'll go back. But he knew it wasn't true. This was goodbye. From that sunset onwards, Portugal, the *Estado Novo*, Madeira, would all shrink away until they were nothing more than a patch of green land, barren, devoid of opportunity and getting smaller, tiny, invisible. His country was bait for bigger fish out in the sea. Or at least it seemed this way to him, as though it hung from the end of a line, trapped, lost in the depths and devoured by the multi-coloured fish. So it became a mythological place in his mind, a new Atlantis of rabbits and their rabbit holes.

Agustina, Granddad's second wife, listened to this story again and again on rainy afternoons. She never understood such prolonged nostalgia, but love for her husband had fortified her with unusual powers of comprehension and, with every new attack of the rabbits, she responded with a simple *ya pasó* – it's done now. These words also helped to allay the feeling of anxiety in her own chest every time she heard his farewell story again. Agustina was not a woman for saying goodbye.

Nevertheless, *ya pasó* did not work for her when, early one Tuesday morning, she found her husband, disorientated, at the washbasin mirror.

'You're brushing your teeth with the shaving foam! Are you going gaga on me already?'

He didn't answer. But she saw his reflection in the mirror, his wrinkles, his shoulders a little slumped, his gaze clouded with memories, and she felt suddenly as though she were being drawn into the eye of a tornado. Her eyes narrowed as she watched her husband grow smaller, tiny, invisible, and she exhaled.

*

'Go via Bellas Artes, please.'

After so many years away from Venezuela, I felt the need to reacquaint myself with some of the old places. Caracas wasn't the same; the air was heavy, the faces of the passersby looked different, the insults of the drivers seemed altered, more vitriolic. Even an afternoon on the tarmac of its streets didn't make me feel as though I'd made contact with home.

On the journey I spotted the tower of Parque Central, in ruins. I took a deep breath. I remembered the day I'd seen on the news that it had caught fire. My grandfather had called me, beside himself:

'Javier, *no sé ou qué vais a facer*, I don't know what we're going to do, look on the internet, watch the news. This is the beginning of the end, *u fim de todo.*'

I looked at the videos and watched the news and, like Granddad, I was devastated.

Nothing hurts more than something that is just not yours: a love unrequited, a private memory in a public place, a life that – though you try – you cannot influence. And yet here I was, suddenly looking at the mosque, the sun shining golden behind it, collecting the crumbs of a city gone dark with secrets. I closed my eyes and the past started to whisper my old secrets into my ears.

'A hell of a sight, isn't it boss, the tower in that sorry state,' said the taxi driver.

The tower was where I had met Laura, during a rebellious moment of my youth. Dressed in XL T-shirts, everything black and covered in AC/DC logos or Eddie holding a bloody axe in his hand. I washed rarely, and kept my hair long and greasy. I was haggard and pale. My parents said they didn't know how to control me, so one day Granddad took me up to one of the highest windows of the tower and showed me the city.

'Recognise its dangers, Javier,' he said, 'a person only respects the place he came from when he can't go back.'

Laura, who was a secretary in the office at the end of the hall, had smiled when she saw us together and I looked at her with my late-night metalhead face, thinking I was Paul Gillman, hating her for including herself in our moment.

The truth was that I had fallen in love. It makes me laugh to think of it, because I ended up spending a whole month's salary on a room at the Hilton just so that Laura might tell me that she loved me too. All that Iron Maiden, Baron Rojo and Doctor Kanoche, all the *I'm coming back, I will return, And I'll possess your body and I'll make you burn, I have the fire I have the force, I have the power to make my evil take its course*, only to end up, years later, whispering sweet nothings in Laura's ear in the suite of that hotel, with no money in my pockets, not even enough for a Cocosette biscuit from the vending machine, and reciting the lyrics of *'Tan enamorados'* by Ricardo Montaner, as though I had written them myself. I recreated the scene with my grandfather, showing Laura the city from the window, hoping she would drop everything and marry me; but no one can make the transition from Gillman's leather jacket to Montaner's white trainers and still keep face.

My grandfather was a good man, always straight down the line, always polite and correct – he had none of my odd personality traits. All my life I've been running from something; from government, from politics, fear, dejection, solitude, in the hope that it will make me a bit more like him, but in the end no one escapes the man in the mirror.

The taxi was approaching the hotel and I, lost in my memories, got ready to greet it with a smile. But instead when I saw it I had a sudden jolting feeling, as though the driver had braked hard and without warning:

'Hotel "Alba"? What the hell is that!'

The taxi driver gave the same response he had given all day, 'These are different times.' At last I understood that I had come back to a different place, a distant place that belonged to other people. So, bereft of any names for my landscapes, with my memories drifting out to sea, I asked him to take the motorway. It was time to see my grandfather.

*

That morning, drinking her coffee, Agustina found herself unable to stack up her memories on the table in front of her, as she did every other day. She was still reeling from the shock that the man who had shared her bed for the last twenty years did not seem to know her.

'Are you sure you don't know who I am?' she implored, but he didn't dare to look, cowered by the fear hanging from the wall beside the crucifix.

Granddad was being scrutinised by a woman he did not recognise, by a strange dog smelling his shoes, by a room that wasn't his. He tried to recognise himself in the clock, the books, the bedspread. His heart fluttered as he touched things. He had no idea where he was.

And then it happened.

Suddenly he felt a little jump in the mattress. He fixed his gaze on the sheets, analysing their waves and undulations, and he made a mental note of the feeling of his weight spread out across the bed. He knew what he had to do.

'*Te vou a trapar*, I'm going to catch you, *rapaz.*'

Agustina stood back to see what would happen next. Granddad launched himself at the nightstand, put his cap on and started searching – first behind the lamp, knocking over the alarm clock, then under the mattress. When a picture frame fell to the floor in the commotion, the dog let out a pitiful howl and went to seek refuge in the living room. Agustina tried to calm her husband down, but he was muttering mortal threats under his breath. He opened the wardrobe and pulled the clothes from their hangers and looked in the suitcases. He found nothing. Eventually he came out of the room, calling for his dead mother, asking her to bring the shotgun.

In the next room he came face to face with his terrorised dog, barking at him. The dog looked at the enormous body of his owner, depleted and saddened. He stopped barking and stopped wagging his tail but did not look away. The two of them were now in a battle for recognition.

Granddad also froze in the middle of the living room, his gaze vacant and his mind blank. His neurons seemed to have stopped making their connections. The lights went out, and in the power cut he lost touch with the present.

A silence lengthened between the two figures, dog and owner. The dog, seeming to understand what was happening to his owner, approached slowly to smell his feet, licking him unthreateningly. In that moment an army of neurons gave way on the battlefield inside Granddad's head, felled by the white flag of this animal licking his feet. Granddad tried to resist, didn't move; he was frightened, thinking that if he lifted even a finger now all the mutilated would be sent back to him again, envelope after envelope with news of the casualties of war. It was getting late, and this time there was no island to run to. Agustina, her fingers in the knots of her many fears, put her hand on her husband's shoulder.

'It's the dog, José, it's the dog.'

Without moving, he looked down at the dog and inside his brain a light came on, as though a grenade had been thrown onto the battlefield.

Granddad understands again.

'It's not a dog, it's a rabbit.'

The rabbit jumps through the apartment, until he finally finds a rabbit hole in a crack in the door. He escapes. Granddad falls, immobile, to the floor.

*

How many memories does it take to pass the time in the Caracas traffic? Four lifetimes' worth? Eight? After the shock of the hotel, the taxi driver helps me to recalibrate my memory in line with the social changes I am discovering.

'Those conquistadores were killing us years ago, and now it's time for the payback,' the driver says candidly, convinced of the linguistic retribution.

Everything has changed: the names of places have mutated – my first dates with Laura weren't on our way up Mount Ávila, but in the Waraira Repano.

243

The last dates weren't in the café at the Ateneo, instead those fights have now taken place somewhere called Unearte. The day that Laura left me, we were in the Parque Generalísimo Francisco de Miranda, not in the Parque del Este. But I don't care about that one. I wanted that place to change, or even to vanish completely, with its herons on the lake, the racket of its migrating macaws, and her Adriatic eyes. For this is the place where Laura shot me down and ended everything. How I wish that in learning the details of my past anew, I could also change some of them. All I can do is try to assimilate myself into this new discourse, with its new names, to make another improvised history. I even tell myself, still grieving, that had the park not been called Parque del Este Laura might not have left me at all.

'That'll be 250 new bolivars, sir.'

The things people say don't change anything. Even if it goes by another name the amount of money doesn't change, it all comes out the same in the end.

I pay, get out of the taxi with my suitcases, and take in the entrance of the building. I'm back. Large drops of water are falling down my chest in the humidity, and rain starts to bang against the zinc roof of the building. I go in as soon as one of the neighbours opens the door. I don't recognize him. The people have changed too.

I know the shiny white tiles on the walls of the entrance. I can make out two red lights, reflected in them, two circles dancing to the sound of the downpour. These lights break out into straight lines just as the sound of a siren is drowned by the drumming of the hail. I turn to discover that there is an ambulance at the door, waiting for an elderly gentleman who lives on the eighth floor. The stretcher passes me in a flash, racing down the hallway. That's how we meet again, my grandfather and I – he unconscious, speeding past me on a pair of greasy wheels which leave a dark trace along the floor until they reach the rain. Things aren't like they used to be.

*

Alzheimer's. Second phase. That's what they diagnose, all those doctors with their white overalls and their spotless faces, busily balancing books and juggling patients. Patient about what, I ask myself, waiting patiently for death? Agustina tries to calm me down, she explains that my grandfather has been like this for some time. I refuse to keep on paying tribute to resignation. It's as though that has been the only sentiment available to me since they stamped my passport. I try to explain to them that for my grandfather, pacing up and down through his memories, turning them over and examining them, has been a lifelong exercise. Taking someone's memory away is like stripping them naked and pushing them out before a crowd, exposing them to a squeamish world that keeps turning around them. They were leaving him with no history, with no memory. What would I do if my history were taken from me? If I were left without Laura? The doctor just tells me that it could be worse, 'At least he still has his life.'

What life?

I see him lying on the bed and I wonder, insistently, what life?

*

The return to infancy, a commonplace among all humans. Agustina, my mother and my aunt are all living in the fear that my grandfather might leave them behind in the search for his dead. It is the dead he thinks of now, the dead he calls out to, the dead he goes looking for. As for me, he only remembers me as I was in a particular childhood photo, recognising me in the past; at the moment, he confuses me with an employee from the fruit shop that he owned in Bello Monte when he first arrived in Venezuela. He called out orders in those days in the same way that now he hides the pigeons' eggs from the window boxes in his pockets. Day after day I sit down with him to hear the new day's anecdote, looking for the laughter in his benevolent glances, waiting for the complicit twinkle of a rascal about to carry out some mischief. He never removes the faded cap, beige with green badges. In old age, his mannerisms have grown more and more childish. The cheeky smile, the constant winking, and the cap – *cachucha*, he liked to call it – always worn sideways.

Seeing him, looking after him, I think of you, Laura. Might this be what I need? A refuge from you.

I get up, he needs help to stand. He wants to go out chasing rabbits again; we try to explain to him that there are no rabbits, and that he's in an apartment in a building in the city, all covered over with asphalt.

He goes to the window and points to the mountain. I explain that Madeira is not outside the window, and that there aren't any rabbits here either.

'That greenery out there is, what is it? Mount Ávila? Waraira Repano? Caracas' green belt? Whatever it's called… It's another mountain, not the one you're looking for, Granddad.'

We give him his blood pressure tablet and he calms down and ends up on the same sofa in the living room, punching it with his closed fist, knowing he's cracking up and watching his memory escape him down little rabbit warrens.

'I'm shrivelling up from the inside,' he says, and goes to his room to cry, determined to forget.

*

One warren, two rabbits, three warrens, four rabbits, five warrens, six rabbits, seven warrens, eight rabbits… They jump, they hide…

He's breathless, without a shotgun… And meanwhile Mount Ávila is sinking into the sea…

*

I drum my fingers on the table, feeling wretched. I lift the telephone. Control my breathing. I know the scene is clichéd. Franco De Vita and Rudy La Scala assail me; I'm a collage of throaty melodies, I'm a collage of you. I hang up. I'm frightened that you'll pick up… that you'll know what I mean.

Agustina had to reorder her days. She woke up earlier to have her coffee and her toasted sesame seeds, sometimes even to eat an *arepa* to give her strength for the new tenor of her days. She didn't wait for her husband to get ready any more; after tying the dog up in the kitchen, she went and got him ready herself. With her daughters, she helped to bathe him, shave him, put his nappy on and dress him. After combing his hair, she put on his cologne for him and, with a kiss on the forehead, placed his cap on his head. In the mornings, Agustina stacked all her hopes in front of her on the table, while she drank her coffee.

She doesn't know how to say goodbye.

*

Granddad was nostalgic for his house keys, he gazed at them where they hung on the wall. He turned them over in his hands, finding himself again in them. In their texture he felt all the places where he used to walk, the streets of Caracas that were interchangeable with the *ruas* of Portugal, the shoes he had worn out, the blue Malibu he always drove. Granddad was nostalgic for going out. The keys oozed this sweet sadness, they were another form of saudade for him, they were the repressed desires of his final journey, his very own enactment of Vila-Matas' *Viaje Vertical*. I read once that saudade is a sentiment that can be whatever the individual wants. His form of saudade was his abstraction. So I decided to take him out.

'Are you sure? Everything's so disordered,' said Agustina, with the hesitation of a mother letting her child out of her sight for the first time. I calmed her down, promised that I'd take him in his wheelchair.

His face changed, and for a moment I wanted to sit in that chair, to try and put myself in his place to understand what he was thinking. He hardly spoke now; it was as though the switching off of the lights in his brain had taken away the desire to speak, the impulse to communicate. In that moment though, he was happy.

We went to Plaza Castellana, where he used to take the dog. He rested his gaze fixedly on a single point, as though he were remembering his walks there. I sat by his side and spoke to him about things that had happened, about my experiences in Spain, about Madeira when I had been to visit, and finally I spoke about Laura. He remained still, looking into the distance as though his keys were hanging from the statue of Isabel la Católica in the middle of the plaza.

'She never came to this country, not like you. You were brave,' I told him, as if I were telling a bad joke, trying to engage him. It worked. In a wavering blend of Portuguese and Spanish, he began to talk to me about Salazar as though I were a fellow Lusitanian. He wasn't telling me his story, he was living it by my side, as though we were seated in *La Serra*. Today he had decided to treat me as one of his hunting companions. Laughing, he repeated *O senhor Esteve*, but he grew sadder at the mention of the *Estado Novo*. He talked of *suas filhias* – his daughters – being taught to respect the boss, of the police, he said that perhaps he ought not be speaking so much, that everything was for the good of the people... but what a poor people it was.

'We are on our own and proudly so... *À sua sacana!*' he said, shaking his head.

I didn't understand half of what he said, but I let myself get tangled in his web of references, listening to him speak so fluently, questioning his country, seeing history repeat itself as he looked at the city. I asked him questions, I encouraged, improvised. Until he said, suddenly:

'*Eu penso, que estesen todos calados* – everyone should be quiet, including you,' he said, as though he were reciting from his favourite film, laughing to himself, '*Agora silencio, se va a cantar o fado.*'

Granddad got out of his wheelchair, whispering some sort of *cantiga*, went over to the statue and stroked it... and in his smile was the sadness of someone who was packing up their past in a suitcase.

*

From the street, Granddad spies rabbits all over. They are scampering playfully amongst his neighbours, the loves of his youth, his parents, and the villagers with their instruments in hand. He sits on an old bench – perhaps in reality he has always been there – and watches each rabbit launch its attack on the darkness, he speaks to an old companion who seems to have frozen in time. Suddenly, the sound of a drum, some church bells, the hollow blast of a tuba, invite people to a grand event. Everyone sits around a wall on which the film *Fado. Historia D'Uma Cantadeira* is projected. They are all mesmerised. The character of Ana Maria, played by Amalia Rodriguez, comes out in front of the audience in a restaurant, and everyone applauds her, enthralled.

'*Agora silencio, se va a cantar o fado,*' says a man in the film.

Granddad gets up, moved almost to tears, humming the fado that Amalia, with her black shawl and her small-town charm, renders for him. He goes closer to the wall to touch the image, everyone whistles and shouts at him to get out of the way. He turns around, waking from his reverie and, in the fog of the projector, between the lights in black and white, he sees the figure of Celeste, who smiles shyly, and helps him get himself out of there. He falls in love with his first wife all over again. Now there is silence, and she moves away to the chords of a Portuguese guitar, with a voice that sings:

'*O mais feliz é o teu, tenho a certeza. É o fado da pobreza. Que nos leva à felicidade. Se Deus o quis. Não te invejo essa conquista. Porque o meu é mais fadista. É o fado da saudade.*'

Celeste, too, goes down a rabbit hole, turning to smoke and going straight out of his head. Granddad doesn't run. He doesn't look for her. He has removed himself again. The film does not exist, nor the friends, nor the village. Everything is white, everything light. He sees himself, younger, meeting Agustina in a street of La Candelaria. He gives her his hand. She kisses his cheek.

Agustina hooks herself on his arm and asks him sweetly, '*Volvemos* – shall we go back?'

*

I sit on the bench in the plaza and watch Agustina's tenderness calm my grandfather's desire to dance with Isabel la Católica.

'You see, your grandfather's always been a scoundrel,' she teases, smiling. 'Oh, my Portugal, I always have to keep my eye on you!'

My grandfather smiles sadly, and strokes his wife's trembling face. He gets back into the wheelchair, a dead weight of goodbyes. Agustina wants to take him for a walk on her own. She doesn't ask, but I can see it's what she wants. They go.

Thought is frightening when it comes uninvited. But it has come, and I see you, I remember you, I conjure you up. You sit down next to me and you are the same Laura, with no other names, in the same flowery dress that you wore to meet me when I visited you in Italy.

'How's it going?' I asked, a pathetic attempt to flirt with you again.

'Oh you know, it's all the same shit over here or over there… the only thing to do is try and amuse yourself along the way.' There you go again, seducing me with that same dissatisfaction with life.

You offered me olives. Your delicious lips could elicit erections, heart attacks, heartbreak. You were still the same. You were open, free and unattainable. And I was still shut in that hotel suite, reciting Montaner songs, hoping that you'd have mercy on me, humiliating myself.

'Did you go back?' I ask your spectre, the one sitting beside me on the bench.

'Go back where? Javier, a person can't go back to a place they've never been.'

You get up again in your white flowery dress, and you vanish. I'm alone again, saying goodbye to you. And I make my decision. This return is over.

I'm leaving.

*

That night Granddad was unsettled, dreaming about his shotgun.

Boom! An escaped rabbit. Boom! Another one who was hiding in a corner. Boom! A swimming rabbit. Boom! A flying rabbit. Boom, boom! He let them all have it.

Boom!

*

My bags are waiting in the doorway. I can't delay my return to the publishing house where I work in Spain any longer. I'm tired of being a repository for the all-consuming memories of *her* in this city. The dog circles me, waiting for a final pat. In the porch, Agustina wipes away a few tears and my grandfather, in his isolation, smiles without knowing that he knows me, but still always affable.

I take a deep breath, as if to empty myself from his smell, and a single intake of this air fills my chest with salt from the sea, working its way into my unshed tears. In an unexpected gesture, Granddad puts his cap on my head; I am an ally. It doesn't matter that the image of the strong man who sat me on his lap every December is a distant memory in the presence of this exhausted human being, a shrunken old man in a shirt stained with the food he has spilt down it. It doesn't matter that he is forgetful, as long as there remains in that smile some trace of satisfaction. In my head there are no wars, languages, ideologies, and no illnesses... Laura is not there... With this cap on I am just Granddad's employee, his hunting companion, a family friend and, occasionally, his grandson... I have all the lifetimes I need to get me back to the airport through the Caracas traffic.

I move backwards, as though I can feel the sea beneath my feet with every step. I hear a splash as my vision blurs. In a moment everything is water and salt.

Yet another goodbye.

*

Granddad smiled from his bed. He knew that his grandson was going, leaving a sinking ship. His body, now an island, undulated smoothly.

The fear fell from the walls and, as though water were coming out of all of the rabbit warrens at once, the sea gradually filled the room. The rabbits came out of their holes, drenched, and Granddad laughed to see them thrashing about in the waves, startled, trying to run from their hunter, his grandson in the background.

Granddad just laughed; he had no shotgun and not much breath left in his lungs, but he was free.

Suddenly there was a tremor, as though an earthquake were shaking the city, or a huge green mountain were being born from a fissure in the ground, launching the bed high into the air. Granddad was enjoying himself. The island is coming back... It's Madeira, it's Mount Ávila, it's Waraira Repano... it's Atlantis. And inside his head, the neurons put flowers into the mouths of all the shotguns firing at him, at his mind, living through a revolution that never was, raising a final white flag against oblivion.

With one last guffaw, Granddad let out his breath, and with it, all his saudade.

ON A BAD DAY IN 1979

VICTORIA DE STEFANO
Translated by Christina MacSweeney

On a bad day in 1979, in the rain, lost, exhausted, seeking refuge in the house of the dead, whose outline suddenly appeared before me in the muted morning light of a corner of the old cemetery of Montmartre, chance led me to Stendhal's grave.

Overhead, the Caulaincourt Bridge thundered, shaken by the drumming of the Metro carriages. Overhead, above he who loved the countryside and beautiful views, who used to say that man is happiest among trees, who explicitly expressed his desire to be buried – if it were not too expensive – in the cemetery in Andilly, in the Forest of Montmorency, under the foliage of the promontory leading to the Seine valley, near to where he corrected the galleys of *Love* – written in pencil, in Milan, as he walked and thought of Métilde – printed in 12°, on poor quality paper, very poor quality and very cheap, just a few steps from where he'd relived, once again, every unmitigated nuance of his love for Métilde Dembowski, née Viscontini. (*I was on the verge of going mad.*) Stendhal, being read at last, all past wrongs redressed, the splendour of his name restored, a name that will endure for ever, venerated, admired, enjoying such prestige, and yet without that small, easily fulfilled wish being granted.

Stendhal was poor, he died in penury, said the Australian man who, seated beside me, holding his umbrella over my head, was enlightening me on the topic.

So why did he admire him so much? Because he was the negation of what he most abhorred: tartuffery. Because he was the affirmation of what he most appreciated in man: the search for happiness for the pleasure of the search itself, not for the finding, which was undoubtedly a trivial, deceptive chimera, a Utopia for idiots, a snare for the melancholy.

Not happiness, he said. How can I explain it? The explosion of feeling, the precipitate of his unbridled joy. Not happiness itself, but the paths of happiness, constantly changing, its marvellous, unexpected avatars, the improbable, the incredible situations which only chance can offer... At times, he considered him to be his saint, to the extent that an unbeliever can consider the noble souls who guide him to be saints. Yes, madam, my saint, my guiding light, the ideal I'm proud of. And he bowed down before him, before Stendhal, before his ingenuity, his euphoria, his fire. Could he be so foolish and insensitive as to do otherwise? To be indifferent to his talent, his fearlessness, his caprices and peculiarities? How could he not marvel at the personification of everything that was great? How splendid Stendhal was! How splendid his novels were! What a pen, my God, what a powerful pen!

Now, come with me.

He took my hand, pulling me along for a good distance, moving away, returning to the roar of the Metro, entering darker spaces, getting into a tangle with the umbrella, determined, animated, following the map he kept unfolded before us.

Look to the left. Can you see the tombstone under that beautiful willow? It was a simple stone. Please, go closer. Do you see? I read the inscription, just a name, a date. Heinrich Heine, the German nightingale who made his nest in France! Heinrich Heine, the Rabelais of emotions! The Voltairean cutting from the German trunk!

So, beneath the heavy drops that continued to drip from the foliage, on the softened earth, amid the scent of moss and decomposing leaves left by the rain, the Australian confided in me that during this, his third tour of Europe, just as he had done on the first and second occasions, faithful to his dead friends and the maxim of his master, his halcyon, indefatigable master, the intrepid hiker of Sils-Maria, according to whom *only where there are tombs are there resurrections*, he intended to visit various cemeteries, those hospitable, roofless cities, those mansions of the spirit, those garrets of the deep, those oceans of silence, those urban appendices of rich humus, those last strongholds at the end of the journey where each person sought his dead, the people to whom he was united, the people he loved.

No better place, he said, leaning straight-backed on the handle of his umbrella, for a choosy necrophile, for a conscientious exhumer of those who, though dead, continue living, for a lover of the past and of those who gained victory over death (*victory over death*, stressed), for someone possessed by the idea of immortality, for a fanatical explorer of enigma, as he defined himself in the most natural way: the cemetery of Charville, deep in the grounds of which the angel of exile, in exile from himself, Arthur Rimbaud, was buried; the cemetery of Battignoles, where lay his master in perversion, the ultra-lyrical Verlaine; the cemetery of Montparnasse, which sheltered the mortal remains of the highest of the high, the greatest image of poetry created by man, Charles Baudelaire (and César Vallejo, I tell myself while writing this); the cemetery of Picpus, in whose imperturbable shadows Rilke loved to shelter at the uncertain twilight hour, and to which the body – by all accounts headless · of the poet André Chénier, among the last of those beheaded during the Terror, was dragged; the cemeteries of La Villette, of Bagneux, of Montrouge, of Auteuil, of Passy, of Belleville, the great forty-four-hectare fief containing the graves of Father Goriot, Esther Gobseck, Lucien de Rubempré, Cousin Pons, Jacques Collin, the last incarnation of Vautrin, and, reigning on its highest point, Marcel. That fertile field which gathered together the worst and the best of France, and where – finally lying together again in the shared peace of the shroud, reduced to barely a pound of impalpable ashes – are to be found Heloise and her husband, the peripatetic, the incontrovertible Pierre Abelard.

*

In relation to ashes, he said, there was a letter, a few lines in a letter written by the learned Abelard – sent to his grieving Heloise, all the more the lover for not being satisfied – that were, he emphasised, beyond any price due to the contempt he shows for his unhappy love and brutal emasculation. And he'd been so fascinated by those lines that he had even set himself the task of adapting the passage for the clavichord, but as was to be expected in an amateur with little talent, for all his evocation of the demon of music, for all the days and nights dedicated to the attempt, it had been an embarrassing failure.

He threw a pebble into a puddle. The fantasies I have from time to time! Me, a musician?, he exclaimed. It's enough to make you die laughing… Another of my crazy ideas. Oh, how awful the impotence of the act of creation for the creator. It's not enough to settle down to the human task, not enough to work, the desire is not enough. No, no way. Something would still be missing, something essential. Courage. Courage and talent. Courage added to talent and multiplied by all the rest.

He stood in silence, a silence that seemed to me to last for ever, and suddenly, with his eyes looking fixedly ahead, he parted his lips to the sweet soft tune of: *Che farò senza Euridice… Euridice, Euridice, sombra cara, ove sei…*

Would you like to hear it? And I, not understanding, bewildered, asked: Hear what?

Pierre Abelard, of course.

Yes, I would.

Clasping his hands and inclining his lovely face towards me: Really? Would you?

He sat on a bench and took a thick black notebook, like a breviary, from the inside pocket of his jacket. Here it is, he exclaimed, and in a voice of beautiful, throbbing inflections, in which his whole being was concentrated, he read, his finger following the letters – spirited, impulsive, enjambed, as I could see as I looked over his shoulder – while his hand moved down the page: *Then you will see me, not to shed tears, the time for that will have passed: shed them now to extinguish illicit passion: then you will see me, to strengthen your piety with the horror of this cadaver, and my death, more eloquent that I, will tell you what it is you love when you love a man.*

He gave me a sideways glance, resting his chin in his hand. He was trembling slightly. A little brandy? It's cold.

From his travel bag, he extracted a small bottle and unscrewed the cap. Before offering it to me, he smelled it, running the tip of his tongue over his lips. Was it brandy or a magic potion? I drank. Was it brandy or a love philtre? I drank again. A pleasant sensation spread through me, as if a warm red glow were expanding my veins to liberate the torrent.

Oblivious to me and to everything else, passing his hand over his face, his neck wrapped in a red and blue check woollen scarf, he repeated: *and my death, more eloquent that I, will tell you what it is you love when you love a man*, twice, three, even four times, raising the intensity of the emotion by half a degree on each repetition.

With almost no perceptible transition and a huge smile lighting his decidedly blue eyes, putting into the pocket of his Burberry the small bottle and the black leather notebook – my treasure, my *vade mecum*, my Baedeker, my book of hours, my beloved ark, the coffer of my memory – in which, in addition to so much else – dates, maxims, ephemera, facts – he made marginal notes of his thoughts and everything arising from his daily readings (he travelled with several – twenty or thirty – kilos of books he couldn't live without, his books were his conscience and should go where he went, for better or worse, however short or long his trips were), he informed me that that same night he was to take the train to Florence, where, in the church of Santa Croce, were to be found, cheek and jowl, Galileo, Machiavelli, Alfieri and Michelangelo, the master of living stone, and, in the nave of the Sepulchre Chapel of the church of San Lorenzo, the bones of the great dukes in their jasper, porphyry and granite tombs.

His trip would last about two weeks. Or however long it took to consult certain manuscripts in the archives of the Laurentian Library. To look through the archives and walk by the Arno, walk in the light of the Arno and enjoy, once more, Bronzino's *Descent of Christ into Limbo*, the Titians in the Pitti Gallery, in particular the *Man with Grey Eyes* and the *Aretino*, undoubtedly not the artist's best portraits, but the ones he admired most. From Florence to Naples to visit Virgil's tomb, and from Naples to Herculaneum and Pompeii. He didn't want to miss the opportunity to explore that area of Campania, where, according to ancient legend, the Gates of Hell were to be found. There, where under black clouds of pumice stone, in the year 79 of the current era, Pliny the Elder had lost his life due to his scientific curiosity; Pliny, that slightly Vernesque spirit for whom he felt a special adoration, to the point of having spent a small fortune on the thirty-seven books of his natural history: *you pay dear for what you love.*

Immediately after that, following his itinerary, he would travel north. Sitting by the window on local trains (shreds of green, fragments of trunks, blackened branches, snow on the roads, clouds, tunnels, rows of small houses, platforms, clocks, halts in stations with their ample dose of annoyance), which offered him, in addition to the calm he required to address his spiritual needs and to keep strict control on a heart overladen with the stress of travel – for want of horse drawn carriages or some equally slow and outdated means of locomotion – the sensation of being topographically and physically transported through the coordinates of space. And if nothing unexpected occurred, that is to say, if he didn't change his mind, tempted by chance, or who knows what sudden mood, depression included, as sometimes happened, he would continue on to the Währing cemetery, where, beside Beethoven, stricken in that organ which was indispensable to his art, lay the good Schubert, the best and simplest of men, and then to the small graveyard in the mountains of Valais that shelters, beneath thick layers of cold and silence, the prudish and, to his mind, intolerably pure but still notable Rainer Maria Rilke. After that, he would take a short rest in some small hotel in the Swiss mountains, looking out onto the Lake of the Four Cantons, scenery, atmosphere, clarity, air – that alpine air that cleans the lungs for deep breathing – sharp thorns, meadows of late-summer plants, ploughed fields, wallflowers, bells, deep gullies, snow-capped peaks, glaciers, blood-red sunsets over the lake, an image, what am I saying, he said, multiple images of unspoilt beauty that had drawn and repelled him since he'd been there with his parents as a child, a very small child. With his unfortunate parents who had died young, so young that they were complete strangers to him. They too were almost children. October 1949, killed in a strange accident. Would the lake bring back the image of his parents? Would the lake exorcise the magnetic force of that absence? Mother. Father. Would they appear together or separately?

He asked himself questions for which he had no answer... Formulated questions for which there were no answers. But if he didn't go there, he would never dispel the doubt (*doubt*, he repeated, *the worst of germs to attack the soul, with the exception of the taste of the poisoned fruit of disillusion*). Will I go? Will I not go? How to live with that uncertainty? Would he opt to let the decision rest on the throw of a die? The toss of a coin? He was blowing bubbles that would ultimately burst.

Then straight on to Antwerp, to St James's church, where the glorious Rubens lay among the greatest gods of a century replete with painters, and by sea, leaving the continent behind, back to England. To Coniston, in order to visit the grave of Mr Ruskin, with his mania for stone, to Canterbury, in whose earth Joseph Conrad had cast his anchor, to Bunhill Fields, the burial ground of the victims of the Great Plague, in which, due to one of those extraordinary interventions of Nemesis – the same that made Swift build the lunatic asylum to which he would be committed in his old age – his fellow chronicler of that plague, the diligent Mr Daniel Defoe was also laid to rest, and to Bybrook Cemetery in Ashford, Kent, where little Simone Weil sleeps the great sleep, and to the country church in Nottinghamshire to which were transported from Missolonghi, on the brig *Florida*, soaked in alcohol and so preserved from all posthumous harm, the remains of the incomparable Byron, the athlete, the songbird of freedom, of whom he had an old bronze bust, placed facing out to sea, in the den of his small house in Newcastle, standing on a pile of music scores. By whom? Schumann. *Another dead idol.*

And he'd already paid homage to Leonardo in the garden of France, that is to say in Touraine, to Chateaubriand on the islet of Grand Bé, in the bay of Saint-Malo. An absolutely magnificent place, like a desire, like an impossible dream, and at some point – he'd promised himself – his pilgrimage would take him to the holy city of Neyshabur, where Omar

Khayyam, pure contemplator of the stars, is buried at the foot of a garden wall, over which can be seen the tops of pear and apricot trees that, in his praise, are maintained like a flowering orchard, always in bloom.

On his arrival, the first thing he'd do would be to get drunk on wine. Then he would enter the garden, handing out alms to the beggars, and he'd lie on the ground, in the nude if possible, at risk of receiving a thrashing, to await nightfall, the fiesta of his Persian night spangled with stars, and he'd greet the new day at the departure of the moon, at the bray of the ass, the crow of the cock, the appearance of the clarifying rays of the sun on its pedestal of peaks, to the cry of *Allah, Allah! Akbar Allah!*

Jumping to his feet, hand on heart, head well forward, in the regulation oratorical stance, clearly emphasising the scansion, he recited some of the choicest *rubaiyats* on wine, women and songs on the fleeting nature of life. Suddenly, with a gleeful flash of brilliantly white teeth and a vigour that softened (or should I say, gave the lie to?) his gloomy mood, and with which – revealing himself in his unique humanity – he was sublimely ironising his own foolishness, he asked me if I was aware that in Athens and Sparta they used to cut off the hand that had caused the death of a suicide and bury it separately. So, it was to be supposed that Socrates' hand and body were to be found in different parts of demotic Athens, beneath the dust of the markets or the floors of the new Greeks. Perhaps feeding the plants in some dirty slum quarter, perhaps getting in the way of some horse or goat. Or caught between the wheels of cars, jumping at the sound of the horns. Unmatched hands, each in turn pushed by the incredible force of the sea breeze, far from their ungrateful land.

And picking up his umbrella again, as he hoisted his elegant travel bag onto his shoulder, he burst out: pitiful life, this one which doesn't allow you to be in two places at once! Not to be able to be here and in the hills of Newcastle, in Brisbane and in Geneva, in Vienna and Syracuse, in Hyde Park and Cuzco, in Veracruz and River Blue, in Sri Lanka and in the Bay of Mombassa, in Paramaribo and in Cape Horn, in San Francisco and The Hague, in Turkistan and on the Dead Sea, on the Danube and the banks of the Volga, on a crag in Genoa and on another, which he knew very well, in the land where he grew up! On the cliffs of Funchal and in Brittany, on the Rialto and the Galata, on the Brooklyn Bridge and the Golden Gate, on the pedestrian bridge in Shakespeare's birthplace and the one in Sydney Bay, on the Via Tuscolana, by the tomb of Eurysaces the Baker, and in Ravenna and in the Piazza San Marco, in Kabul and on the islands of the Homeric sea and the Clarence Islands, in Inútil Bay, in Puerto del Hambre, in Tierra de la Desolación, in the far south of the American continent, in Detroit, in Chicago, in Damascus, the oldest city in the world, and in Trabzon and in Smyrna, in Nepal and in Alexandria, in the British Museum and at the kiosk on the corner, in the Tuileries and in the Bastille, in the heart of London and in the heart of the heart of the jungle, surrounded by Eskimos and platypuses, by Comanches and Vikings, by Greeks and Tartars, by Malayans and Guaranis, by Kaffirs and Cook Islanders, by the best of present-day society and the intimacy of the great departed! And so on, and so on, and so on... Not to be able to fish from the quays of the Seine and the banks of the Hudson, hunt leopards in Kenya and hippopotami in Harare! And so on, and so on, and so on. Not to be able to be here and under the sun of the Arctic Circle, not to be able to unite the day with the night, to be at once nomadic and sedentary!

Not to be able to be simultaneously here and anywhere else. If you're here, you're not there, and if you're there, you want to be here... Constantly having to give something up. Ah, how do we navigate up the river of that frustrating nostalgia for not missing out on anything? Constantly having to choose. Constantly burning your boats. One thing or the other. Constantly having to defer something, constantly sacrificing something. Constantly in discord with our dearest desires. Constantly looking for what isn't there. What was left for us, then? Given that we couldn't rupture time, or spill life out over the map of the world. All that was left was travel. Travel as a substitute for that contemplative zeal, for that endemic disease of the soul. Errancy and freedom. And of course, only if you were exempt from the ignominy of paid employment.

Whoever does not have two-thirds of his day for himself is a slave, his master Nietzsche had stated. A truth to which even monkeys would subscribe with their left hands... There's nothing else for it: take joy in travel... Naturally, if you were rich enough to take that joy, which was undoubtedly his case. I'm a man whose whole life is spent in leisure, he said. *I don't earn a living, I earn life.* Ah, those journeys in which our imagination would be always occupied with the next stage, with the anticipation, the effects, the marvels of those events full of meaning that were, in themselves, life's charm. God never aspired to anything else! *Journeys that added life to life,* it was not he but Mr Nerval who had said that.

J'ai fait trois fois le tour du monde dans mes voyages, he crooned. *J'ai fait trois fois le tour du monde dans me voyage...*

If he had his way, no one would see him in the same place for two months at a time. Unless he, George Bilfinger – citizen of the world, it must be said, from no city, from every city, a native of Australia, a country bigger than a hundred countries put together, Occania, an island, a continent, the largest sea on the planet, a tightly stretched horizon, stretched along all its wide liquid surface – decided that it should be so...

But let's not slander the world. What can it matter to it that we are owed so many other lives, so many landscapes and experiences, that so many doors are closed to us and never re-opened? What can it matter to the cherry tree whether or not we like its fruit? What can it matter to the thrush whether or not we love its warbling? What can it matter to the world that its successive occupants be carried off to death? What does the world care about this continuous, unequal battle of ours against miserly, turbid life? The ridiculous failure of mortal creatures? No, he said, don't misunderstand me. I accept the world as it is… I'm not complaining. There's no grievance. *To understand is to forgive, to forget is to forgive,* as Spinoza said. *Ego te absolvo.* Reality always imposes itself. I'm a philosopher too, and I take my hat off to the triumphs of its indicative power.

And now, how about going to a small bistro near the Rue des Petits-Champs, that medieval relic of the old mud city, around the corner from the Bank of France? A very hospitable place, impeccable service. They do a delicious kidney brochette, marvellous cutlets *à la Barnave*, almost blood red. And the wine is superb. *Allons, allons*, it's getting late, we need to hurry… Where there's hunger there's no conflict… Assuming that it can be satisfied, of course. Would you mind holding my hand? You wouldn't? Really? I'm dying for some sign of friendship. These huge cities! And always so lonely. And my life so full of people I'll probably never see again. *Alors, oui ou non*?

In the vicinity of the Place Clichy, escaping from the swaying dances and bells of a tailback of Buddhist monks, authentic Tonkin Buddhists, in orange and brown, we slip into a side street. In mid-flow, as if some delayed memory had come into his mind, he stopped: when he rose from the table, Mr Talleyrand liked to say that fate could not reach him because he had already eaten. And in a few hours, we'll have eaten. We too will be out of its reach.

And I laughed. I laughed out loud. We were going down the steps of the underpass, and I laughed, and laughed, unable to stop. Without warning, he let go of my hand and started doing some very strange dance, all high kicks and arms held aloft. Suddenly, I felt an enormous, deep explosion rising up inside me, that explosion of pleasure where we are rolling down an invisible slope and everything around us vanishes. My God, who knows how this will end? For my part, I only have one life, one life… a life I don't want to let slip through my fingers like a stream of water. Not so fast, not so fast, stream of life.

It's a Scottish jig, he shouted, tossing his red and blue check woollen scarf into the air.

As we emerged from the tunnel, the hurried footsteps of the imperturbable French passed us by. Just one glance, from the eager eyes – framed by dark rings – of a child, and the convulsive, vertical and lateral tremor of the chin of a blind harpist, stretched out on the ground, while the thread of bones that were his hands rattled the coins in his hat.

Phew! I'm exhausted. I learnt that cancan so I could dance it at Joyce's tombstone in the Fluntern cemetery, with its marvellous views of Zurich. Did I? Oh yes, oh yes! And how! For want of bagpipes with their tassels and ribbons, I was accompanied by the harmonica and third violin of a local orchestra. They thought it was crazy, taking music to the dead. I made an effort to explain to them that although Mr Joyce might be dead, he was of that line of people who hadn't stopped being alive. Is Christ, the second person of the Trinity, dead just because he's not present in his fleshy raiment? Yes, but Christ is in heaven, and the emeritus Mr Joyce is underground, they retorted, as if wanting to demonstrate to me how imperfectly they had applied their brains, not only to the minutiae of theology, but also to the highest flights of dialectics. I had no option but to follow Iago's advice: put more money in their purse. They'll understand that, I told myself. Everyone understands the truth of that language. Money, hard cash, ready cash, small change, loose change, pocket money, pin money, pounds, shillings and pence... Poetry is good, but not that good. Poetry is good but francs are infinitely better.

He moved closer and stared into my eyes. *N'ayez pas peur, ma chère,* he said. I'm timid, you're timid. Let's be daring... Today I feel romantic. No, I won't disappoint you. So far, I've only shown you a minute part of the immense riches I have in my head...

THE OTHER ISLAND

FRANCISCO SUNIAGA
Translated by Chris Lloyd

The day Wolfgang first went to a cockfight was a Saturday. The rain on the beach had scared the bathers off early and the reservations he had, which so far had kept him away from the cockpit, vanished at Renata's consent, who saw nothing wrong, if he had little else to do, in his seeking to satisfy an extravagant curiosity. Quite the opposite, if nature had decided to give them a break, the best thing he could do was take it, she said, and likewise she'd make the most of it by going to the mall and hitting a few shops.

He picked Fucho up in the estate car they used at the kiosk and together they went to a cockpit in La Asunción. The place had nothing in common with his friend's cockpit, which, although ramshackle, had evidently seen glory days. It lay on the outskirts of the city, on a large piece of land encircled by a rough adobe wall, in front of which the spectators' vehicles were pulled up any old how. Admission was through a half-opened iron gate, guarded by a doorman who was in charge of selling the tickets – numbered slips of paper he tore from a small pad. The pit, some fifty metres from the entrance, was half-hidden behind a barrier of mango trees, papaya, sugar cane, coconut palms and other tropical plants whose names Wolfgang didn't know. It was a crude construction, made from rough materials: bare blocks of cement, unpainted steel girders and a conical roof of grey asbestos sheets, raised to lessen the effects of the heat. The path that led to it and to the surrounding wasteland were covered with coarse gravel, worn stones compacted by the tramp of people passing over them, littered with cigarette ends, bottle tops and plastic glasses of assorted sizes. At the end of the piece of land, behind some banana trees, were the urinals: an irregular whitewashed wall, with no roof, and outsized signs saying 'gents' and 'ladies' on each end, daubed in green with a thick paintbrush. Next to the pit was a hut made of blocks of red clay, covered with rust-stained corrugated zinc sheets that had once been part of other roofs elsewhere before ending their days here. The front wall went up only halfway and was crowned by a wide, untreated wooden board that acted as a bar. Pressed up against it in noisy uproar, clutching their tickets in their hands, the cockfight fans clamoured for whatever it was they sold there. Fucho explained that they filled up on beer or flasks of rum before the fights began, they had to buy them outside because nothing was sold inside the pit and no one wanted to go out to buy them while the bouts were on. The gamblers drank their beers in a rush, so they could get ringside as soon as possible, and when they finished them they chucked the cans to the gravelled floor without the least display of conscience. A little old man, the closest thing to a beggar who's not seeking money, picked them up and placed them in a plastic fibre sack slung over his shoulder. Wolfgang had seen many 'tin men' before, as they were called, scavenging among the palms on the beach or searching through the kiosk's rubbish bags, but none with such a desolate expression as the man in the cockpit. To complete the local wildlife, children carrying huge aluminium pots went among the gamblers, selling them corn *arepas* stuffed with meat, fish *empanadas* and soft-boiled eggs. By the looks of it, no women ventured there.

Wolfgang looked around for the owner of the red cockerel among the men huddled around the beer counter, among the ones talking together outside, among the ones coming or going to the bathroom, but he couldn't see him. He asked Fucho about him and the fat guy reckoned he'd be inside, sitting in the front row, as was only fitting for anyone with a fight arranged. Fucho left him to go to the hole in the hut wall and join in the shouts of the other men looking to buy a beer. After a time, he came back with two cans, he offered one to Wolfgang and suggested they drink them before going into the cockpit as there was still a bit of time before the fight started. When they finished, Fucho chucked his can to the ground without a moment's hesitation while Wolfgang debated whether to take it to a metal drum some twenty metres away that was overflowing with rubbish, throw it to the ground like he'd seen everyone else do or give it directly to the tin man, like it was alms to the poor. Before going, he beckoned the old man over, placed the empty can in his hands and hurried away so he wouldn't have to look him in the eyes. Most of the cockfight fans were in the pit. Some, the minority, stayed in their seats waiting for the next bout, the others were clustered around the arena, surrounding the stars of the show and their owners. Fucho told him that the fans wanted to see the fighting spurs being put on the cocks, to make sure no one gained any advantage. The spurs vary in shape and size, and how they're to be used in each fight is part of the agreement that has to be reached beforehand by the owners. Wolfgang asked him how they were fitted and Fucho told him that they used a knife to cut the cockerels' natural spurs and then, with wax and thin adhesive tape, they fixed razor-sharp plastic or metal spurs in their place, he'd show him in the cockpit, he promised.

The circular structure of the ring and the concave shape of the roof created an acoustic that raised the volume of the voices several notches, and to make themselves understood, the fans either had to shout to each other or talk in the brief gaps when the din died down for a moment. In a smaller huddle, far from the uproar around the combatants, Wolfgang espied the trader from Porlamar who owned the red. He had a red cloth bag slung over his shoulder, and inside it you could make out the outlines of a cockerel, which Wolfgang supposed would be the red. The man saw them, and to greet them without shifting from where he was, he called out something that Wolfgang couldn't understand but that must have been funny because Fucho let out a guffaw in reply. Wolfgang watched the man's movements until he split off from the group and clambered over the low wall around the ring to take a seat like any other spectator. For now, he and the red would have to wait.

Someone they called 'the judge' rang a handbell and, like a heavenly force bringing order from chaos, the spectators hurried back to their places and fixed their attention on the two men in the arena, who were each holding a cockerel. The fight was about to start, the heat given off by the asbestos of the roof and the dust that rose from the ground, mixed with the dioxide breath of the spectators and the sweat of every skin, condensed inside the pit in a cloying, yellowish steam, a heavier atmosphere than the rest of the air, where passions could float at will. The tumult of the fans fell silent, with barely the nervous murmur of bated breath, a foreshadow of a barely contained uproar. The cockerels, however, were calm, absent, imperturbable under the rain of human adrenalin that fell on them. The judge gave a signal for someone to lower a wooden box that was suspended over the pit by a piece of rope that passed through a pulley and was tied to one of the posts holding up the roof. Without once removing from his mouth a cigarette with the ash hanging in a gravity-defying arc, an assistant diligently obeyed the order and lowered the contraption to the centre of the arena. Holding the end of the rope, he didn't once take his eyes off the judge, waiting for the sign telling him to raise it again. The owners of the cockerels, their faces pinched and pallid, as though they were the ones about to kill or be killed, lifted the lids from the closed compartments in the box and placed the animals inside. The judge waited for them both to return to their seats and signalled to the assistant with the cigarette in his mouth to raise the box so the fight could commence. The imminent onset of the fight, like a hand slowly tightening around a throat until all breath was snuffed out, imposed an absolute, unnatural silence that was broken by the roar of euphoria unleashed by the crowd the moment the box was raised and the cockerels stood facing one another.

The animals, stunned by the oppressive air and the noise from the stands, took a few seconds to come to their senses, before they were moved by the impulse of a natural order seared into their bones, and set to in a ferocious fight, without cause, like soldiers in an ancient war. The cockpit roared, gasped, calmed and rose again, lively as a March sea, as the fortunes of the bout ebbed and flowed. Bets were waged on one creature or the other the length and depth of the grandstand in the midst of a deafening uproar and at a dizzying speed that Wolfgang couldn't even follow with his eyes. The difference between the face-off and the real fight in front of him seemed to him so great that he felt like a teenager discovering sex with a woman after years of lonely imagination. Once in Andalusia, on a long weekend with some friends, he'd watched a bullfight and it left an impression on him, but the sight before him now in the cockpit was different. In a bullfight there's no competition: the matador invariably kills the bull. Thousands of bulls killed for every bullfighter. If it weren't for the ritual of the corrida, the death of the bull would be as bare as in a slaughterhouse, but with the fighting cocks it wasn't like that, here it was a fight between equals, an ultimate struggle, without rite or artifice, without justification or calculation, one of the cockerels, or both, would die, no one knew, nothing was set in stone.

As the fight progressed, Wolfgang became increasingly isolated from the overwhelming sea of noise crashing through the crowd. He slowly drowned in a hitherto unknown inner silence, as tenacious as the two cockerels who were killing each other in the pit without a single sound emerging from their throats. In the depth of the silence, like a remote echo, he heard the blows of the spurs on their skulls, the beating of their wings and the muted crack of the pecking that lacerated skin reddened beyond limit. He was convinced that he was the only one there able to hear the deaf clamour of the battle, to see how grandiose was the fight, to discern the meaning of the tribute being paid, and without his conscience taking part in deciding the course, his soul fused in an indestructible identity with the cockerels, the only other inhabitants of the mystical dimension into which he had passed. It was in that instant of unprecedented submission when he witnessed the moment that catapulted him even further beyond his ecstasy and – like the sorcerer who has crossed the threshold of a satanic mystery and been trapped by the demon that has revealed himself – made him a prisoner of the animals that would be his downfall. A captivating moment that would forge a perfect communion between the cockerels and Wolfgang, blessed by a brutal liturgy, which would never again be broken. In a swift movement, one of the cockerels managed to immobilise its opponent's head, seized it by the fleshy seam left where the crest had been clipped and, without releasing it, gave a powerful leap, moving its feet in a parabola like a murderous knife blow; with one of its spurs, Wolfgang couldn't see which one, it caught its adversary right in the exact spot on the neck where the unfortunate bird's jugular would be and opened up a deep wound, from where blood began to spurt out in jets to the beat of its heart. Wolfgang watched the animal recoil from the force of the blow, he saw every single one of the sequences where death steadily routed its arrogance, twisting it into an ungainly creature, keeping on without keeping up, its legs tangled in the longest of its wing feathers. With its dying breath, the wounded cockerel let slip a deep gurgle, brief, mortally brief, a croak that lasted an infinitesimal fraction but that took a lifetime to flee from the wound opened up in its throat, before collapsing gracelessly, the way that all things collapse, its head bent forwards, its beak resting on its chest, inert, lifeless. Dead.

With the surprise finale, the cockpit let loose a shapeless roar that – like a roll of thunder whose echo dies into the distance – slowly faded to become diluted into intelligible shouts and laughter from the winners, confused with the expressions of dejection of the losers. Some hugged each other and clapped each other on the back, others mourned, all shouted. Only two people remained silent: the defeated cockfighter, who looked at his cockerel with the impact of its death reflected in his face, and Wolfgang, who looked at them both. The man, slumped in his seat, was lost in his thoughts for a long while before leaping into the pit and, with a mixture of shame and anger, picked up the cockerel by the legs and went back to his seat. He left the bloodied body on the edge of the wooden ledge and, with more sadness than serenity, parsimoniously unravelled the adhesive tapes that fastened the spurs to the legs and placed the plastic contraptions into a little box he kept in his pocket. Then, with the look of someone placing the lid on a loved one's urn, he picked up the cockerel, placed it in its red cloth bag, got up from his seat and walked out of the cockpit at a funereal pace. Only Wolfgang watched him go.

Fucho had bet on the winning cockerel and was talking effusively at the top of his voice with the people sitting on the stands above and below them, who bounced along with him like excited children, their body language unbound. But not Wolfgang. Wolfgang sat in silence, not moving from his seat, unable to weather the wave of emotion that crashed over him and drowned his senses. His mind was a whirlpool that spooled over and over again through the terrible image of the final crushing blow and the standing death of the cockerel. Never had he thought that the violence he had seen unleashed would reach such a powerful climax, that an animal so small would be capable of killing with such efficiency. He couldn't recall anything that had ever had such a huge impact on him, he felt his blood course quickly and he knew that the reason for that wasn't the overwhelming heat of the atmosphere or the beer he'd had to drink before going in. It was something that came from much deeper within, that challenged him to remain motionless, drunk on a liquor that flowed from his very being, drifting on the primitive current that ran though his veins.

Some cockfight fans call that blow the blood shot: the sharpened tip of the spur punctures the artery in the neck and the cockerel dies instantly, drained of blood. It doesn't happen often, but it's an expectation that's hanging in the air at every fight and that serves to feed the bottomless and morbid longing of the fans. Wolfgang didn't know that, he thought that that was the normal way of things, and he felt that he no longer had anything left in him to face the reality of seeing the red cockerel be victorious or die in a pool of blood. Fucho must have seen something in his look because he paused in his noisy exchange with the other fans to ask him if he was all right, concern in his voice, and suggest he went outside to take a deep breath or two. Outside, Wolfgang confided his ill ease to Fucho, who comforted him, explaining that it was rare to see a blow like that, that most fights didn't end like that, that he'd been really lucky to get to see one on his debut as a cockfight fan and that he'd probably have to wait hundreds more fights until he saw another one as clean as the one they'd just witnessed. He spoke to him of the brutality implicit in every cockfight, that even if the death wasn't jaw-dropping, like in the last fight, each one saw the spilling of blood. That there were blows that he reckoned were even worse. That he yet had to see the blow that cockfight fans called the 'club': the spur snaps a vertebra in the neck and the cockerel can't lift its head. Or an even crueller one, the 'butcher': the cockerel takes a blow from a spur that doesn't open up an external wound but bursts the veins in its neck and causes internal bleeding. The blood collects beneath the skin and darkens until it forms a sort of black sausage, which grows with every beat of the bird's heart and ends up killing the cockerel, drowning it. It was an agonising death because the animal didn't know what was happening to it, it simply carried on fighting and with each movement it died a little more. But even in these cases, fighting cocks should be seen for what they were: the privileged few in the bird kingdom. That the cockerel that had just been killed at least had the good fortune to fight for its life, that in that one moment, in South America alone, thousands of cockerels and chickens will have been killed by much more cruel and despicable means. That if Wolfgang wanted, he'd take him to one of the fresh chicken stalls on the island so he could see for himself what he meant. Wolfgang, calmer after Fucho's lengthy speech, offered to buy him a beer and went to one of the huts to get them. His quest took him some time because he refused to join in with the shouting match to get served, waiting patiently instead until one of the barmen asked him for his order. He came back with two cans and a small bottle of rum and told Fucho with a smile that the beer was for the heat and the rum was for his nerves.

It didn't take long for Wolfgang to see that Fucho was right. That afternoon didn't see a repeat of the sudden death by the spur blow to the neck, but the fights were no less exciting for that. The battles that followed, including the red's, were also sensational and showed Wolfgang another side to cockfighting, one that was, to his way of thinking, much more majestic than the ability to kill one's opponent: the strength to resist and to fight to the death. In the remaining fights, the cockerels came together in long and extremely tough battles, wars of attrition in which they used every last ounce of energy until they were drained, completely drained, lacerated to the point where they were unrecognisable, even blind, and even then they still drew on a strength from somewhere to lift their heads and seek out their enemy. That was the type of fight fate held for the red. Its adversary, a Salamanca grey, battled with great tenacity, it resisted charge after charge by its opponent and inflicted severe wounds before being consumed, completely, with no strength left to hold its head up. But with the agonising strength it had left, it still tried one last attack with its beak, though it was little more than a clumsy feint that crashed to the ground, where it languished in its death throes. The red didn't kill it, it died from fighting so well, and Wolfgang clearly saw the difference between the two. These fights of resistance, where he learned just how far courage can go, sealed off any escape for his captivated soul and rooted in his consciousness an incurable fascination for fighting cocks, the animals that would be his downfall.

CARACAS
CITY OF FRAUD
& FEAR

WHAT DO THEY CALL
THOSE BORN IN CHIVACOA?

HÉCTOR TORRES
Translated by Tim Girven

> *I never feel sadness*
> *I never feel pain*
> *With my cunning and stealth*
> *I don't need a brain.*
> Emir Kusturica

You don't inhabit Caracas, you endure it. To cross the city from point to point, east to west, it's best to intoxicate yourself using one of the many recipes for stupefaction. The idea, after all, is to convince yourself that you're enjoying it. You can lose yourself, for example, in the soundtrack of your iPod played at ear-splitting volume. There's weed, glue, alcohol. There's the temerity of ostentation: a Chevy Avalanche that's as long as it is unsafe, a fast and powerful BMW, a big handgun, a hard face in a leather jacket. Or you can *mainline* party rhetoric and fill yourself with political hatred. You can mount the kerb and roar down the pavement, hit the horn impatiently, run the lights – or exercise whatever mode of irrationality helps you tread the perpetual knife's edge, emptiness on the one side, death on the other.

Or take a swig of suicidal euphoria. The one activated by Friday's catchphrase: 'What are you up to tonight?' The one that doesn't know the words danger, inflation or crisis – nor pays attention to the slowest striptease in the annals of dictatorships.

It was with this placebo that Andreína and some of her workmates from the bank went out that night. After various luckless wanderings in Las Mercedes and El Rosal, they ended up finding space in a bar on Avenida Solano. A table for five, danceable music, cold beer: who could doubt that God does indeed keep an eye on things once in a while?

Come the third round of drinks they'd forgotten what they were celebrating. Come the fifth, they were hungry and asked for a *parrillita*. Come the seventh they concluded that Ordóñez's promotion had a suspicious connection to the fact that he lunched with the boss, and come the eighth they didn't notice that only four tables remained occupied, although they did clock the sudden appearance of three guys sat at the table to one side of the corridor leading to the washrooms and facing the till.

It's not that they were poorly dressed. Nor that they looked like delinquents. It's not that they were ugly (*Noooo!,* the three girls opined in unison). It was something indefinable, elastic, elusive; something disquieting for reasons that no one managed to nail down.

The ninth round came as a surprise. 'These are on the gentlemen,' said the waiter, twisting his lips in the direction of the table to one side of the washrooms.

That was reason enough, so to be cautious they were going to ask for the bill, but with the first notes of a song by Willie Colón, a hand reached out towards Andreína.

Upon raising her gaze, her fears were confirmed. At the table, everyone looked at them out of the corner of their eyes, pretending to concentrate on the conversation, but she panned her gaze round and with her look signalled a sort of 'stay calm, everything's okay.' She took his hand and they walked to the dance floor. Tall, dark, slim – a description apt for one in every four guys who approaches a girl in a nightclub. Close up, Andreína confirmed that, effectively: a/ he wasn't badly dressed, b/ he certainly wasn't ugly, and c/ there was something intimidating about him that was difficult to define.

And also, that he danced real sweet… And that she had been wanting to dance for a while. Perhaps for that reason they danced something like five songs one after the other, and although he didn't lose his disquieting air, she found herself gradually becoming accustomed to it, feeling as if it were something impersonal, as if it emanated from him naturally, without his even knowing.

We're talking about a girl who's had ten beers and who really wants to dance. We're talking about the fact that in Caracas you have to submerge yourself in whatever form of stupefaction does it for you. And this one came in a 'friendly' package.

But we're also talking about the proverbial heads or tails. Because after the fifth tune she returned to the table and said softly but firmly: 'Let's go.'

It was the hour of full-on salsa. After Willie Colón came Sonido Bestial. Then, 'Where are you going Chichi?' She, heir to a dancer's ancestry, didn't scare easily. Her partner's companions conversed in low, relaxed voices, seemingly far from them, tracing imaginary maps with their hands. The youngsters spoke among themselves but didn't cease to observe the dancers out of the corners of their eyes. He stood out with his stylish steps. She honoured her heritage.

And he spoke like he danced: about everything and without order. He told her that the salsa musician Larry Harlow didn't speak any Spanish; that the gays who lisped and became hairdressers were always children without brothers or sisters; that to ensure cocaine didn't leave you impotent you had to accompany it with whisky; and that he had a son in Chivacoa, and that the little one had asked him for a Wii (how the fuck do the kids in Chivacoa even know that Wiis exist?); that the town didn't offer anything to the young and that it was shitty; that only the town of Nirgua was worse and that was only because it was the den of so many retired robbers and thieves. And then: 'Let's see if you know, princess: what do they call those born in Chivacoa?'

Andreína realised that this wasn't a rhetorical question and that her dance partner (Ernesto was the name with which he'd introduced himself), was waiting for an answer. When he saw her hesitate he said to her with a disappointed air:

'You don't deserve the present that I have for you but I'm going to give it to you anyway. Do you know why?'

'A present? No,' said Andreína, feeling that all the beers, the dancing and the situation were pushing her way beyond her daily dose of bewilderment. 'Why?'

'Because you're alright. A guy asks a girl for a dance in a club and she'll always look him up-and-down. But you didn't. You danced with a stranger. And did anything bad happen? No. The only thing that happened is that the stranger is going to give you a present. You're going to get a gift even though you don't know what they call a kid born in Chivacoa.'

He paused as if seeking the precise order of his words.

'You and your friends have exactly five minutes to get out of here. We came here to take the place down. But then I fancied stretching my legs while we waited for the car to arrive. And you're a sound girl but the car has arrived so we'll be getting to what we came here for. Five minutes. Do you like your present?'

'You're pulling my leg,' Andreína said to him with a composure she was far from feeling.

'I'm pulling your leg?' he repeated, imitating her voice and raising his eyebrows, his face grave. 'Lower your hand a fraction to see if I'm pulling your leg.'

Andreína slid her hand down his back, across the smooth surface of his jacket and hit a hard object stuck into the waistband of his trousers. She drew her hand back as if she'd received an electric shock.

'Shhh, calm down, it's a present not a party.'

'But why are you going to do it?'

'Listen baby, the question here is whether you want this present or not. If you do, we'll finish this dance, you pay for your drinks and leave. It's the present I give to the pretty girls who don't look down their noses at a guy who wants to dance for a while.'

When she returned to her table, the expression on her face was enough to ensure that her 'Let's go' convinced everyone to ask for the bill and leave some notes on the table without asking any questions. They understood without understanding, from the depths of their own stupefaction. As they walked towards the exit, the guy – who was explaining something to his mates at their table – followed them and, after opening the door, said to the huge bloke smoking outside:

'This lot leave.'

'You're such a playboy,' the gorilla said, throwing his cigarette butt to the floor and drawing a pistol that made a blood-curdling metallic sound when he loaded it vigorously.

The playboy, turning his back to the road, did the same with the pistol that he drew – surely enough – from beneath his jacket.

'*Chivacoense*, princess. My kid is *chivacoense*,' he said to Andreína as she passed by his side and he threw a quick glance down the silent street.

'Let's move, Romeo,' said the other, 'tonight's feature is an action movie.'

And they pushed in through the door, brusquely.

As the group sought to convince their legs to last until they reached the car, they heard through the glass, as if reaching them from the loudspeakers of a vehicle in the distance, the insults and aggressive orders of the assailants.

'Don't look up, don't get any smart ideas,' Andreína heard as if in a slow motion film, recognising the timbre of her dance partner's voice with clarity.

BLANES IN FLASHBACK

HÉCTOR CONCARI
Translated by Katie Brown

> *Because there is this thing with the past. There is always so much more where it came from.*
> Jack Nicholson, *The Two Jakes*

I don't know at exactly what point of my life Blanes appeared, his bulging eyes swimming in his happy round face as he recounted his projects. I place him in some misty moment in the late eighties, when I was working at the travel agents in Sabana Grande and the afternoons melted into a placid routine, a permanent four o'clock on a Friday afternoon. Perhaps what first caught my attention about him was that at a certain point Blanes was able to locate me, despite me moving offices and jobs, to share his ideas with me and offer me work. For some reason – as enigmatic as his appearances – Blanes had declared himself my friend and didn't hesitate to remind me, without listing them, of the favours that he owed me and that he insisted on repaying. I remember that over the years he suggested that I took charge of a quarry in Yaracuy, a sugar plant in Apure, and a hotel in Margarita, swearing that I was the right person for the job, because it wasn't about knowledge but attitude. He was living proof, using his economic think tank to reach the highest echelons of power, which generated indescribable opportunities for him.

'The Slovenian embassy is mine,' he told me in a serious tone over a *fabada* in Urrutia. 'My friend Pedrique was promoted in the ministry and he just confirmed it. Can you imagine what that means?'

I nodded, gently inclining my head towards my ribs. He sighed at this veiled confession of ignorance and began to explain.

'I have a friend, a great friend, a professor of "organisational behaviour" at a school of management in Singapore. The Slovenian government contracted him, a few months ago, to carry out a study. How to move from a centralised and planned economy to the free market. The result? It's the most successful country of former Yugoslavia. What a luxury. Imagine the opportunities that are open, in such a context, to a guy like me, as ambassador. So, filled in by my friend, the one from Singapore, who rubs shoulders with the president of Slovenia, I talk to Pedrique. Pedrique and I used to play marbles together, a few blocks from here, when we were kids, and he's made a career as an economist, consulting for the Foreign Ministry. He's a genius, Pedrique, and he owes me many favours. I'm packing my bags now. We're just waiting for the president's signature. A salute to the flag, and bam, off to Slovenia for two or three years…'

He sunk his spoon into the soup, swallowed and repeated, 'So, get ready – you'll be visiting me on holiday, I imagine.' I remember this lunch well because when it came time to pay I had to handle the bill, which was added to the countless favours that he would one day pay me back with interest.

Two weeks later, I got a call from Blanes, begging me to meet him in La Belle Epoque. I got held up in traffic on the way there and when I arrived I spotted him at one of the back tables. He was sat with his legs apart and his hands palms up on his knees, as if expecting something to fall from the sky. He was staring into space, hanging by the scruff of his neck from an imaginary hook which drew him towards the ceiling and left him gazing blankly at his drink, adrift on the table. I sat down and clapped him on the shoulder.

'Pedrique fucked me over,' he said without acknowledging my greeting. He then explained that the Slovenian embassy had vanished before his eyes. That the president had designated a distant nephew of one of the most generous contributors to his campaign, and that Pedrique had done nothing to defend him. 'Nothing, nothing, he didn't lift a finger,' he repeated various times, heartbroken by the betrayal and the need to come up with a new project.

I tried to console him, confessing that the Singapore-Slovenia-Caracas triangle had always seemed a bit fantastical to me and that – as Sheridan always said – whatever happens is for the best, but Blanes, lost in thought, only repeated, 'Nothing, nothing, Pedrique abandoned me,' while he drank his Old Parr on the rocks, unhurriedly, almost methodically. A few hours later, I left him at the door to his house. Before getting out of the car, he gathered what energy he had left in a sigh, and for a moment it seemed that he had sobered up. He announced:

'Tomorrow I'm starting an excellent new project I've got up my sleeve. I'll call you.'

That line opened a large parenthesis of six or seven years, during which I heard nothing from Blanes.

*

He reappeared with the triumph of the revolution to inform me that, as a service to the fatherland, he had accepted a position in the Ministry of Finance, to advise the minister and quite often the president what to do at such a critical moment. 'The country doesn't have enough money to operate for more than two months, and in the hands of those brutes,' he sighed, 'if it weren't for me, I don't know, I don't know...' he confessed to me, rattling a whisky in the hotel bar where I worked and where he had found me to bring me up to date and ask me to keep him in mind.

I decided to put him to the test three weeks later. At customs, an inspector had taken a look at the cheeses that we were importing for the Swiss food festival and refused to release them if we didn't pay him off. I called the ministry and his secretary put me straight through to him. Blanes asked me the details dryly, sighed several times, pointed out that it was complicated, that his diary for the day included a meeting with the president and that he would see if there was anything he could do. We started to think about how to imagine a Swiss food festival without cheese, or how to get hold of them locally when, that afternoon, a colonel from the National Guard announced himself to my secretary. 'The gentleman says it's urgent,' she whispered to me, sounding serious.

I let him in. He was a tall man in campaign uniform, who bowed his head slightly, without taking my hand or responding to my 'How can I help you?'

'I recovered the cheese, following Dr Blanes' instructions. I have it in the patrol car. Where should we unload it?'

Blanes explained the awful state of customs to me three nights later, accompanied by the colonel, at the cocktail party to open the festival, drinking a Fendant. He took small sips, swirling it in his mouth and explaining to his companion, who stared at him, 'This is a fruity young wine, typical of the Jura region. Excellent before cheese.' The colonel thanked me for the invitation and the complaint. They were cleaning up customs and the inspector in question was at the top of a large list of civil servants who would receive exemplary punishments. The night dissolved into chatting, giggles, and raclette. Before leaving, Blanes pulled me to one side.

'I can't stand the official sector any more. The minister is perfectly mediocre and I can't tell you about the people who accompany him. They're exploiting me. But you have no idea the amount of money they handle. A unique opportunity. A few more months to polish some contacts and I'll go back to the private sector.'

It took him six months to call me again and invite me to lunch at Le Trou, the hotel's French restaurant. Courteously, and despite the vice president's pleas, he had left the government. 'I don't want to imagine the fuss the president would have kicked up about that guy not managing to keep me there. Luckily I could convince them that I'm more useful outside of the government than inside.' He went on to explain that he now represented a bank in Lugano, opening credit lines for the state, and that his position was key for both parties. 'But I didn't call you to talk about this, I have bigger fish to fry,' he said, lowering his voice. I leant towards his seat, turned my head from left to right to create an aura of secrecy with my gaze, and listened.

Two Sundays earlier he'd woken up craving paella and traipsed between every restaurant he knew without finding one that satisfied him. Carried by this minimal defeat, he retreated to a Chinese restaurant in Las Mercedes. An absurd and incomprehensible series of events that was to define his life, because it was there that he found it. There was a Chinese guy, really skinny, drinking beer after beer at one of the back tables. As soon as he'd spotted him, he'd tried to communicate with him through signs, to take the coincidences of that afternoon to the extreme. Blanes had believed he recognised him from one of the top government meetings. He'd invited him to his table and they'd talked all afternoon in snatches of Spanish, English and French from which Blanes had been able to reconstruct a bizarre journey. He was an IT expert hired by the government, he explained, wide-eyed. The Chinese guy had refused to give more details and when he asked him, smashed on beer, he only repeated 'seclet, seclet,' raising his fist to his eyes, then lowering his thumb to slit his throat with a horizontal movement.

But the story didn't end there. In fact, it only started there, because on that afternoon – which stretched into the early hours of the next day – and through who knows what trick of human communication, the dejected Chinese man had related his drama. Once the work was finished they had abandoned him to his fate, and he had escaped so as not to return to Canton. That's not the important bit, the most important thing was still to come. He had in his hand an invention that would revolutionise consumption and would never see the light of day in China, and he had to stay in Venezuela at all costs. At this point, Blanes lowered his voice further and made me come closer to follow his story.

A device that captured memories, he told me. A magical appliance that you stuck to the pillow before going to sleep and would extract the furthest, most deeply buried memories from your mind, and store them in a tiny box for you to enjoy later on your way to work like a new treat. And then exchange them with friends, upload them to the office computer to savour in a free moment, share them with the family, or even sell them, in the case of some bighead – there's always one. He raised his eyebrows in a sign of complicity to encompass the millions that this idea would make him, and continued. He had used all his savings to rent this Chinese guy a penthouse in Altamira in which he could work at ease because he was defined by two characteristics: he was a workaholic who only interrupted his sessions in front of the computer to satiate his sexual appetite. He was an incorrigible sex addict who required two or three different women a day to keep working. 'A weirdo. I think he's a bit autistic,' Blanes confessed, 'because all he does when he's not working or shut in with some women is make lists of all the martial arts films from Hong Kong from 1900 to today. Then he eats some white rice, works feverishly and occasionally shouts, "More pussyyyyyyy, I need more pussyyyy…"'

I walked home stifling a laugh. At that point I still lived in La Florida and I needed time to air the anecdote and make it believable before telling it to Sheridan, who would listen to it with her usual look of scepticism.

He arranged to meet me urgently the following Friday in the Tamanaco hotel bar. 'It's more discreet,' he explained. He was at the bar and when he saw me come in he took me by the arm and made me sit at the back, away from everyone, while he asked the barman to bring his whisky to the table and another for me.

'Eighteen years old. Enjoy it, we're celebrating,' he told me, showing me a white box that appeared from nowhere in his hands. He raised his glass, clinked it with mine, put the box in my hands, sat back and announced:

'It's called "Flashback" and this is the prototype. I want you to be the first to try it.'

There was no way to get out of it. He insisted it was an honour he was saving for me. It would be his pleasure, but above all a necessity. Once it was on the market, it was only a matter of time before Bill Gates or Steve Jobs or Larry Ellison would be calling, and he didn't speak English. He needed a translator he could trust implicitly, who would also have a share in the business. He repeated, incredulous, 'Don't you get it? Do you not realise what we're bringing to the market here?'

Hours later I waited for Sheridan to breathe the little sigh with which she bid goodbye to the world until the next day, and slipped out into the living room to set up the machine. I read the simple instructions I found when I opened the lid and took the device out with great care. It was a piece of transparent plastic, the shape of an ostrich egg, with a pebble, white and asymmetrical, floating immovable in the centre. I shook it a little, just to make sure that nothing affected it. Then I connected the cable that came next to it in the black case, in the slot labelled 'in'. I placed the other end of the cable, shaped like a headphone, in my ear and went back to bed. I hugged Sheridan and went to sleep.

I woke early the next morning, remembered happily that it was Saturday, and heard noises coming from the kitchen. I put my hand beneath the pillow and pulled out the egg while I rubbed my eyes and took out the cable. At its core the pebble had acquired a light turquoise tone, and for a moment it seemed to twinkle. Sheridan was silhouetted in the bedroom doorway with a jar of coffee in her hand, pointing her jaw towards the device.

I told her everything, while her face treated me to expressions ranging from incredulity to rage. Finally, to convince her, I unplugged the cable from 'in,' turned the device around, and plugged into 'out'. Sheridan sat on the bed with her legs crossed, drinking her coffee, while I brushed her hair aside and placed the headphone into her ear. She left her cup on the bedside table and concentrated. I pressed play.

I watched as the little light began to twinkle a little more, giving off a weak sparkle of a darker turquoise. Sheridan smiled distractedly, then her eyes widened little by little in that mix of attention and surprise that bathed her when something drew her in. Her expression became fixed, then I watched as her eyes filled with tears, while she started to slowly shake her head and repeat, 'poor, poor thing…,' and then she lifted her hand to her ear to remove the cable. She stroked my face, almost laughing, and repeating tenderly, 'poor, poor thing…,' while she took my clothes off and then undressed herself and lay on top of me, scratching my neck and kissing me slowly. I stayed on my back, feeling how she played with me and together we reached the heights of pleasure. I felt her tears run down my neck while I played with her hair falling over me, and she kept repeating, 'poor baby, my poor baby,' between giggles and moans.

I slept a long while and when I woke up, I was alone. I remembered once again that it was Saturday and that Sheridan had gone to her yoga class. I stretched a hand out to the rocking chair, groped around without finding anything, took a long breath as my hand slid about underneath, explored beneath the pillow that had fallen to the floor and touched the Flashback. Still not looking, I found the cable and lifted it to my ear.

I'm sitting in the laundry room at home, on a high chair, watching my mother, who's humming as she puts clothes into a white washing machine. It starts to rock, softly at first and then with more rhythm. It's a bright day and the sun starts to bathe the small space. For me this routine act is a spectacle I follow attentively, because my mother is facing away from me and I can see her, tall, agile and happy, organising the clothes. Every now and then she turns, looks at me, wrinkles her nose, I do the same, and then she stops humming, looks at me and laughs, before returning to her task. My gaze travels along the wall, very slowly, pausing first at the sun that comes in through the window and plays with my mother's hair, then on to the mirror that returns my mischievous and amused image back to me, before landing on the sink. I stop on the black plughole and look at it for a long time, because it's the only thing out of tune with the joy of that morning. Then, as all my attention is focused on that black hole, I watch one long grey leg peering out of it, planting itself firmly on the rim of the hole, seemingly gathering strength to pull up a bulge it's dragging. It doesn't manage it, and calls for help from another leg, which sticks out and repeats the operation, while I feel like the sun has escaped and I shout to stop a third leg coming out of that hole and to stop it coming towards me, dragging the body of the spider which is now out of the plug, and it looks at me, enormous, and I can't do anything from my watchtower but shout and shout for my mother, too late, because fear has already darkened everything, to turn on the hot tap and wash the bug back into the void from which it could return to attack me at any other happy moment of my life.

I looked at the pebble, at the core of the egg. It was still, barely showing the turquoise I had noticed early that morning. I stretched for a long time, too tense and shocked to get up. It was better than remembering. It was living things for the first time *again*.

I put the device back in its box, very carefully, as if I were handling a loaded gun. Then I made sure to respect the original packing and called Blanes to give it back to him that same day, as soon as possible.

He arranged to meet me at his new office. He had rented a whole floor in La Castellana, and was at the reception giving instructions to the carpenters when I arrived. He showed me in hurriedly.

'What did you think?'

I explained that it was too much for me. That it struck me as an incredibly dangerous device and that I wished him the best of luck, but I definitely didn't want to have anything more to do with the Flashback.

He guffawed, took out a Cuban cigar, pressed it between his fingers, raised it to his ear to hear its rustle and then lit it.

'From Honduras. They want me to import them, but I don't have the time. I've called off all my other business. Even the bank in Lugano. The guys were furious. Some Swiss blokes who speak Italian – can you imagine? Well, this is going places. First we'll sell this model, but we've already got everything lined up. Jackie Chan's working on a dial that will allow you to locate memories by year. And in the strategic plan... I've spent nights working on the company's strategic plan... we hope to have one that allows you to find them by type and by period. And I solved the finance issue.'

I sighed, nodded and tried to get up to go, but he stopped me with a wave of his hand wreathed in a cloud of smoke.

'And I sent Gates, Jobs and Ellison packing. I don't even want to speak to them. Forget it. The government's paying for it. "Rebopopate.'"

I stuck my head out and widened my eyes.

'Support for SMEs. Rebopopate. The technical sergeant who runs the ministry's office was fascinated by the idea. Luckily for me he flashed back to his first brothel. He spoke to the minister and they told the Big Man. They've authorised me however much I want.'

Spreading his thumb and forefinger wide he described an arc in the air, as if imitating a poster, and repeated, 'Rebopopate'. Then he started to uncurl his fingers, one by one, while he hammered out the syllables.

'REvolucionary, Bolivarian, POpular and PArticipatory TEchnology.'

He spread his hand in a triumphant five, swivelled in his chair, let out another mouthful of smoke and clarified:

'Don't think I'll forget about my friends. As this grows, I'm going to need people like you.'

I excused myself, blaming Sheridan who was meeting me for lunch. He promised we'd be in touch and that he was counting on me for marketing, because he still hadn't ruled out floating the company on the New York stock exchange, we'd see.

*

It was one of the best Saturday mornings of my life, which is saying something as Saturday mornings are always glorious, a kind of parenthesis between the recently ended weekday-war and the slow threat of Sunday which begins to form in the afternoon. I walked a long while, still a prisoner of my flashback, as if some morning from my past, buried in the depths of time, had come back to swear that it had never gone away and to demand my attention. I thought for a moment whether it was right to try to forget things with the same effort that we sometimes put into remembering them. And while I wondered about how the fantasies of my friend Blanes, who always walked with one foot in the future, were making a space for themselves in this world, I relived the memory again. I slowed down, because part of me wasn't in the present and I was at risk of getting run over or knocking somebody down. I realised then that the Flashback held me captive, that it had installed itself in my head and started to grow tentacles that had taken hold of my insides. Worse still, I began to sweat as I felt that this memory wasn't mine, wasn't one of those that you can alter to make it fit a better history, embellishing it with what you wish had been. No, this monster was something different and delicate. Being mine, it had all the weight of something solid that lived within me but had a life of its own, as if someone had put it there to stay.

I sat on a bench in Plaza Altamira and it took some time for me to breathe normally again and convince myself that I was in the present, that it was one of those sunny Saturdays I liked so much, and that the world was still turning as if nothing had happened and there was no reason to worry. I calmed down and thought I could start walking again when it hit me, as if I were struck by lightning, that what the damned Flashback did was return the past to you like a present that would never go away, that wouldn't let itself be trapped by later events, and that you, the victim, would re-live again and again and again – a lost and domesticated memory. It would keep coming back to attack you, unrelentingly, forever, to ruin your life, because life is nothing more than taming the past, polishing it day by day, with the patience of a craftsman, trying to bend it to your will. I asked myself what could happen if, instead of one, we had to live with two, three, one hundred, one thousand wild flashbacks, fighting among themselves, each one demanding its space in our lives, without control or a rope to rein them to the present and to what we had come to be after so much time. I sat for a while, watching people walk by and repeating that it was just an ordinary Saturday, thinking that that was the only way to save myself from the spider that had returned again and again to pursue me, and which would never retreat. After half an hour, I managed to control myself. I tried a few steps without venturing too far from the bench, and when I felt stable again, I began to walk towards Blanes' office. I felt safer with every step and I realised that the exercise and my interaction with the street and the everyday world were helping me place that episode back in the Pandora's box from where it had come, which didn't mean that Blanes' device didn't scare me or that there weren't things that I'd prefer not to re-live, even if this amounted to a mutilation of sorts. I arrived at the building and went up. The office was closed and I knocked several times, shouting his name, thinking that the damned device had to be destroyed, knowing that Blanes would never allow it and that the business was on a roll.

In the days that followed, Sheridan repeatedly asked me about Blanes and his Flashbacks and even suggested that we try it again with another memory, but I refused emphatically. From Monday on, I immersed myself in work, hoping to bury that glorious Saturday.

I often had to go to the centre for procedures with official bodies. I preferred to take the Metro, for speed and to avoid the traffic, but also because the centre of Caracas had the peculiar charm of diversity and amid the grime, the peddlers and the most bizarre objects, I found a grotesque poetry that hurt and amused me in equal measure. One morning, a few months later, I was walking down the road when I saw it for the first time. It was a small cube, hanging from a market stall by a wire, like a scarecrow. In front of it a tall man was telling a teenager, 'All your memories, sweetheart, your past in this box...' while he swapped the pebbles. I wasn't brave enough to approach, but I understood that, in a country where success is measured by mass consumption at informal street markets, Blanes had triumphed. I walked a long while, focusing on worthless objects, people's gestures, passing cars, and the cries which protected me from the abyss. I took deep breaths, trying to concentrate on the upcoming meeting, and to my surprise, I realised that the spider was not coming back.

I wasn't shocked that Blanes didn't contact me. I imagined he was in a phase of euphoria, of unstoppable work, from which he would eventually emerge to find me and offer me work or ask for my help. Several months passed and I remembered him from time to time, but it was a lovely spell, and Sheridan and I escaped to Morocco and killed hours wandering the streets of a country we didn't know, haggling in shops and eating couscous. One afternoon, in Marrakech, while we were waiting for our guide to pick us up at the hotel, I started to leaf through *Le Monde Diplomatique* which I'd found next to me on a lobby sofa. On the third page I saw the headline *'La Térébopopa: Le pari informatique de la révolution Bolívarienne'.* It was a long report on the Flashback phenomenon, presented by Blanes and peppered with reflections from intellectuals, who welcomed the sovereign recuperation of the past and the rescue of the country's purest mysteries and culture in an original form, uncontaminated by a dependent present. 'With this invention, no one can snatch our past away from us, as they did before,' asserted Blanes, in a paragraph which included quotes from Galeano and Saramago.

I was tempted to take the paper, but at that moment the guide arrived, and I left it behind to avoid being captured once again by the ghosts of the Chinese guy's invention and Blanes' commercial prowess. I strolled through Marrakech's main square, laughing with Sheridan, enjoying the snake charmers and choosing rugs for the apartment, while I told myself that it was all just a fantasy and that distance would not save me from returning to a present in a constant state of siege, whose meeting I could only postpone for so long.

When I got home I tried to track down Blanes, but it was impossible. His phone gave the same message as always: 'It's Blanes. I'm very busy. Leave a message and I'll call you,' with mambo as background music. No one answered at his office. It made me sad to think that success had taken him away and that he'd probably never contact me again, before I realised that the Flashbacks had disappeared from the market and peddlers were no longer offering them in the street. I tried to find out if anyone in the office had tried one, unsuccessfully.

He called me back on a Saturday afternoon two weeks later, sounding like a ghost, asking me to meet him at La Bastille.

As always, he was at a back table, in the now familiar position of a tired boxer who has decided not to rise for the next round. He heard me sit down without looking up and told me:

'A hit, it was a hit. We'd opened the first shop in Sambil, and we already had the contracts to expand to Maracaibo and Margarita. And then abroad. We sold eighty Flashbacks on the first day. On the third day we had to close because we ran out of stock and I had to triple the shifts in the factory in Guarenas. Jackie Chan was happy with his whores and yours truly even took the opportunity one Sunday to tell Bill Gates that he was an arsehole and that we were much smarter and we'd be waiting for him at the Exposhow in Las Vegas. And the people, the people were the best bit, swapping pebbles like gold coins, like kids with marbles. Don't tell me you didn't see them...'

I said yes and heard him sob. I told him that I'd seen peddlers selling them.

'Those motherfuckers. I think that's the root of the problem, but then I also think I'll never know. That's what annoys me most, that I'll never know.'

He downed his whisky and ordered another. I asked him to tell me everything. He sighed and repeated the part I already knew about the Chinese guy, his suspicions about that pervert, that damned hacker, always playing with bidirectional devices, his speciality, you know, devices that talk between themselves. 'They communicated, they communicated,' he said, lacing his fingers together and then separating them furiously.

'I had the same suspicions as you, I wondered who in the government had hired him. Now it all seems so obvious to me. And I insisted, insisted that the Flashbacks were for personal use. To remember happy times, to go over the details of things that happened to you, that you recall. But I don't remember. I never remember anything and I don't learn – that's why I don't learn, because I don't give a shit what happened yesterday. The only thing I want to know is what's going to happen to me tomorrow and that fucking weirdo got it into his head that the pebbles could communicate and that people could swap them between themselves and give them as gifts. I said no, I insisted on privacy, and I even asked for a legal study but it's such a new area that they couldn't tell me a damned thing. And that's where the bloody Flashback had repercussions, first one, then another and another and another in an open circuit that we couldn't control. Dirty memories, disgraceful. I ask myself why I couldn't stop it, why I didn't think, couldn't see it coming. Memory is shit, it's a curse, goddamn it! I asked that Chinese degenerate to think of something to block the avalanche, but it was unstoppable. Women stole the pebble from their husbands at night, men delved into their wives' brains to find their first boyfriends. Police connected to suspects and Amnesty International got involved in the whole mess. It was a catastrophe and the press just added fuel to the fire. And it got worse once politics got involved. The president trying on a Cartier, the minister appropriating part of the secret budgetary expenditure, that other cretin at an orgy. It all came out, all the shit that this city dumped into those gadgets, and I felt like that torrent sent me reeling and was going to ruin me and that there was nothing I could do about it. I arrived at the office one day and found it shut down and occupied by the police. I didn't ask anything, I escaped down the stairs and raced to the penthouse. It was open, and they'd taken everything – the computers, the girls' clothes, everything. Jackie Chan never came back. I hope they haven't harmed him, but wherever he is, he'll never have it as good as he did with me, with his computers and his women. I thought about taking refuge somewhere safe, but I decided that if everything was going to be lost, it was better to lose it all at once. I went home, opened a good bottle of Burgundy and began to drink. They rang the bell half an hour later. A military committee. Straight to a safehouse. Pedrique appeared, that motherfucker. He knows me well, very well. We've done many deals together. He calmed me down, told me not to worry, that it had all been a mistake, and not to worry. He repeated this several times, that there was nothing to worry about, and then he did what I feared. The final nail in the coffin. He grabbed a briefcase, opened it, took out a sheet of paper and showed it to me. He fanned me with the paper, like it was all a joke, before holding it up to my eyes. It was a decree nationalising the Flashbacks for reasons of sovereignty, strategic interest and other nonsense. He gave me a long look and a self-satisfied half-smile. Triumphant. Then he sighed and told me if I wanted a fight, there would be a fight. Afterwards, he put the document in the briefcase and left. Do you know what they did? I found out a few days later. They collected all the memories and auctioned them off to psychiatric societies in the US. For research – they're making a fortune. One of the gorillas took me home to finish my bottle of Burgundy and cry like a little boy.'

I kept quiet a little longer, knowing that I wasn't going to go anywhere and that Blanes would stay drinking for some time, slowly burying his story, first with reproaches, then vague phrases and finally monosyllables. He did exactly that, and two hours later asked me to please take care of the bill. While I paid he struggled to put his hand in his pocket, with all the grace of a manatee. He brought out a packet wrapped in a handkerchief and opened it unhurriedly.

'It's yours, the first prototype. I managed to rescue it. I want you to keep it.'

I considered protesting, but it seemed too cruel to poor Blanes. I silently accepted it like a dangerous trophy which could explode at any second. He sat looking at me for a while, then sighed and asked me to take him home, and whether I didn't mind picking him up early tomorrow to go to Betania because it was Sunday and he wanted to pray in the church before Monday, because on Monday, early, he'd start on the next project he had up his sleeve.

WHILE THE BLOOD DRIES

ROBERTO MARTÍNEZ BACHRICH
Translated by Tim Girven

How long it takes to get home. It's slow and gruelling.
But finally – 'one day' – the tube-train reaches Los
Cortijos. Leaving the platform below, I already sense
there is something amiss. As I approach the turnstiles
it's confirmed: a growing murmur that becomes a roar.
I don't even reach the exit stairs that would take me to
the street: people are coming down at full speed and
they trample each other, yelling, pushing, some even
rolling down the stairs. Those of us in the ticket hall
don't understand what's going on but instinct makes
us recede and lead this hasty race back towards the
depths. Back within the turnstiles, we're in the front
row when the cause is revealed to us – both in theory
and in practice. A confrontation between teenage
gangs has arrived here below. Bottles fly, sticks,
stones. Where have they got sticks and stones from in
a city stripped of nature? They're kids. They can't be
older than fifteen. And their hormonal rage dominates
them, drives their fury, generates their acts. One of
the boys takes a wrong step or isn't fast enough. The
rival gang is upon him, have him cornered, beat him.
Everything is over in a matter of seconds. The sound
of shouts. Sticks that rain down blows upon his body
time and again, bottles smashing against the floor, or
maybe against his skull. It's five, six against one. Then

in the blink of an eye, the assailants disperse and melt away. Some take the stairs to the street and are lost on the avenue. Others descend to the platforms and take the first train that arrives.

In the ticket hall, which is neither the street nor the depths, a bloodied boy remains: he gets up, helped by one of his gang who reappears now that the worst danger has passed. Adrenalin drives the body of the injured boy, who bleeds profusely from his forehead. He leaves the corner where a pool of blood, sticks and smashed glass remain like an imprint of the attack. People are crying, shouting; some are hidden behind the ticket collector's booth. Not many help the lad. Fear establishes itself as the lord of this place, of these times. Fear is the only law that can guarantee a minimal survival in this savage city. A man unleashes his horror on the staff: why are there no guards in the underground? Can no one defend anyone else anymore… is no one safe? Idiots! Cowards! The employees hear him out and agree mechanically. One doesn't know if they're trained to deal with insults or simply tired of witnessing such events. Be that as it may, the answer is more than clear: no guards, no security, no one is safe.

A woman is having a crisis, she is on the floor, crying. She says they're coming back, that they must protect her and her children… that she wants to be at home. She is attractive and an entourage of men rapidly approach to help her. The irate man shouts at the staff to call an ambulance. They're taking the wounded boy toward a corridor off the main hall, to an office where he can lie down and be given first aid while a doctor arrives. But half an hour later there's still no sign of a doctor. A few of the injured boy's companions turn up in ones and twos and accompany him inside. But then other voices begin rising, start to shout: this time from below, on the platforms. Once again people stampede – this time upwards. One of the friends of the casualty – he must be twelve or thirteen, this one – passes his bag to his girlfriend, encouraging her to go inside with the wounded boy. He steels himself, jumps the turnstiles and runs down the stairs. The cries and shouts from below can still be heard, people calling for help, the whistle of a train pulling out, the doors of another that has just arrived opening. A few seconds later the kid comes back up. He seeks the door which his friends entered, but it's closed. He knocks, but the staff member who opens the door tells him that if you go out you stay out. The boy accepts it without causing a fuss. You can see he's not accustomed to expect anything from anyone, except to be left alone in the world – that's his daily bread. And in that moment his body is like an open book: he moves as if jumping, ever on guard – he's learned the rhythm of the hunter; the rhythm, too, of one who has probably been hunted all too often. His gaze shifts in a millisecond – automatically, instinctively, naturally – to the mouth of the stairways that lead to the platforms, to the exit that leads to the street, to the turnstiles and the booths that could hide – behind darkened glass – an enemy. He rubs one fist with his other hand, moving some sharpened blades that, back on his wrist, appear to be a simple bracelet. He has the eyes of one who is getting ready to kill; ready to defend what's his, whatever that may require.

Now a band of girls, some in the blue secondary-school blouses, a few others in sixth-form beige, are coming up from the platform. They hug and protect one of their own who is having difficulty walking. It appears that someone pushed her during the battle – down the stairs, from the platform on to the rails? She's crying, shaking, and she shouts something unintelligible. At the same time there is an unassailable something in her look of giving thanks to life. She's alive and could very well not be. Pathetic happiness: our daily bread and oft-recited psalm. Another half an hour has passed and there's still no sign of a medic or an ambulance. At the end of the ticket hall appear two blue uniforms, darker than those of the underground staff. I look for the hunted hunter, but I barely catch a glimpse of him disappearing up the stairs to the street where he'll never be caught by those who are only arriving now and don't have any idea of the honour of a youth, of the improbable excuses that could bring him to kill or be killed. Ridiculous for those who look from outside, for them it is a heartbeat, the movement of the Earth.

The angry bystander who'd protested about the station's security, now with an expression that promises a little more equanimity, approaches one of the staff members to ask him to remove the sticks and stones, the murderous bottles that have remained untouched and seemingly useless in the corner: if there's another confrontation, the weapons would be on hand. The police ask and ask. They receive stories – vehemently told, haltingly related. They receive raised shoulders and I-don't-know-anythings. They receive fear. Over the PA system it is announced that there have been student disturbances; that the time is 5.30; that one must cede the blue seats to pregnant women, and that they have been obliged to close the station: Los Cortijos, for now, will not continue to offer services. Passengers are kindly asked to go to the stations Los Dos Caminos or La California. Passengers are kindly asked to keep moving along and not stand and stare. Passengers are kindly asked to go about their business and forget. Passengers are kindly asked not to talk about this with anyone, that's life, that's Caracas. Passengers are kindly asked not to write little *crónicas* about these events and to find better things to do with their time.

The blood on the tiles has dried.

CLOWN

RODRIGO BLANCO CALDERÓN
Translated by Katie Brown

For Salvador Fleján.

Hit me, Clown.
Korn, *Clown*

Forgotten Files. That's what the blog was called. It couldn't have been called anything else. That Monday, Alex Bell had come into the newsroom early to update it, making the most of the calm which lulled the newspaper's headquarters until ten in the morning. It was the second entry to what readers, after many comments, had spontaneously baptised 'The Episode of the Erotic Policeman'. The photos – which showed a police officer wearing only underwear, a bulletproof jacket and a helmet, gun in hand – had caused a storm. So much so that Alex Bell had begun to doubt the benefit of publishing the second batch, which was even more compromising than the first.

Thanks to these photos, his readers had multiplied like a virus. Nonetheless, neither the regulars nor the new followers had asked themselves about what in visual arts is called 'perspective'. Perhaps they thought that the policeman had taken them himself. Or, at most, that it had been a lover with a weakness for men in uniform. Nobody seemed to consider other possibilities.

Deep down, he didn't have any doubts. He hadn't felt so strongly about anything since the first time it occurred to him, in an internet café in central Caracas, to open the temporary files folder on the computer he was using. The find – and the need to share it – became an electrical pulse which took form at that exact moment. Like a fleeting monument to the place of discovery, he created the blog in that dingy internet café and gave it the most transparent name he could: *Forgotten Files*. A perverse homage to the intimacy stranded in the limbo of a computer as anonymous as its users.

Alex Bell prepared to finish his task. The night before, he had written the texts to accompany the images: detailed, ironic and brutal descriptions of postures, clothing and expressions. Imaginary situations that he dreamt up based on the photos, which had allowed more than one attentive reader to recognise his distinctive writing style. Now he just had to put all of the material together on the screen and click 'Finish'.

First he wanted to check his emails.

There, in his inbox, was the news that would change the course of that morning, the following weeks and, perhaps, the rest of his days.

The invitation to the press conference was explicit. It announced in large letters the return of Fonsy. Not 'Fonsy, the Clown'. Just Fonsy, because this was the genuine article, the most famous TV clown in Venezuela.

The Fonsy Show had maintained an unbeatable audience share from the mid-seventies until the end of the eighties. It was in 1989, when the economy crashed and the *Caracazo* riots took place, that the programme was taken off air. During the following decades Fonsy's reputation had had its ups and downs. He was an embarrassing episode in the collective memory, the recollection of which proved strangely pleasant. For those who had been children at the time, he was a kitsch emblem of childhood. Fonsy was that feeling of ridiculousness that hits you when you see yourself in the past with absolute sincerity.

Fonsy's career, like that of every other show business star, was always shrouded in controversy. It was said that in reality Fonsy hated children. And it was also said that Fonsy not only hated children, but in fact, hurt them.

Bell knew all about this dark legend, and moreover he knew from experience that it was true. He could remember this because he worked for the newspaper, because he was the lead entertainment reporter, and because he was sure to be assigned to the press conference. Otherwise, the anecdote would have remained as it had been until then, in the cloud of memories that you want to erase. Latent but disconnected from their references, like a forgotten file.

The wordplay worried him. Alex Bell had a hunch that something was going to happen. He felt with perfect clarity that life, out of amusement or malice, was preparing to tell itself stories. Stories in which little people such as himself were like cogs in a machine which, after crafting a plot, constructing a useful sentence or demonstrating an idea, would be dismantled by time.

He relived the incident with photographic precision. No television camera captured it. It didn't happen in the studio but in Fonsyland, the theme park that Fonsy had opened close to the boulevard in Chacaito. After repeated tantrums his parents had agreed to take him on a Saturday when Fonsy would be there in person with the children.

Alex Bell would have been about eight when he learnt that hell was made of garish colours, balloons and a multitude chained to jobs requiring forced fun. As soon as they arrived they realised that their only purpose in that park was to queue: half an hour for a miserable slide which turned out to be more dangerous than the Bajada de Tazón highway, due to its sharp angles and the dried up Pepsi-Cola spilled all over the bottom which made it stickier than a glue trap; another half an hour to get into the toilets, which were very similar to those in the worst bars he would frequent in his university years, given that children and drunks tell the truth and urinate anywhere; long queues to buy cold popcorn, to try the shooting gallery, to take an impossible photo with Fonsy, the clown.

His parents didn't squander the chance to teach him a lesson and forced him to queue for every one of the rides. At the last one of the attractions, when his mother was already waiting on a far-off bench while his father paid the parking ticket, the meeting occurred. He spotted him hurrying down one of the corridors. Alex Bell abandoned the long line of children immediately and ran in that direction. As he reached the corner, he saw that he was headed towards a door at the end of the corridor. He began to race again against the possibility of Fonsy disappearing and against the two boys who had followed him and might try to ruin his special moment.

The boys ran after him and soon closed in. Alex Bell wasn't going to let anyone get ahead of him and that's when he cried out:

'Fonsy!'

Alex Bell hollered and kept running, arms wide open, like a fugitive in search of sanctuary. Fonsy turned and swatted away the swarm of children pursuing him with his elbow.

Alex Bell was flung to the ground. He didn't cry. The two boys were already at his side and looked at him and then at their idol, not knowing what to think. For a millisecond, Fonsy didn't know what to do either. But then he reacted in the manner of what he was: a professional clown. He pulled his ace from his sleeve, his characteristic exclamation, the monosyllabic switch to turn on the laughter machine:

'Hwe-ep!'

Fonsy said this with the corresponding wiggle of arms and hips.

The children started to laugh and, when he saw that the situation was under control, he opened the door and disappeared.

Alex Bell peered around him and found the usual bustle of the newsroom at eleven in the morning. He wasn't surprised that no one had greeted him. His unhealthy shyness was common knowledge at the newspaper. Everyone accepted his way of being, his dressing like the last of the grunge Mohicans, as the dysfunctional flipside of his talent. A talent which consisted of extracting from the banal (be it celebrity gossip, the routine of anonymous people, Venezuelan culture or, above all, himself) perfect texts that made readers cry with laughter. As if all his daytime behaviour were only the first part of that big joke which was his real life.

He'd never seen it like this. In fact, before this morning, he'd never seen *himself* like this: in the third person. He glanced around suspiciously and had a feeling that in another dimension someone had discovered that childhood vignette and was putting his story into words.

By the time of the planning meeting, news of Fonsy's return had spread. Conversations were filled with the old rumours about his temper, the refrains of his songs, tentative names of the other clowns who accompanied him. Everyone was embarrassed but at the same time happy to share the shameful memory of Fonsy. Alex Bell felt that, in some way, the laughter was directed at him.

'You go to the press conference,' he told the intern.

The editor of the entertainment section and the other reporters fell silent.

'I want an exclusive interview,' said Alex Bell.

They all burst into laughter and looked at him like a naughty child.

'Only you can do it,' the editor told him with an air of complicity.

'Only me,' Alex Bell confirmed, and left thinking about how stupid people look when they laugh without knowing why.

It wasn't difficult to arrange the interview. The manager was Glenda de Fonseca, the famous Fonsyna, a love-struck fan who at fifteen was part of

Fonsy's ballet and later ended up as his wife and the mother of his children. The interview was scheduled for the Wednesday and would take place at Fonsy's own home. This surprised him, but no more than the fact that even a clown can find the love of his life.

He made the most of the 2pm drowsiness to post the second part of 'The Episode of the Erotic Policeman'. The officer of the first photos was joined by three more to form a dangerous and tender little train. They wore only their helmets: a ploy to hide their faces. The first officer held his gun aloft, confirming with this gesture either his rank in the force or his condition as the locomotive of the train. Alex Bell had never endorsed the words with which he had presented the blog, *Forgotten Files*, on that first day as much as he did then: 'Photographs and other files found on the computers in the internet café I visit. Forgotten by foolhardy or consciously shameless strangers. Is this legal? Is this moral? I doubt it. But it is fun.'

Yes, it was fun.

The next morning, the number of comments surpassed that of the previous entry. Alex Bell sensed it when he arrived at the newsroom and everyone greeted and congratulated him. Since he had begun the blog, he had tended not to log in at home: he didn't want to waste the opportunity to exploit the pearls stored in the bowels of the internet cafés lost in the city. Settled in his cubicle, he saw that the link to *Forgotten Files* had been shared by the majority of his contacts on Facebook and Twitter. Then he realised what was happening.

The problem wasn't that people had turned a joke into a denunciation of the robberies and kidnappings carried out in uniform and in daylight by the Metropolitan Police; nor that they had made a joker, an amateur comedian or virtual clown like himself, into a hero. The problem was that they identified him, with name and surname, as the author of the blog.

To calm himself down, he concentrated on his work. He gave his intern some instructions for Fonsy's press conference at midday. Afterwards he dashed off two pieces about the premiere of a film and a *telenovela* and then he turned to his preparation for the interview.

Online he found pages made by nostalgic fans, videos with clips of his shows, photos from different eras, the lyrics to his songs, brief bios, and last but not least, the names of the clowns who had accompanied him. It was well known that after Sony Fonseca hung up his alter ego in 1989 he became an important and forbidding television producer. As for Fufurufo, Chirrinchi and Mr Wikili, however, those clowns on whom Fonsy had always played dirty tricks, nothing more had ever been known of them.

It was Guillermo Cabañas, a retired telenovela writer and great connoisseur of the media, who gave him some hints. Of Fonsy's three assistants, Fufurufo had always been the most ambitious. He had even managed to film a pilot for his own show. The project fell through at the last minute and Fufurufo ended up in an ill-fated drug business which landed him in jail. When he got out, he had become a hardened addict.

'Did he die?' asked Alex Bell.

'I don't know. In the end, it doesn't really matter. When you can't tell the colour of your skin from the filth on the street it means you've already been wiped out,' said Cabañas. 'Of course, Sony was always thought to have been behind the failure of that pilot.'

'And the others?'

'Chirrinchi also wound up in jail. More or less the same story: robberies, drugs. Only he was also accused of rape. You know that they don't forgive that inside. He was killed in a brawl after a visiting day.'

'And the other one?' Bell insisted.

'Mister Wikili?' Cabañas said, squinting. 'I never heard anything about him again.'

Without really understanding why, Alex Bell was angry. At around four in the afternoon, the intern returned.

'And?' said Bell.

'A real cretin. You'll see.'

Alex Bell read the summary of the press conference, Fonsy's statements. He made a few suggestions to the intern. Minutes later, on the way home, he began to plot his revenge.

The lift door opened and Alex Bell let the photographer pass. Glenda, Fonsyna, greeted them. He had to admit that she was a beautiful and warm woman. The apartment was a spacious penthouse in Santa Mónica, a neighbourhood to which many middle class families had emigrated in the seventies in the truncated race up the social ladder. The clown's abode, like the area, had lost its lustre over the years. The decor, the furniture, the pictures, all had the same waning sheen, like a varnish about to evaporate.

331

After a few minutes' wait, Sony Fonseca appeared in the room. His dark skin, weather-beaten but with a healthy glow. His dyed black hair held in a ponytail. His eyes too seemed to be dyed black. They were ruled by an almost hypnotic stare.

Alex Bell was undaunted.

At first, he let Fonsy's ego expand at will. He gave him free rein to tell the classic story of deprivation and achievements: his arrival in the capital city with the desire to succeed; the multiple jobs he had to work during the day – waiter, ice cream seller, ministerial office boy – while at night, in a room in some boarding house, he learnt little acrobatic stunts, card tricks, conjuring acts; the long days at the gates of television studios waiting for a chance. All the roadblocks to self-improvement that move the masses, Sony Fonseca raised them during the interview.

There was a pause. Fonsyna brought in a tray of juice and biscuits. Alex Bell seized the opportunity.

'How old are you?' Bell asked.

'Just put that I was born "in the forties."'

'It's never been easy for the great clowns to return to the stage. What reasons does a man of your age have for making a comeback? Is it money? Do you feel like you need to recover your fame? Are you bored?'

'I'm coming back because every time that I've been invited onto a programme, on the radio or on TV, the lines collapse from people calling in, crying, begging me to return.'

'And why do you think that is?'

'I think,' he said, puffing out his chest, 'it's because I left a deep impression on people's hearts. Generations of children loved Fonsy and wanted to be like Fonsy. Even I wanted to be like Fonsy.'

He chuckled. He looked pleased with himself.

'Cary Grant,' Alex Bell said abruptly.

'Pardon?'

'I was remembering how a reporter once told Cary Grant that everyone wanted to be like Cary Grant. And the actor replied that he would also like to.'

They both fell silent.

'Let me see if I understand. You're comparing me to Cary Grant?'

'No. I just remembered the anecdote. Although, Cary Grant did start his career as a comedian and a clown in the Bob Pender group. He also did acrobatics. Did you know that?'

'No.'

Sony Fonseca was completely serious.

'Are you not scared of the public seeing an aging Fonsy?' asked Bell, taking up the interview again.

'I may have aged, but Fonsy hasn't.'

'Why do you insist on talking about Fonsy in the third person?'

'Does it annoy you? I talk like this because Fonsy and I are not exactly the same person. Each one is the mask, the character, the double of the other,' Fonseca said. His eyes darkened.

Alex Bell swallowed. The moment had come.

'If that's so, what does Sony Fonseca have to say about the infamous rumours that surrounded Fonsy's career? Is it true that he hurt children?'

The silence filled the room. For an instant no one made the slightest movement, not even the

333

photographer who was discretely covering the interview. Sony Fonseca, with his eyes fixed on those of Alex Bell, relaxed his expression and a wide smile opened across his face.

'I like you, you know?' said Fonseca. 'Don't ask me why, but I like you. Fonsy himself is going to reply to that question.'

Then he gestured to the photographer and called for his wife.

Two hours later he had Fonsy in front of him. Sony Fonseca had slowly disappeared, covered by successive layers of make-up, by the seventeen rollers put in his hair to give it its characteristic bell shape, by the drawn-on tears that always fell without flowing from his eyes. Fonsy had some time ago baptised this whole process of transformation, which the photographer captured step by step, 'the ritual'. And there was something mystical in the abnegation with which Fonsyna helped him with each stage.

Alex Bell knew that the interview, together with those photos, would be a smash hit.

The question had hung in the air and the whole ritual was the setup for the lie. Alex Bell knew it and yet he felt uneasy. As if, despite his own memory, Fonsy could convince him. As if he couldn't help but find a profound truth in Fonsyna's beauty and movements.

When he was ready, he sat back down beside him and with a completely different attitude – 'theatrical' was the word which came to Alex Bell's mind – he answered.

'Look me in the eyes so you believe me,' Fonsy told him, putting a hand on his leg. 'Never. You hear me. I have never hurt a child.'

The interview was published on the Friday and, as he had suspected, it was a great success. Alex Bell remembered the sad fate of Fufurufo, Chirrinchi and Mister Wikili and thought that, like them, he had let Fonsy trample him to reach the top.

Despite himself, Alex Bell had to admit that he had also reached the top himself. That irritating affinity between him and the clown was confirmed by the last few dozen comments left on the blog. Insults against the police, sardonic joy at Fonsy's return and appreciation for Alex Bell's undeniable talent intermingled there. He didn't know whether to be worried or happy when the site's omniscient administrators put up a warning to users of the explicit content of *Forgotten Files*. This step fuelled the readers' rage, the polemic intensified, and by Monday Alex Bell found that his blog had been officially shut down.

From then on, Alex Bell was the object of an unbearable wave of solidarity. A famous talk-show host even claimed in an interview to be an avid reader of *Forgotten Files* and lamented the strange circumstances that had led to the closure of the blog. Alex Bell, by contrast, experienced it as a release. No longer having to descend into the hell of Caracas to seek out forgotten images, he allowed himself the peace of wandering along roads and avenues, capturing the no less anonymous potentiality of everyday activity.

On one of those afternoons, he ended up almost without realising it, at the Centro Plaza. He went in the Noctua bookshop and scanned the tables. In the bestsellers section he found a novel that, ever since he'd seen the film version, he'd been searching for in vain: *It* by Stephen King. He started reading the first few pages when 'Bellina' made her appearance.

Her shrill voice, like a child's, shattered the hushed atmosphere of the bookshop, barely pierced by the filigree of the background music. Alex Bell, raising his head cautiously, observed what was happening. She was a blonde woman, thirty-something but dressed like a twenty-year-old girl. She had skinny jeans, Converse, a sweater tied around her hips, a T-shirt with the seams on the outside, and a perfect body. That body was a bookshop too, a space with millimetric harmony that had been disrupted by a voice and words from somewhere else.

After listening to her speak to the bookseller for a while, he realised that the woman was mad. He returned his gaze to the book, but her presence distracted him. He kept up his self-absorption, which worked so well for him in the newsroom, when he felt that they were watching him. Indeed, when he lifted his head he found the fascinated expression of the woman who was watching him with her eyes wide open. She approached him, and, unable to contain her excitement any longer, said:

'Fonsy.'

Alex Bell was paralysed.

'Pardon?' he said.

'You're Fonsy. I'm your biggest fan. I've already got my ticket for this weekend. I've been waiting years to see you.'

Alex Bell looked at the bookseller, who shrugged his shoulders, unable to hide a smile. Then he started to look around, towards the shelves, as if he expected to find a hidden camera behind the books which would explain what was happening.

'I'm not Fonsy.' He realised that he'd started to sweat.

The woman laughed and covered her face.

'Of course you're Fonsy,' she said after. 'I read your interview with him. Besides, I always visit your page and I know all about you. I'm your biggest fan. I already have my ticket for the concert. I haven't forgotten a single one of your songs.'

Then, without warning, she came closer, hugged him and stamped a kiss very close to his mouth. Then she turned and skipped away.

When he went to pay, the bookseller smiled at him again.

'She's so beautiful. It's a real shame.'

'Who is she?'

'We don't know. She comes in now and then, always with a different name. But at least she's clean and she has some money. She sometimes insists on buying books from us. You can tell she comes from a good family.'

'Just as well,' said Alex Bell. He paid, said goodbye, and as he left the bookshop he noted with shame that he had an erection.

On the street, Alex Bell once again had the feeling that he was on the edge of a stage, observed by hundreds of masked people who were enjoying his performance. He began to walk and the impression that Fonsy was not only the producer but the director of that production muddled him up. He went up the Avenida Luis Roche and took refuge in the Casa Rómulo Gallegos. Throughout that month, in the underground cinema, they were showing a cycle of North American comedies. He bought a ticket without stopping to see what the film for that day was. There were only two people in the front row. He walked by them, went up the stairs and sat in the back row.

The lights went out and the details of the moment started to get lost in the darkness. Alex Bell told himself that he could be calm, especially when he realised the splendid coincidence: *Limelight*. He settled in to watch Calvero's misadventures for the nth time when the door opened and he saw her come in. The woman located him, crossed the space that separated them, and sat down beside him with absolute calm, as if she had arrived for a date.

Alex Bell observed her while she watched the screen. He thought about getting up, saying something. Then she put her hand between his legs. He knew there was nothing to be done. She spent a long time massaging him and then started wrestling with the button and fly of his trousers. Alex Bell helped her.

'You are Fonsy, aren't you?' she whispered.

'Yes,' he replied.

Then the woman bent over and in those moments Alex Bell forgot even about the darkness. After the episode with Bellina (as he called her every time he thought of her), he called in sick and shut himself up at home. He couldn't remember which of the two had left the cinema first. What he did remember clearly, although he couldn't quite understand it, was the automatic decision to throw away the King novel. As if Pennywise had had something to do with what had happened in the cinema. The fact is that during his isolation he saw himself enveloped in a chain of identical nightmares: Fonsy devouring him with revolting fangs. However, the image of Calvero, musing by a window and telling Teresa 'Life can be wonderful if you're not afraid of it' wasn't much more comforting. Calvero and Pennywise were the paths to a crossroads which left him paralysed. Wasn't it too much? A clown with coulrophobia? A shy clown? What was a shy person if not a living creature afraid of life?

He never thought he would be pleased for that Saturday to arrive. That's why he was surprised to note the lack of movement around the Caracas Theater Club. If it hadn't been for the logistics staff, no one would have guessed that that was the day of Fonsy's official return. The show was meant to start at eleven o'clock and Alex Bell arrived at 11.30. He tried to avoid being recognised. Especially by Bellina, if she had actually turned up.

He showed his press pass and the doorman's yawns gave him a sense of the flop. Sure enough, the theatre was half full and that was only the first of six planned performances. It didn't take long to work out the audience. One part was made up of those with nostalgia who wanted to show their children an important episode from their own childhood. The children cried with fear every time Fonsy approached the audience. The others didn't have children and had come only to laugh at Fonsy: they sang the songs at full belt like at a drunken birthday party at four in the morning.

After the first interval, half of this half took the opportunity to leave. Fonsy didn't come back out. No one would ask for a refund, as the only people left were Fonsy's friends and family, and a few spectators who would return home with a juicy, pathetic and well-earned anecdote.

Alex Bell left his seat and with his press pass made it into the dressing rooms. It wasn't hard to find him. The place seemed like a garrison breaking camp. A technician showed him the door. He entered without knocking and saw the couple. Fonsy raised his arms to the heavens and then buried his head in those same arms. Real tears fell down his cheeks and their short course dragged down the others, the ones that had remained suspended for more than twenty-five years. Fonsyna withdrew from her husband for a moment and was about to ask Alex Bell to leave, when Fonsy recognised him.

'Leave us alone, Glenda.'

Fonsyna left the dressing room.

'What a fuck-up, ey?' An ironic smile fought to impose itself on the smudged make-up.

'Yep,' Bell said.

'I never thanked you for the article.'

Bell kept quiet.

'What's going to happen with the other performances?' he asked after a while.

'Cancelled. The producer just told me.'

At that point, Fonsy started to cry again. He cried and cried without stopping. Alex Bell distracted himself eying the clown attire strewn across the room: the ashes of the ritual. He thought about Chaplin, about Stephen King, about the intricate architecture of future laughter.

He was thinking about these things when he saw that Fonsy was practically on top of him. Like a nightmare from the past, Fonsy, inconsolable, with his make-up cracked by his tears, was pouncing on him for a hug.

With an elbow that had been brewing for more than twenty years, Alex Bell pushed off the clown.

Fonsy was still on the floor, baffled, when Alex Bell left the dressing room.

He walked across the car park and headed to the exit. Then he felt a knot in his stomach. A void produced by the total absence of any enthusiasm. Revenge, more than a dish served cold, was a dish reheated.

'He deserved it,' Alex Bell said, without much conviction.

And Bellina?, he thought. Did she also deserve what had happened? The blonde tones of her hair made him think of Virgina Cherrill, of how Chaplin had met her during a boxing match, of her making her acting debut in *Limelight* to end up in the arms of Archibald Alexander Leach, her first husband, better known as Cary Grant.

Alex Bell was wrong. Claire Bloom had dark brown hair and although she played Teresa in *Limelight*, she married, to cite a reference that could interest him, Philip Roth in 1990. Virginia Cherrill had starred in *City Lights*.

Anyway, Alex Bell asked himself looking up, who'd care, at that moment, about such a clarification? Hadn't Bellina confused him with Fonsy? Who, then, was responsible for that mistake?

Alex Bell thought, or perhaps even said out loud, that the two errors, between them, cancelled each other out. And something like a gust of wind, the kind that closes doors, signalled that the end of his story was approaching.

He felt another tight knot in his stomach.

A taxi passed and he signalled to it, but what pulled over a few seconds later was a Metropolitan Police patrol car. The driver stayed at the wheel. The other three got out. They asked him for his ID.

'That's him,' the one with the ID told the driver.

They handcuffed him and put him in the car. At that moment, he identified the only extraneous element, like a prop, of the whole ensemble. The four policeman in the car were wearing helmets. Could it all be a farce?

Alex Bell noticed that the uneasiness in his stomach was moving to the rest of his body, and from there it spread, like a plague, to the entire city. The idea pleased him and he clung to it, while a torrent of blows removed him, too, from the stage.

THE BRIEFCASES

JUAN CARLOS MÉNDEZ GUÉDEZ
Translated by Katie Brown

They punched him in the stomach a couple of times. They were competent at their job. The blows barely made a sound, but he fell weakened to the floor and waited several minutes for the beating to continue.

'We'll leave you alone for a while to think things over properly and loosen your tongue.'

Once he'd gotten his breath back, he dragged himself across the room until he could lean on the wall. He dozed off for a few moments. The air seemed to ring with the sound of a distant sea. Blue sparks speckled his retinas. He heard a buzzing. He thought about a beach covered in rubbish bags that the sea brought in on its waves.

As the pain lessened, he remembered his mother. She never exchanged too many words with him, but on one occasion, as they watched a spy film on TV, she did say: 'The important thing when you're hit is not to let anyone know that it hurts. That's something your father simply doesn't get.' Donizetti never understood this phrase, and although it came back to him now like a whistling sound, he knew that it wouldn't help him much.

It was always a little tough for Donizetti to imagine how his mum and dad had built a life together. All he could recall from his childhood was the silhouette of an absent woman and the face of a man who was always making a bad joke; who always arrived too early or too late; who bought fish when she wanted to eat smoked chops, or smoked chops when she craved a tuna salad.

It would seem that, when first married, his parents had a few peaceful years. Then she fell pregnant and had Donizetti. She looked after him. She drew up lists of her daily chores and carried them out meticulously. Whenever she completed a task, she'd cross it out with a red line.

When the time came for Donizetti to go to school, his mother led him by the hand and smoked thin cigarettes. There she met other mothers. She used to join them in greasy spoons that smelt of coffee. She listened to them talk about their jobs, their projects.

One afternoon she mentioned at home that she was going to go back to school, that she wanted to work in communications. Donizetti's father smiled. He came home that night with a beautiful and very expensive dress; he told his wife he was taking her to Aruba so they could relax for a few days, she could show off her dress, she could dance.

Perhaps they took that trip, Donizetti doesn't remember. What he can recall clearly is that several years later his mother told them that she had just been accepted at Central University, that they'd have to help out more at home, that she'd be there less. It sounded good to Donizetti, the thought of his mother having a degree thrilled him. His father said nothing. He buried his gaze in his plate of lentils.

The first Monday that his wife had to attend classes, Donizetti's father came home from work especially early. Around five o'clock he started to look closely at his son, to put his hand to his brow, to check the back of his throat. Then he insisted that the boy looked ill, sent him to bed, took him blankets, took his temperature countless times. 'Dad, I feel fine,' he said. 'No, no, my boy, you don't look well, it's a virus, or worse, hepatitis, you're a bit yellow, at the bus station they said that hepatitis is going around, you go to bed, go to bed, and you, woman, look at your son, look at him, damn it.'

A little before six, Donizetti's father, head in hands, pulling his hair out, spoke of the imminent death of his son: 'He's leaving us, he's leaving us.' Realising that he was getting no reaction from his wife, the man coughed violently: 'Me too, I feel ill too, I'm dying, woman, I'm dying, and you want to go to the university, precisely today you want to go.' But the wife remained calm: 'Calm down both of you, you both look fine, I can't see anything wrong with you.' And the husband: 'No, no, no, those are the most serious cases, when someone looks okay it means that they're about to die.' And the wife: 'If you feel very ill, go to the hospital and leave me a note.' And the husband: 'Don't take this the wrong way, my love, it's not so you look after us or to stop you going to class, it's because of the contagion, you must have the same thing, you'll start an epidemic at the university, we have to be responsible, woman, you're going to infect the entire class, and through them a load of families, and in two days you'll have unleashed an epidemic in Caracas, then in Venezuela… be responsible, my love, there are enough journalists in the world already, and anyway, once you've killed everyone off there'll be no need for journalists.'

Donizetti got out of bed and whispered to his mother to go and not to worry about them. He couldn't be sure that she had heard him, but he saw her go, her heels clacking sharply. He watched her from the balcony, contemplating how she walked the length of Avenida Victoria before crossing to the left. He thought that she looked beautiful in those blue trousers she was wearing, carrying those books in her hand.

During the years that followed his father had some strange ideas. He suggested that the family move to Barquisimeto; he tried to get into the coffee growing business near the village where his grandparents were born; he changed his working hours so it was impossible to know when he would be at home; he wanted to open a photocopier business so his wife could run it; he proposed that they have a second child.

The fact is that Donizetti's mother skilfully dodged every onslaught. It wasn't hard: her husband's enthusiasm was a combination of resigned tenderness and fleeting euphoria. And the fact is that although he made puppy eyes every time he placed a note on the table, through all those years he paid for every book, every trip, every typewriter that his wife needed to continue her studies. Donizetti understood that his father held a deeply engrained fear; that when his wife obtained her degree she would leave him. She wouldn't need him anymore. Perhaps it would have done some good to talk to the old man: 'Relax, calm down, stop annoying Mum, she looks so happy taking these classes.'

When she graduated, father and son bought similar ties. They took photos with the radiant woman. They went for lunch at the Casa de Italia so that she could enjoy an exceptional lasagne and a slightly bitter and expensive Chianti. They toasted the new graduate. The old man's hands were shaking as he raised his glass and four drops of red wine stained the tablecloth.

Donizetti's mother left home six months later. She'd gotten a modest job with the local council in Margarita. In shaky, unenthusiastic words, she asked Donizetti if he wanted to go with her, 'Even though I'm sure your dad would like you to stay. I don't mind, son, I'm strong, but he probably needs you more than I do.'

The door opened again. The woman in the baseball cap carried an iron rod wrapped in cloth. Donizetti tensed his stomach muscles anticipating another blow.

'Calm down,' she said, throwing the rod into a corner, 'my hands are enough for now. Are you starting to remember some of the things I've asked you? You look like you're remembering a lot of things. Who has the Glock you sold?'

After much shouting, forcing him to stay standing for hours, threatening him with the rod and another shower of blows, the pair retired bewildered. Donizetti accused all of his co-workers of stealing the pistol from him. One by one. Not pointing to anyone in particular, not leaving anyone out. Even the doorman, an arthritic little old man who walked with a hunch and barely moved since he'd lost his sight, was included in the list of names that he recited without pausing for breath.

Once again the major and the man with a face like a shaved armpit appeared.

They asked Donizetti to sit, inquired whether he wanted another Ricomalt or perhaps another *cachito*?

'No, thank you, I've lost my appetite.'

'The *cachitos* are really good,' said the major, 'they put lots of ham in them.'

'Thank you. Right now I don't want anything else. But I would like to know if I've collaborated enough and can go home.'

'No, no, comrade. Your explanations are very strange. How am I to believe that an entire office conspired to steal your weapon? What do you think I'm doing here? Wasting my time? I want to help you and go home. We're both tired.'

Donizetti felt the sting of the punches. For a while he considered whether to tell them that they were making a mistake: he had always thought that there was meant to be one good cop and one bad cop; but they had distributed themselves all wrong; first two good cops appeared, then two bad ones. He ran his tongue over his lips: a mixture of blood and chocolate. His knees creaked. He tried to take a deep breath.

'How long have you been doing these international missions?' whispered the major, his face like a rock.

'Is that what they're really after?' thought Donizetti. In a steady voice he recounted how for the last year he had transported green briefcases without a hitch until now. When he finished the sentence, he looked closely at the two men. Seeing their ironic looks, he explained that some strange things had happened on the trip to Geneva which he had planned to report upon his return to the agency, which hadn't happened yet because of the abrupt invitation from the two men who took him from the lift at gunpoint.

'Dear comrade,' said the major lifting his finger as if it were a hole punch, 'drop all this, save your tomfoolery, we don't have time for jokes and bourgeois faggotry. You misplaced a military weapon, you nearly lost a briefcase in Rome and you were acting strangely in Geneva.'

Donizetti took a breath to speak:

'No, Major, that wasn't my intention, please forgive me. What I wanted to tell you was that on that last trip, the one to Geneva, it was as if the staff had different instructions from the other occasions.'

The major lifted his chin and his face seemed to light up. It was the face of an affable man. Paternal almost.

'Major, this time, arriving at Geneva was a bit strange; at the airport, the comrade soldiers checked inside the briefcase.'

'And before that, what happened?' probed the man with the face like a shaved armpit.

'Before? Nothing strange, the same as always, they called me with a mission, they gave me the ticket and I received text messages once I was there.'

'Everything was the same as always?' asked the major. 'Don't hide anything.'

'The weird thing for me was that they checked the case and took out loads of clothes.'

The major was unfazed. He didn't even make a note in his pad. Donizetti picked up on that detail. The clothes didn't seem to surprise him.

'You're saying that you were given the instructions the same as always? Listen closely, I want you to think specifically about the trip to Geneva. Only that. I'm not interested in the fuck-up you narrowly escaped in Rome, perhaps you were checking out some Italian girl's arse so hard you almost got robbed… that doesn't concern me. I want you to tell me about Geneva. I want you to tell me that you didn't make an agreement with anyone to carry that briefcase at your own risk?'

Donizetti smiled and discovered that his bottom lip hurt. In that moment he also noticed again how the Ricomalt had stained his shoes and trousers.

'Nothing different, Major. How could I take those kind of decisions by myself? What for? It never occurred to me to disrupt a mission with a plan of my own.'

'Everything was the same then… You went to Prague, you took a twirl around Wenceslas Square, you tried a sausage, then you went to the hotel, from there to the airport, you flew to Geneva and, after eating Peruvian food and buying a book by Julio Ramón Ribeyro from a bookseller named Rodrigo Díaz, you were alone in that nightclub, without speaking to anyone at any point, and then you gave the briefcase to the doorman.'

Donizetti made an effort not to smile. They'd missed a detail when they'd spied on him in the club. They hadn't seen him talking to that blind man who was drunk and walked off like he was following a labyrinth. Well I'll be damned. Even professionals made mistakes. He lifted his face a little to the right. Breathed deeply. Made a special effort to detect any unusual detail.

'Well, now that I think about, the text messages I received were different, they were well written, they're normally a mess.'

'Aha,' said the shaved armpit, looking uncomfortable, 'well written texts. Anything else?'

'Nothing,' Donizetti confirmed, 'it was the same procedure as always.'

'Did it not seem to you as if one of your colleagues was especially interested in this delivery?' insisted the major.

Donizetti looked at the ceiling. Within seconds he calculated which answer would be the least compromising. The one that would let him survive. Keep going.

'I knew very little about this mission. I only knew what I needed to know to complete it. It was difficult for me to be aware of too many details.'

The shaved armpit and the major sighed. Then they stood up. The dim light seemed to thicken, as if someone were pouring a jar of ink over the room. The armpit whispered something that Donizetti couldn't quite make out; something like: 'What's important is the content, comrade, not how it's written,' and strode off. Only then did Donizetti realise that the man wore sandals and had a disgusting blue toenail.

The sound of trumpets and some kettle drums seemed to ricochet from the street. 'Life is full of useless details,' thought Donizetti stroking his swollen cheeks. 'If I manage to persuade them to let me go, in a few days I will remember much about this place, this moment, but that music will have been completely erased, as if it had never happened.'

'Let's see,' said the major. 'I think we can forget about that Glock that you lost. The matter could be very bad for you, because why shouldn't we think that you sold it to one of those thugs who go around massacring people; or worse, that you gave it to an enemy of the government. But I'm going to trust you on two conditions: the first is that you are going to report every detail of what goes on at the agency to me. A hand-written report, in your writing, that I will ask you for once a week.'

Donizetti nodded and, at a sign from the major, stood up.

'The other is that you are going to give me a contribution,' insisted the major. 'The boys that work with me don't forget for nothing. They have a great memory and could keep bothering you, but I can convince them to leave you in peace. So first thing tomorrow morning you'll deposit the money you earnt for these last trips into my account. And not a word to anyone. This city has become very dangerous. Choose who you meet with carefully. Remember everything you saw the other day, when those people were killed outside your house.'

A shiver ran down Donizetti's spine. He saw that the major's face remained impassive. 'Is he threatening me or is he just recounting my life so that I know that he knows?' The golden sound of the trumpet seemed to return: a distant piece, indecipherable. Donizetti continued nodding as they blindfolded him again. He let himself be carried. He did the maths, subtracted amounts. For a few seconds he would have almost preferred them to kill him rather than put such a big hole in his savings account, but when he felt the humid air of the street he felt euphoric: 'It doesn't matter, I'll see what happens, it's good to be here, smelling this unmistakable mix of petrol and eucalyptus, ripe mangos and women's perfume: Caracas, once again Caracas, breathing Caracas.'

THE STATE
OF THE NATION
(AND HOW IT GOT TO
THIS)

PATRIOTIC STUFF

EDUARDO LIENDO
Translated by Jethro Soutar

Fly-man Temístocles Pacheco guzzles down a baby-bottle of condensed milk, spiked with twenty drops of valerian, and hits the sack. He lies down on his circular bed and unfurls his beautiful transparent wings. He closes his left eye, keeping his right eye open. He will alternate between them throughout the night, the modus vivendi of a creature forever on guard. A peaceful night's sleep is simply not in his nature.

At dawn, his fly hearing detects the distant rumble of metal caterpillars, an unusual sound even in a city accustomed to strange indiscriminate noise. The thrum of the caterpillars has thunder in its belly. The roar melts the motorway tarmac and the shudder sends ants scurrying to sound the alarm in their geometrically complicated underground cities. Moths become flustered as they flutter about light bulbs. A black cat dashes across the road seeking safety and a ledge to watch the drama unfold. Word has already reached the cockroaches, not for nothing have they survived all manner of calamities through the ages, although a straddler, failing to propitiously heed the call, is crushed unceremoniously along with empty beer cans that litter the road and now explode like toads' stomachs. Rats instinctively sharpen their teeth, sensing that the surprise appearance of the metal caterpillars heralds a feast of freshly felled flesh.

Street dogs hug the sides of city boulevards ready to take refuge inside buildings, aware that no ribs are spared when caterpillars are on the prowl, not even those of a stray dog. A mad old lady crosses herself when she sees the caterpillars, as if she's just glimpsed the devil, then lets out a terrifying cackle. The caterpillars have stirred memories of death and destruction, resurrecting fears that had largely lain dormant.

Flying requires each wing to be the precise counterweight of the other, a difficult balancing act: the fly's left wing flickers excitedly, anxious not to miss a moment of the action; the right wing glides carefully, conscious that the route the metal caterpillars are taking augurs catastrophe. Homeless folk curled up in avenue doorways feel their bony bodies shake as the ground crackles. They think it's part of their dreams, for in their nightmares they always flounder on the edge of a precipice. Bags of rubbish dumped outside buildings await the dawn arrival of the dustmen, spilling out their stench though not their contents: they have not been torn apart by ravenous dogs this morning, for the hounds are too preoccupied with saving their own hides. Newspaper kiosks have yet to open but front-page headlines are already out of date, reports of the unexpected march of the metal caterpillars having failed to reach newsrooms, despite the din. There are not many cars on the roads this early in the morning, but a few pass the caterpillars going in the opposite direction. Their drivers look on in amazement, whether in curiosity or fright. The fly, and the fly alone, hears one driver cynically mutter: 'The president's going to get it tonight.'

A soldier pokes his sleepy helmeted head out of a tank turret, all the while gripping his automatic rifle. He was fast asleep when the sergeant told them to line up in the yard ready for combat. The order took everyone in his artillery squadron by surprise. If war had suddenly broken out, then nobody knew who it was with. The lieutenant who inspected them said the time had come to perform an important manoeuvre, but he didn't specify which one. As they climbed aboard their caterpillar, a soldier asked the tank sergeant what this was all about, but the sergeant answered irritably: 'Don't ask dumbass questions, soldier. Do you want to be imprisoned for cowardice? This is the stuff of patria.' So now the soldier finds himself in a metal caterpillar on his way to perform a mission he knows nothing about. The coolness of the early morning caresses his sleepy face.

The fly, who has been accompanying the caterpillars on their journey for quite some time now, flies down and lands on the soldier's shoulder. Why this soldier and not one of the many others journeying into and unto the night? This soldier is a native of Caripito, a town in the country's interior, and this is the first time he's seen the city under stars and nightfall. Perhaps it is the image of the novice provincial soldier that attracts the fly. A queer in platform shoes and two hookers with heaving breasts and necklines that leave little to the imagination spill out of a bar of the ill-most repute. The passing of the roaring caterpillars alarms them not in the least, for they are creatures of the night, they walk the tightrope between pleasure and pain and fear not the devil himself. The fly knows their hideouts. One of the hookers, dressed in a bright yellow top, shouts *ciao!* to the passing soldiers and raises a plastic glass to them. The soldier from Caripito looks at her curiously, but she merely makes him think of Rosalía, the girl he's in love with, who works in the town billiard hall and who is doubtless asleep right now, for Rosalía, at least in his mind, is a good girl, not a loose woman. She commands respect. But he's a long way from home, and he has no idea what this 'stuff of patria!' the sergeant talked of might be.

The fly-man takes flight again and rides the current of a gentle breeze. He senses the tension in the air, the agitation, the warning signs of mortal danger, for he understands, through some ancient learning, how space fills with foreboding when death approaches.

The government palace appears on the horizon. The fly counts as many as 507 working spotlights versus only three faulty light bulbs, and 150 guards on duty, with many more still in their dormitories at the military barracks. Their duty is to watch over the palace, the symbol of power and occasional overnight abode of Mister President. To take in the whole panorama, the fly heads up to one of the sentry boxes where a soldier stands on guard. The soldier is a native of Tucupita, a town in the country's interior.

Perhaps it is the image of the novice provincial soldier that attracts the fly, because there is a certain naivety to the soldier's expression.

The coolness of the early morning caresses his sleepy face. The fly, who has been accompanying the metal caterpillars for a good while now, lands on the soldier's shoulder. The soldier looks out at the apparent tranquillity of the night, the calm disturbed only by a few drunks shouting somewhere in the palace vicinity and the monotonous hum of lorries and buses on a nearby boulevard. Tonight is the first time the soldier has been on guard in the sentry boxes. He can see the city's tower blocks from where he stands and he watches as they become submerged in darkness, contrasts of light and shadow brought by the night.

The omniscient fly, like a tiny God, sees and hears a great deal more, but for the soldier, the city before him bears little resemblance to his internal landscape. His mind is elsewhere, looking out over an immense river, the mighty Orinoco, greys, browns and greens coming together to colour the eternal waters of the great river. That is what he sees from his sentry box, along with an indigenous girl in a red dress, Rosalía, who waits for him. He barely notices the palace courtyard and his fellow soldiers in their sentry boxes, and he's not in the right frame of mind to sense the coming of the caterpillars, which become confused in his imagination with the rumble of the river. But they will soon roar ferociously and spit fire from their jaws at the palace gates.

Soldiers in camouflaged uniforms and helmets jump out of lorries clutching rifles and machine-guns, then blend into the shadows, sheltering in doorways. The first detonations are heard. This stuff is lead, the soldier in the sentry box tells himself as he grips his rifle ever-more tightly, ignoring the fly that moves from his shoulder to his ear. Somebody shoots at somebody else. Stomachs churn, hearts pound. There has been no word of a foreign invasion, which means this must be the beginning of a battle between soldiers from Caripito and soldiers from Tucupita. In other words, as the sergeant said: the stuff of patria!

Where the fuck have we been sent, Corporal? Cover me and quit asking bullshit questions, rookie. Move in from the flanks. Ah! Christ almighty, I've been hit. Clear the wounded. Keep advancing, get behind the tanks. Enemy at ten o'clock! Enemy at ten o'clock! They're shooting at us from the sentry boxes. Sweep the sky, goddammit, sweep the sky. Disperse, for fuck's sake! Sergeant, lead your men over to the wall and cover us. The fly hides at the rear of a soldier's helmet. The soldier is crawling and doesn't know if he's bleeding or if he's pissed himself, but the fly can smell urine. Nevertheless, the soldier keeps advancing, thinking how he never imagined combat would be like this, so terrifying, so perilously close to losing the one thing that is truly his, the only thing that matters. The fly listens to the soldier's panted breath.

A particularly aggressive caterpillar hammers against a palace gate that refuses to yield. Why the fuck hasn't the Kommander sent back-up yet?, a lieutenant barks angrily. We've already lost a lot of men, adds the corporal. Got him, I finally got that son of a bitch up in the sentry box, took him down, hit him right on the money. The fly watches, now nestled behind a cartridge holder, sees courage beside fear, urine and blood, the sound and the fury. A couple of grenades go off inside the palace courtyards and the smell of gunpowder reminds the fly of patron saint festivals in the towns most of these soldiers come from. But this is no party. Here death is lord of the dance.

The fly, curious – horrified? – enters a bloody tunnel made by a projectile travelling faster than the speed of light through a soldier's body. The bullet entered the soldier, practically a teenager, via the throat, piercing the oesophagus, causing a vomiting of blood and penetrating the guts, which had never seemed so soft, softer even than the heart, its palpitations brought to a sudden halt by the foreign body, which was especially tender because the soldier was in love. The tunnel passes through the liver, a liver that appears to be in perfect order to withstand many celebrations, to keenly process the fifty thousand bottles of beer that make up a lifetime, and ends where the bullet has lodged in the femur, as if to accompany the soldier on his march into the back of the beyond. The fly has to turn back, embark on a sticky return journey through a body that no longer feels pain, but he doesn't exit via the same hole in the throat, rather he does so through the soldier's open mouth, from where the soul was released, for he will shortly have to seek and find its companion soul, such is the fly-man's calling. But first he lingers a moment on the soldier's lips. The fly has met the young man before, earlier in the morning, as dawn was breaking and the soldier rode into the city on one of the caterpillars. For this is the soldier from Caripito.

The fly perceives a small hatch being opened in one of the palace kitchens, specifically in one of the kitchen's walls. The hatch, perfectly camouflaged amongst blue porcelain tiles with golden arabesques, leads to a tunnel that runs under the palace grounds, beyond the perimeter wall and out into an old building that was once a nun's convent. We'll escape down here, Mister President, says a general carrying a torch, as he plunges into the dark tunnel. These pricks won't have the satisfaction of stringing me up, replies the head of state, in his checked pyjamas. They didn't count on your cunning, my dear President, adds another general, turning to close the camouflaged door behind him. Then he mutters under his breath in the semi-darkness: Better dead than caught up in a blood bath.

The fly rises up, flying in spirals in order to avoid becoming a sitting target, lest some envoy of the Persecutor endeavours to take advantage of the situation and liquidate him. He returns to the sentry box where the soldier, practically a teenager, is slumped over a railing, his head hanging, a bullet travelling faster than the speed of light having penetrated his throat. This is the soldier from Tucupita.

The fly, curious – horrified? – enters the short tunnel made by the projectile. The bullet snapped his vocal chords, causing a vomiting of blood, cut through the jugular and came to rest in the cranium, as if to accompany the soldier on his journey into the back of the beyond. The brain, that perfect mass of infinite wonder, harbourer of every sensation, was shattered in a millisecond, the tiny neurones wired to make the billions of connections that make up a lifetime instantly deactivated. Words, songs, hopes, dreams, fears, pains and loves, because the soldier was in love, all shattered along with his magnificent brain and turned to shit. The fly goes back the way he came, a sticky journey through a body that no longer feels pain, but he doesn't exit via the hollow in the throat, rather he does so through the open mouth, where the soul came out, for he will now seek to find its companion soul, such is the fly-man's calling. He pauses for a second on the soldier's lips. Only the fly knows that the final thoughts of the two soldiers coincided, for the soldier from Tucupita saw a billiard hall in an unknown village where a dark-skinned girl with a ponytail works, whose name is Rosalía, whom he's in love with and who's waiting for him, and the soldier from Caripito saw an immense and stunning river where an indigenous girl with loose black hair and a red dress sits on a rock, her name is Rosalía, he's in love with her and she is waiting for him.

The fly flies up to the window of an apartment in a nearby tower block. The battle is almost over, the shooting has become sporadic, like epileptic spasms. The fly, curious, looks through the window and sees a television being watched by the stunned inhabitants of the apartment, who lie flat on the floor. The Kommander, binoculars hanging from his neck and sword of vengeance held steady in his left hand, solemnly and proudly declares: Patriots! I'll step down if I have to, there are no flies on me. The vile constitutional president has slipped away. But you know all this, you're not fools. This is the stuff of patria!

Morning having broken, Temístocles Pacheco, the fly-man, returns to his neighbourhood and courteously greets the concierge of the Coromoto Residence. He goes up to the tenth floor in the lift, then walks down to the seventh floor and enters the Flykave. He's unlikely to sell any encyclopaedias today. It has been a long night, too long.

I Want the Bones of My Son

Maye Primera
Translated by Joanna Josefina Thomas

1

Water, a change of clothes, toothpaste, a hot dinner. If Edgar was still alive he would need the same as any other living inmate of the Retén de Catia. Water, a change of clothes, toothpaste, a hot dinner. Maybe one or two other things, if by chance he was only wounded. But in her hurry, in between fruitlessly searching for her son at the morgue and the hospitals and then returning to the prison, Inocenta had only managed to throw those four things into a bag. Once at the prison, she would try again to find out what had happened inside those walls five days before, on 27 November 1992, when dawn broke on two battles; one in the skies over Caracas, and another in the hell that was the Retén de Catia.

At four in the morning on Friday 27, a group of armed rebels hijacked the airwaves of three television channels, including the state channel, Venezolana de Televisión. From there, they broadcast a message from Lieutenant Hugo Chávez, who at that time was captive in the San Carlos barracks. In the four-minute message, the commander of the failed coup of 4 February promised that this time the tyrant Carlos Andrés Pérez would fall, the '*junta patriótica*' would take charge of the government, and the ignominy that was desecrating Venezuela would end, 'for now and forever'. The recording was broadcast six times over the two and a half hours the rebels maintained control of channels Eight, Two and Four. It was interspersed with footage of an official – the sleeves of his uniform rolled up – whose speech lauded the nineteenth century Federal Liberalist soldier Ezequiel Zamora and announced the triumph of the previously unknown '5 July Movement'. The rebels had also taken the Libertador airbase in Maracay and, along with it, the F-16, Mirage and Bronco fighter planes that went on to carry out the bombardment of the La Carlota airbase, the headquarters of the Venezuelan Intelligence and Protection Services (DISIP), the Fuerte Tiuna military base, and the presidential palace of Miraflores, all in Caracas.

At 7.20am, President Carlos Andrés Pérez took back his place of command behind the cameras of Televen, from where he announced that half an hour earlier troops loyal to his government had retaken control of the armed forces, that very shortly they would also take back full control of the media, and that the man appearing on their television screens – Hugo Chávez – remained incarcerated, and harmless, in the San Carlos barracks.

When Inocenta Martín turned on her television at 6.30 in the morning, she saw neither Chávez nor Pérez on the screen. Instead, she was confronted with the news that a battle had erupted in the Retén de Catia, where her son Edgar José had been incarcerated for the previous two years, awaiting trial for the armed robbery of a passenger on a local bus. Inocenta stood rooted to her spot before the stove. As the water for the first coffee of the day boiled away, she stayed as static as the silent image of Chávez that appeared over and over again on Venezolana de Televisión.

She can't remember what the time was when her legs finally carried her down the eastern lane of Propatria's Mario Briceño Iragorroy barrio towards the entrance of the Retén de Catia. She does remember that when she arrived the air was alive with bullets and tear gas, and that from an armoured police truck a water cannon was forcing families away from the main gate. The street that ended at the entrance to the prison was heaving with mothers, wives and sisters shouting the names of their sons, husbands and brothers, straining for a glimpse behind the railings, where bodies were piled around the courtyard.

When the commander of Zone Two of the Metropolitan Police, Rafael Barrios, informed the waiting journalists that the mutiny was under control, the sound of machine gun fire was still audible beyond the gates. The windows of the prison were crowded with more arms than bars, displaying banners made of bed sheets, revealing the situation that was unfolding, barely audibly, beneath the racket of the bullets: 'Alert the United Nations. They are killing us'.

There are two versions of events from that fateful dawn. Both versions end in the same way: with the Metropolitan Police shooting from the watchtowers. Approximately sixty-three inmates were executed, more than fifty-two were injured, and another twenty-eight disappeared. The shooters claim that the prisoners were attempting to escape. Survivors say that the prison guards shouted that they should flee, deliberately drawing them into the courtyard to be slaughtered.

The version of events provided by the inmates of the holding cells where Inocenta's son, Edgar José Marín, was incarcerated along with another eighty men, begins at five in the morning. Everyone had their eyes glued to the television, and the alternating faces of Hugo Chávez and Carlos Andrés Pérez. 'The government has fallen!' yelled someone. Then came the voice of a guard: 'Come out, you're all free.' At least, that's how the inmates remember it – that the police shouted 'You are free,' opened the cells, and then began to extort money in return for freedom. 'If we paid, we were free. Those who did not pay were killed. If you showed your face without paying, they shot you in the forehead,' says Douglas Liscando, from cellblock two. One of his many cellmates says that Edgar Marín didn't pay, and that the warden pulled the trigger. That story ends there.

The statement given by the Metropolitan Police to the press the following day tells a different story.

They claim that at the cry of 'Coup d'état!' a group of prisoners seized security post number four, killed the sentry, and took control of the machine gun, killing their fellow inmates.

The revolt was eventually quashed in under an hour on the evening of Sunday, 29 November, when five hundred members of the National Guard, under the control of Brigadier General Jesús Rafael Caballero, leader of Regional Command number five, took control of the prison. General Caballero himself did not encounter the machine gun mentioned by the Metropolitan Police. 'We found no firearms, aside from one or two old improvised rifles. We have seized approximately five hundred handmade blades of various sizes, but no firearms,' said Caballero on 30 November.

It was the forces of 'order' that carried the firearms. According to the report presented fourteen years later by the Public Order Brigade of the Metropolitan Police to the Inter-American Court of Human Rights, over 28 and 29 November a total of 485 police officers quelled the uprising using 126 firearms. Autopsy reports showed that at least sixty-three inmates were killed with bullets from those weapons. Another fifty-two survived, but suffered gunshot wounds to the back and sides.

Another report provided to the court by the warden of the Retén de Catia determined that the day before the uprising, 26 November 1992, the morning count showed that there were 3,618 inmates in the prison. The next count, taken on 30 November following a search carried out by the National Guard, showed 2,540 prisoners. It is known that of the 1,178 missing, nine hundred had been transferred to other prisons in the days following the uprising. The remainder make up that 'indeterminate number' of dead, injured and missing men who are referred to in the records archived at the national courts.

3

What finally dispersed the mothers waiting at the gates of the Retén de Catia on the night of 27 November was neither the teargas nor the curfew. Instead, it was the whisper that passed through the crowd that dozens of dead and injured prisoners had been transferred to the morgues and hospitals of Caracas, where they were jumbled together with the bodies left behind in the wake of the military coup. Inocenta went to the hospital of Magallanes de Catia, to the morgue at Bello Monte, and finally to the hospital at the port of La Guaira, where she was forced to stay, pacing between the hospital and the jetty, until the curfew lifted at six in the morning.

That Sunday the National Guard assumed control of the prison. New lists appeared on the walls, of the dead and the injured. The name Edgar José Marín appeared on none of them, and a member of the National Guard advised Inocenta to return on Wednesday, the prison's regular visiting day.

As the sun rose on Wednesday 2 December,

Inocenta had already been standing in line for six hours, clutching her bag containing water, a change of clothes, toothpaste, and food for her son. A procession of families filled the square and shuffled slowly forward. 'Lower your trousers, bend over, shake, push,' shouted the same female officer that body-searched them every Wednesday and Sunday. Carlos, Inocenta's husband, carried no package, and as such entered the prison before her. When she found him inside his head was clasped in his hands, and he was being consoled by one of Edgar's cellmates. 'What happened?' she asked. 'Be calm,' replied the prisoner. 'They killed your son.'

4

Edgar couldn't have been guilty, says Inocenta Marín, because he had served his country. When they accused him of armed robbery aboard one of the local busses that stops on block eight of Propatria, he was barely a year out of military service. And what is more, he had not been recruited, but had joined up of his own accord. Inocenta holds up his military recruitment card, the reverse of which bears the legend: 'irreproachable conduct'.

The day of the holdup of which he was never declared guilty, Edgar visited his mother in her house on the small road in the eastern corner of Propatria's Mario Briceño Iragorry barrio. Just a few days earlier he had found work in a boot factory, and his blue overalls were stained with the yellow glue used for the soles of shoes. An hour after Edgar said goodbye to his mother, one of her neighbours knocked on the door. 'Your son was taken away in a police van. He's locked up,' she told Inocenta. They accused him of trying to rob one of the passengers.

Edgar spent fifteen days locked in a cell at the headquarters of the Propatria Police Department, unable to communicate with the outside world. From there he was taken to the holding cells of the Retén de Catia, where he remained incarcerated for two years without ever seeing the inside of a courtroom. He lived in a room forty metres square, without a bathroom, where more than eighty presumed criminals waited for months, for years, for a judge to decide whether or not they were guilty. The prison – a small two-storey building for administrative offices, two five-storey towers of cells, and an area with workshops and a dining hall – was built originally for six hundred inmates. Later development upped capacity to nine hundred. But in 1992 more than three thousand prisoners lived within its walls. The thirty square centimetres afforded to each was shared with rubbish, raw human sewage, flies and maggots. The authorities had no reliable data on how many men were behind these bars, nor the details of their legal situations.

Inocenta Marín peddled corn and corn meal on the Boulevard de Catia. 'With that money I managed to take Edgar food on the weekends.' But she didn't earn enough to pay for a lawyer to defend her son. She was his lawyer.

Twenty years on, Inocenta cannot be sure if her son is dead or alive. Records of the massacre at the Retén de Catia – which are held at the office of Venezuela's Attorney General – list him as 'disappeared'. The only thing Inocenta knows for sure is where Edgar isn't.

After visiting all the morgues in Caracas in the days following the massacre, and after a fruitless search of the prison cells of the Retén de Catia, Inocenta received a call from the Attorney General's office. 'We have news of the boy. He has been located and he is dead,' said the voice at the end of the phone. 'But there is worse news' – continued the voice – 'the body was buried today, at two in the afternoon.'

The voice gave Inocenta the address of the cemetery at San Pedro de Los Altos, some thirty kilometres outside of Caracas. She found the grave, but there was no proof that the body buried there was that of Edgar José. Since then, every Tuesday, Inocenta searches the archives of the morgue of the Victorino Santaella Hospital in Los Teques, where the names and photographs of those prisoners killed in the massacre and buried at San Pedro de Los Altos are kept. 'Are you prepared for what you are going to see?' asked the pathologist before showing her a series of images of the bodies that had arrived at the morgue already decomposing. 'Despite the state of those bodies, one knows one's family, and there was no photograph of Edgar,' says his stepfather,

Carlos Barreto. 'From that moment until now, life has become an epic quest in search of the truth.'

'I don't know what to think. Perhaps it is true that he is buried there, but it is equally possible that he was taken by the River Guaire,' says Inocenta. It is known that several corpses were thrown into the tributary that flowed, full of sewage, behind the southern wall of the prison, right up until the building was demolished in March 1997. Over the course of twenty years, Inocenta has exhausted every possible resource. She can't remember exactly how many public prosecutors have taken on the case of her son, or how many months are made up of the hours she has spent waiting outside courtrooms.

The cases of Edgar Marín and thirty-seven other victims of the massacre at the Retén de Catia were presented before the Inter-American Commission of Human Rights in 1996. In October 2004, the Commission admitted the suit, which finally came before the Inter-American Court in 2005. On 5 July 2006 a sentence was passed in favour of the families, establishing responsibility for the deaths at the Retén de Catia on 27 November 1992 firmly with the Venezuelan state. The sentence urged the state to carry out every possible measure to identify, judge and try the individuals responsible for the acts of violence committed that day, and to exhaust all avenues in an effort to locate and return the body of Edgar José Peña Marín.

The Bolivarian Republic of Venezuela has obeyed neither this sentence, nor others passed down by the

Court. But Inocenta chooses to continue her odyssey: 'I only hope that the day comes when they tell me "these are the bones of your son." That they give me his bones so that I can bury him, and so that he can rest in peace.'

THE LIVING RUINS OF THE
TOWER OF DAVID

ALBINSON LINARES
Translated by Tim Girven

In its vicinity, everything appears to be small scale. The skyscraper – which today is nothing but the memory of its former owner's ambition – still defies the heights and towers above practically every other building. Like the Babel of antiquity, where the laws of man collided with those of God, the building offers the counterpoint that provides the best metaphor for the country: a stylistically *first-world* structure that houses the immense social debt of an underdeveloped state.

A VERTICAL VIEW OF THE LANDSCAPE OF THE CRISIS

From afar, the intense gleam of the block blinds pedestrians. With its forty-five storeys covered in glass and steel, the old Confinanzas Tower dominates Avenida Andrés Bello, a false crown for what was once the financial centre of Caracas: San Bernardino. It is a reflection, the illusion of a postmodern ziggurat, which, when one approaches it, casts its shadow and shows the toothless smile of decades of neglect capped by a hasty squatters' invasion. More than five hundred

378

families have found shelter in this skyscraper which, at 190 metres tall, was conceived as a monument to the success of the banker David Brillembourg, whose aggressive financial handiwork marked the 1990s.

In the entrance, an enormous hoarding proclaims to the four winds that the structure is controlled by the 'Caciques of Venezuela' Housing Cooperative, founded back in 2010. This Saturday in January is a day of celebration in the two 'habitable' towers of the complex. The local evangelical church has called a fair which features sports and cultural and spiritual events, along with the sale of a beef stew, the daily ration of the squatters who have invaded the building. The children are running about every which way, avoiding the loudspeakers that repeat without pause: 'Renew me Jesus / I no longer want to be the same / Renew me Jesus / Place in me your heart'.

The contrast between the magnificence of the 121,741 square metres of reinforced concrete spread across the twelve hectares of the complex as originally envisaged, and the precarious constructions thrown up since the invasion could not be greater. The red block walls that capriciously divide up the towers run this way and that. 'I arrived three years ago because a group of friends called me. There were a lot of people camping out, nothing worked and rubble was scattered everywhere, the stairwells were full of excrement, debris, dirt and rubbish. Tramps were living here, tin can scavengers and crackheads. It was a den of lowlifes that we recuperated through dialogue and togetherness,' opines Alexander Daza, president of the cooperative and pastor to the towers' evangelical souls.

Those who initiated the takeover describe with pride the complex organisational system that allows them to live here. Apart from the members of the principal counsel, there are sixteen coordinators, various cleaning squads and more than twenty 'co-workers' charged with watching over the good order of the residents in this vertical city.

Each floor has a delegate and sub-delegate who report any incident to the coordinators, including late payment of the 150 new bolivars that each 'condominium' costs. For Gladis Vargas, secretary of the cooperative, it is the efficiency of this structure that has allowed the building to pay off the 80,000-new bolivar debt it owed to the Caracas power company. They proudly show me the meter that has just been installed and as a result of which each family pays the modest sum of 2.5 new bolivars for its monthly power consumption. Now they are in discussions with Hidrocapital, the water utility, to arrive at a similar agreement and end their dependency upon the pneumatic pumps that currently lift the water to the tanks they themselves constructed.

'As coordinators we don't do what we wish but rather what the people want. The decisions are taken by majority vote on each floor and we support them as long as they don't hurt anyone else but are rather of benefit to the floor and the whole community.'

So much do they stand up for the preservation of this harmony that they even intervene in domestic squabbles that get out of hand: 'We're not going to let women be mistreated, nor allow any bloodletting. If anyone arrives drunk and starts raising hell then we'll take them out until they calm down – just because we come from poor neighbourhoods doesn't mean we have to behave poorly,' she explains in a categorical tone.

Like many others, Gladis arrived at the buildings as a result of a frenzied recommendation. Three years ago, her housemate told her about the invasion and she arrived with her children to live under canvas and tarpaulins for ninety days, until they began to build the 'apartments'. Today, by their own count, the inhabitants of the towers number something over 584 families – a tally greater than ever since the rains of last November, which obliged them to receive the flood victims who ended up occupying a further three floors, from the twenty-sixth to the twenty-eighth.

Complaints regarding the supposed sale of living spaces in the towers for prices that oscillate between 15,000 and 30,000 new bolivars are innumerable. When I mention this issue the secretary refutes it vaguely: 'That's not true. What happens is that when we arrived the walls were covered with blood, scorched and there was rubble everywhere. People have done these places up, painting them, installing electricity and lighting because the community generates a sense of ownership. For that reason, when people leave, those that take over compensate them for all the improvements.'

In this commune with socialist airs incrusted into the heart of a capitalist superstructure, the contradictions are permanent: 'We recovered this building and we want to live here with dignity, like human beings. But there are places here with false ceilings and a jacuzzi, of course they are worth more than one that's just painted,' Vargas admits. As the day comes to its end, in the concrete towers the youngsters congregate in the improvised basketball court where they dribble and shoot furiously. A few metres away, Pastor Daza reads the Gospel in an animated spiritual celebration as the light grows weaker.

The flyers inviting everyone to the fair lie scattered all over the bare cement floor and, paradoxically, show a digital image of the Confinanzas Tower which on paper appears shiny and luminous.

KING DAVID'S STEELY TOWER

The Confinanzas Financial Centre was the ultimate dream of David Brillembourg, regarded as one of Venezuela's most successful bankers at the beginning of the 1990s. The initial public offering of the brewing company, Cervecera Nacional, the negotiations with Banco Unión, Mantex, Atlántica, and the foundation of the Confinanzas Financial Company were milestones in the frenetic economic history of that decade. In his book *El dinero, el diablo y el buen Dios* [money, the devil and the good God] Juan Carlos Zapata recalls that back in 1989 stock market operations in Caracas totalled barely 12 million US dollars. But in 1990 the curve broke the limits of any graphic when it reached 5 billion dollars.

The money flowed into the coffers of the bold and Brillembourg was one of them. For that reason he didn't hesitate when it came to investing capital and energy in a forty-five-storey, 190-metre skyscraper that would be the ninth tallest in Latin America and which in Venezuela would be second only to the neighbouring twin towers of Parque Central.

In total, six buildings were envisaged: the Atrium (a lobby and meeting room), the 190-metre Tower A, with its heliport, Tower B, Building K, Building Z, and a twelve-storey car park that would cover a dozen hectares of the property. In addition to being the headquarters of Confinanzas, it would accommodate a hotel, rental apartments and various retail outlets.

No one imagined the debacle that only four years later would sweep away a third of Venezuela's commercial banking sector and oblige the government to provide an economic bail out to the order of 1.272 billion old bolivars.

In 1994 Confinanzas went into administration and the 121,741 square-metre megastructure, having been transferred to the Banking Protection and Deposit Guarantee Fund (FOGADE), passed into the hands of the state – along with a further three thousand properties belonging to other crisis-stricken institutions. It was only about 60 per cent complete.

The rest is history. Since 1994 government agencies haven't known what to do with this mirage of concrete and steel forged by Brillembourg. In 2001 it was offered for auction with a starting price of 60 million dollars but there were no bidders. In early 2005 the metropolitan major proposed installing his operations there and – given the building's strategic location – a number of ministries also showed interest, but nothing ever came of it. In 2006, it was included in the negotiations for Public Offering FGFPB-I-06-129, again without success. The property was there for the taking and before long those anxious for somewhere to live, social *colectivos*, the homeless and other citizens of every sort, fixed their attention on the concrete colossus which by then everyone simply called The Tower of David.

THE BARBARIAN INVASION

2007 was a year of marked economic contradictions. At the very same moment the country reached a growth rate of 8.4 per cent as a result of the burgeoning of both investment and consumption, its inflation rate also outstripped those everywhere else in Latin American, registering 22.5 pcr cent per annum. Despite this state of affairs, Caracas was feverish with economic activity and political diatribes that were changing the face of the city.

One of the biggest changes was delivered by Juan Barreto, at that time the capital's major, who expropriated or seized more than two hundred properties valued in excess of 4 billion new bolivars.

At the same time, the Association of Property Owners and Urban Real Estate (APIUR) decried that 154 of Caracas's public buildings remained in the hands of squatters and that eight hundred private and individual properties (private land, warehouses and empty homes) had also been illegally occupied.

The destiny of the colossus on Avenida Andrés Bello was already decided when, in October that year, a battalion of nine hundred families took possession of these modern ruins. The memory of those days brings a smile to the face of Gerardo Morales, a security guard of the Ministry of Justice and Home Affairs, and one of the first coordinators of the complex.

'I lived in Catia and I got word that there was going to be an invasion of a building that had been abandoned for twenty years (sic). There were a lot of us – something like nine hundred families who came from the Propatria, La Vega, Petare, El Junquito, San Martín, Caricuao, El Valle and La Yaguara neighbourhoods. We lived for something like three months under canvas before we could build and we had to evict crackheads, delinquents, tramps and tin can scavengers. Subsequently we had to clean up our own act.'

Dark and muscular, Morales is dressed in shrill colours that highlight the sheen of his ebony skin. He looks more like one of Daddy Yankee's backing singers than a man who risks his life everyday covering the backs of important people. Leaning on an improvised brick balcony, he makes claims with the airs of Robin Hood: 'Among the first coordinators here were people who worked with (Mayor) Barreto and he knew exactly what was going on. But what they wanted to do was put families in, then get rid of them so as to be able to sell the spaces. We weren't going to let them mess with people, we come from a background of community struggle in the poor neighbourhoods and we'd suffered; so we got rid of them.'

Between one calculation and another, it's thought that some five hundred families had to leave the towers for not complying with the rules of the coordinators.

They were frantic months during which the improvised communes looked after what they had seized for fear of a 'counter-takeover'. Many of the 'founders' of this cooperative, such as Morales, recall the period with fear: 'Thugs turned up and stole whatever they could find, peoples' belongings; they raped women and hit children. All this went on with members of the Sin Techo street gang, who sought out the coordinators, killed them, and moved in.' The result of this lawless struggle – more reminiscent of something tribal or medieval than of a South American metropolis – was the fall of Pastor Alexander Daza's predecessor. 'Frank' was what they called the first leader of the community. The most common version of the story tells how another coordinator, enraged by a decision that affected one of his sisters, took him to Catia and pumped thirty-eight shots into him in a dark side street.

The only serious altercation with the law that today's inhabitants of the complex recall happened a couple of years ago, when three members of the national forensic police force – the CICPC – burst into the communal areas, shooting. Elvis Merchán, a resident of the thirteenth floor, a coordinator and also treasurer of the cooperative, hasn't forgotten that day: 'They were dressed as civilians but between all of us we managed to grab one of them and when we pulled out his wallet we found out they were policemen. Shortly afterward the whole building was surrounded and they started shooting at us freely. We responded throwing stones, bricks and bottles.' His daughter was injured in the leg along with another child and one of the vigilantes. The following day the community lodged complaints before the relevant bodies and since then there have not been any further violent actions on the part of the authorities.

THE LABYRINTH OF THE LAWS

The phenomenon of invasions, so in vogue in Venezuela in the twenty-first century, is seen by some experts as the systematic violation of everything articulated by the jurisprudence of western democracies. Without delving into the detail of the successive legal reforms that have occurred in the last few years, the lawyer Luis Alfonso Herrera is of the opinion that, at least in the case of state-owned properties, such as the three towers, these invasions are a violation of the constitutionally established laws of National Public Expenditure, Anti-Corruption, and

General Auditing, apart from what is established by the Law of Public Municipal Power.

Perhaps what most preoccupies this specialist is that real estate such as this complex was turned over to the state upon reaching the hands of FOGADE, for which reason he notes: 'Such properties cannot, in fact, be given over to individuals under any circumstances, and certainly not so as to allow them to resolve their problems. They cannot benefit certain persons in an exclusive – and exclusionary – manner, because this perverts their nature and the legal regime itself by creating a sort of privilege. It is as if they were giving, in a hidden manner, a private property contract. Until there is a formal act via which the state leases or sells these goods to particular parties, all of this remains irregular.'

This researcher from the Legislature's Economics Observatory has not remained untouched by the frenzy of legal changes and political actions which the present government periodically unleashes. This has caused him to reflect on the ownership which the members of these invasions establish with this real estate: 'The most likely outcome is that the people who live there will end up arguing that they have generated a right to remain there as the legitimate inhabitants of these spaces. They are going to say that there is an accumulated right which means that they cannot be thrown out until they break some regulation.'

Felipe Benítez is a man of numbers. As the coordinator of the Private Property Observatory, he is frequently in the midst of the denunciations of the many invasions that occur in the country. 'Between 2005 and 2010 we registered 1,730 property rights violations. The figures we've collected during 2010 up to November total 140 property invasions but projections coincide with the number of expropriations that occurred in 2006, a presidential election year, when a total of 176 were registered. I believe that the scale of the cases last year, and the publicity given to them, had a serious impact upon public opinion and that this has had repercussions upon government actions.'

Like Herrera, he questions the future of spontaneous communal experiments such as that which has occurred in the Tower of David: 'Between 2006 and 2008, Mayor Barreto took over more than 188 buildings that were for lease or which belonged to some sort of private owner. I doubt that they will give the squatters the title of the property they want when to date they've not even indemnified the owners or the state. This is the powder keg we're sitting on.'

THE RUINS OF HOPE

It's not the first time that an emblematic building has ended up being used, after years of abandonment and transfers, for ends other than that for which it was designed. The Helicoid, the Humboldt Hotel, and La Candelaria's Sambil Centre are other cases of buildings whose destiny has mutated.

Modern ruins tidied up with inept care, the desperate rehearsal of an architecture emerging from amidst the rubbish – these are the fixed images of the squatted towers. Buildings where structures of steel reinforcing-rods, turned into improvised banisters, prevent the inhabitants from falling to their death in the emptiness that surrounds them as, floor by floor, they climb the stairs. In the past, before the precarious security provided by the enclosure of steel railings, a little girl who left her mother's side died, broken, on the floor thirty metres below. And it is this populous ghetto, where people have opened businesses including grocers, off licenses, hair dressers, a stationers, a video-games arcade and even a church, where thousands live side-by-side, which fascinates artists such as Juan José Olvarría.

'I've dedicated a lot of time to thinking about what is going on here. I've looked at the time under canvas spent by those who arrive before a space becomes available, and I've drawn and sculpted the towers throughout the entire process,' he explains gazing steadily at the buildings. His sculptures in clay show the tower emulating the mass production models of the Eiffel Tower or the Empire State Building that are given away as tourist souvenirs. Beyond the irony of these pieces, the artist's discourse weaves history and image into each proposal: 'I feel that this structure is a reflection of the country. A replica on the scale of the debacle of the oil industry, nothing represents Venezuela better than a vertical neighbourhood, a community recreated in a skyscraper. This is what we are.'

It's a Sunday morning in the middle of February, calm reigns in the building and Christian pop music draws the faithful to Pastor Alexander Daza's church. From the parish of Catia to the prisons of El Rodeo and Guanare, from keeping questionable company to the redemption of the Gospel, his life etches an erratic pilgrimage.

Anointed leader by the acclaim of the majority of the Tower of David's residents, he avoids his enemies and admits only to being the follower of one word: 'Here we depend on God, not the government. We accept help from wherever but we look after ourselves. The day they come to throw us out or something like that, they'll have to relocate all of us since we're united. Here we battle against delinquents, false prophets, robbers, satanists and all those sorts of people, and it's for that reason we've achieved all this.'

As he talks he plays with his five-year-old son, who jumps the void between one narrow strip of concrete and the other. Seeing his son on the edge, he recalls the three years he spent in jail when he counted the days and hours until his release. He talks of the plans he has. A centre for social reinsertion for those – like him – who are released from prison and have nowhere to go, as well as his hopes to help drug addicts who want to get over their habit. One project overlaps another but all have at their base the space that surrounds him: 'We can do many good things here and for that reason we ensure the delinquents don't cause problems – which is why they've come to hate me. But one has the backing of God and a community that knows that what we're doing is for the good of all.'

Piles of rubble, rubbish and the stench of sewage still reign in the first few floors of Tower B, the taller and better constructed. As one ascends, the order amidst the chaos becomes more noticeable and explains the permanence of the inhabitants who have become a rare breed of squatting renters.

From floor twenty-six upwards, many of the victims of the floods are found improving the spaces, for which reason long caravans of brick-layers snake up the stairs, laboriously bringing up cement, bricks, paint and sacks of sand. The steel rod railings that prevent one accidentally falling to one's death are the first structures to go up.

If you carry on climbing you get to the twenty-ninth floor, a space designed to house boardrooms with huge windows from which you have a 360-degree view of Caracas. The sensation of vertigo in this enormous concrete esplanade, crowned twenty floors further up with a ruined heliport, provokes nausea in those who approach its edge. Eighty metres below, the cars look like toys and the people like ants running here-and-there in an unreal miniature model. The debris of heavy security glass gleams everywhere, along with kilometres of rubber stripped from the mechanism of lifts that never arrived.

The asbestos dust forms a reddish desert between the ventilation ducts that lie scattered everywhere in the interior area, and where signs remain of the windows that were to divide the spacious offices of the emporium Brillembourg dreamt of having. Outside, the cold wind that blows down from Mount Ávila sweeps the magnificent terraces and leaves their neglect clear to those who would see it.

From the twenty-ninth floor upward stretches the realm of great ambitions truncated; below reigns the deaf hope exhibited only by the dispossessed – by those who have lost everything, those who on one of the heavy doors of one of the six executive lifts have written in chalk, 'Ciao, regards David'.

THE LONG ROAD TO NOWHERE

DOMÉNICO CHIAPPE
Translated by David Swift

Around the Fuerte Tiuna, the gigantic military complex in the centre of Caracas now deployed as an ad hoc chapel of rest for the body of Hugo Chavez, the streets have been transformed into a bustling open-air market. There are mementoes for sale: baseball caps sporting the Venezuelan flag and the words 'Chavez, true heart of my country,' as well as photographs and posters of him at different stages of his military career, from the slim lieutenant at the time of the first coup d'état to the bald and bloated invalid of his final years. The photos cost 20 new bolivars (or 20,000 old bolivars, the ones in circulation before, in a ploy to gloss over internal devaluation, they created a new currency with exactly the same name but a thousandth of its value). The posters are 15 bolivars each or two for 20. Young women wear their red '#IamChavez' T-shirts knotted at the waist for a tighter fit and to reveal the lower part of the back. People swarm towards a lorry, their arms outstretched to catch the bananas, apples and oranges thrown down from it. A huge screen with a powerful speaker towers over the heads of the traders and mourners alike. More of these systems appear at regular intervals along the route to the chapel of rest, and whatever happens in the air-conditioned hall where the VIPs are gathered is transmitted live.

Around ten in the morning, before the official ceremony gets underway, a rap duo repeats the phrase 'you'll live and you'll win' over the PA. Government propaganda is the creative source behind a number of different songs, recorded in top-quality studios, with lyrics eulogising the leader who's been in power for almost three full terms. Some salsa music follows the hip-hop. People queue up along Los Próceres, the wide, tree-lined avenue where, some years ago, they scattered obsolete armoured cars – no more than scrap metal painted olive green – like exhibits in a theme park. A little girl ventures inside one of these huge-wheeled vehicles, before leaping out moments later, yelling, 'Yeuch! It stinks of pee in there!'

Everywhere is a sea of red. After a while, *'Canta, camarada canta'* [sing comrade, sing] by the late Ali Primera, rings out. Among those listening in the queue is a man in a red T-shirt with another line by the famous Venezuelan songwriter on it: 'Those who die for life aren't dead'. The complete lyrics of the song have been written in white marker pen across the roof and bonnet of an old blue pick-up truck, parked on the motorway near the start of the queue of people waiting to see the deceased president. For almost two years, since May 2011 when he first appeared with a walking stick due to what he claimed was a knee problem (later diagnosed as a tumour and finally as some unspecified form of cancer), the then president underwent medical treatment, including an operation and a number of chemotherapy sessions, in Cuba. Chávez announced he had beaten the disease every time he returned to Venezuela. The fact that he was frail and getting worse was hidden from the public by means of propaganda, just as governments never admit failure on the battlefront during a war. Death, in other words, was the ultimate defeat: a surrender that left his supporters in disarray, confronting their own particular interests under a leadership that had been forced upon them. Hours before his death was announced on 5 March, they were still claiming he was well and on the road to recovery.

The day before, in the *El Nacional* daily newspaper beneath the headline 'Chávez Tells of his Sorrow at the Death of Cabello's Mother,' an unattributed report stated: 'From the hospital bed where he has spent the last eighty-four days following an operation, Chávez penned an obituary telling of his sorrow at the death of the mother of his comrades-in-arms Diosdado and José David Cabello.' In a press release the government said was by the president himself, he expressed his condolences to her relatives, describing her as a 'mother, wife, friend and comrade'. The article continued with comments from the Minister for Communication and Information, Ernesto Villegas, who said: 'How could any right-thinking person imagine that we would dare to lie about the president's health or that his daughters would willingly conspire in such a deception?' Statements like this were put out over the more than three months that Chávez remained president of the republic even as he was being treated in an ad hoc clinic in Cuba. During this time, he was neither seen nor heard in public, and there was a complete absence of any medical report or information about what was wrong with him. Even after his death, those who were watching over him in the run-up to his demise have not revealed its causes.

The government announced his death as though it were unexpected, despite the prognosis of independent medical experts who based their analysis on the rare snippets of information filtered through to the press and on what they could discern from his physical appearance during an electoral campaign that ended only days before his self-imposed exile in the Caribbean. Once he was actually dead, it was necessary to reverse any impression of defeat and the relentless repetition of Ali Primera's song was just one of numerous attempts to turn death by natural causes into martyrdom. Then, unattributed pronouncements would be tossed out that only served to fuel conspiracy theories: he'd been injected with cancer; the president had been assassinated. Nonetheless, the only thing one could be certain of regarding his treatment was the tight and impenetrable security measures that shielded his privacy. Who could possibly get near him? In an apparent attempt to dispel any doubts, the government was quick to pin medals on the Cuban doctors who looked after him on his deathbed.

There's an air of genuine loss among those queuing to view the president's body, though no one is crying and there are no dramatic gestures. People wait patiently in line, while vendors walk up and down the columns hawking their wares. There are lots of children and more women than men. Zaida García, forty, has come from Guatire, a satellite town on the edge of Caracas. She is almost at the back of the queue, along with her colleagues from the refuse collection department at the municipality of Zamora. They arrived four hours earlier at eight in the morning.

'He's the love of my life,' she says, adding, 'He was my husband, my partner, my lover. When they made him, they broke the mould.'

'Did you ever see him close-up? Did you ever speak to him?'

'No... I went to his birthday celebrations on 28 July last year in Petare.'

'Did he not look ill then?'

'He looked better than ever. He still looks well.'

She said the president helped arrange her operation.

'What for?'

'On my jaw.'

'When was this?'

'They haven't actually operated on me yet but, thanks to him, they'll operate on me soon.'

'And what's wrong with your jaw?'

'It's dislocated.'

'What happened? Did you have an accident?'

'A big mango fell on my head when I was sixteen.'

Her colleague pipes up:

'I should have had his child!'

Yamelis García Navas laughs. Quietly, so the

others can't hear, she tells me she's forty-one and shows me her poster of Chávez. She works in the print department of the national post office, Ipostel.

A man, also from Guatire, joins in:

'We're all from the borough of Ezequiel Zamora.'

'The "revolutionary borough" to be precise,' says Yamelis.

'Yes, we work for the council of the revolutionary borough of Ezequiel Zamora,' the man says, before adding, 'He gave us dignity.'

'What do all you do there?'

'We work for the hygiene department, we deal with solid waste collection. Not rubbish, solid waste collection.'

'Isn't that the same thing?'

'No, it's not the same thing: now we've got dignity. Everyone who works at the council is here.'

Euphemisms such as 'solid waste' instead of 'rubbish' feature widely in the language deployed by the government through their radio and television stations, newspapers and news agencies, which are estimated to comprise more than five hundred different media outlets. These euphemisms include 'deprived of freedom' for 'prisoner'; 'street dwellers' for 'homeless'; 'live-in employee' for 'caretaker'; 'lowlifes' for 'opposition'; and 'mission' for 'government subsidy'. The words 'Bolivarian' and 'revolutionary' are applied as an adjective or prefix even to the country itself, whose official name was changed in the most recent draft of the constitution, drawn up in 1999 at Chávez's own request.

The last verse of a folk song from the Venezuelan

plains comes over the speakers: '… your ten million votes will never be seen again'. The song ends, and is immediately followed by a pop song: 'Mercenary, rioter, dog of war, traitor: my people say "no, no, no!"' From another screen a few yards further on, the phrase 'feminist government' can be heard. The air is thick with propaganda. There are organised groups of a dozen or so moving around with placards. They stop wherever there is a television camera, wave their flags and surround the presenter. Behind the cameraman, a short, fat man in a state oil company baseball cap begins to shout, 'The people are safe with Chávez and Maduro!' As if a fuse had been lit, the refrain is taken up by the others in the group until the television journalist is hemmed in by chanting from all sides.

At the end of the Avenida Los Próceres, members of the National Guard – soldiers performing the role of policemen – block the way and allow those who are standing in an orderly line to pass through. At the barrier, motorcycle taxis are available for 10 bolivars. White smoke begins to pour from a fireman's motorbike. He quickly dismounts. People laugh when a man behind him shouts, 'It's going up! Call the fire brigade!' Someone else tells the fireman to disconnect the cable to the battery. He does so, and nips the problem in the bud.

Enerva Figueredo, a native of the city of Puerto Ayacucho in the far south of the country, wears an I-am-Chávez shawl over her head.

'I was given it during the campaign,' she explains.

Now it protects her from the blistering sun and

the thirty-plus-degree heat. She's still only halfway along the queue. During the first couple of days, people made their own way here by bus, motorbike or car. Afterwards, government-chartered coaches began to arrive. Long lines of them are parked up in adjacent avenues, guarded by soldiers.

The Simón Bolívar Symphony Orchestra appears on the screen, conducted by Gustavo Dudamel, currently the public face of 'El Sistema,' the state-funded music education programme inaugurated in 1978. They start with the national anthem. People sheltering from the sun in the covered stands rise to their feet. The respectful silence is broken only by two men unloading eight Portaloos off the back of a lorry. Up until this point, no one had foreseen the need to provide toilets for people who have been queuing for hours. If they'd left it a day longer, the smell here would have been unbearable.

When the national anthem finishes, 'Viva Chávez' rings out. Then the dignitaries attending the funeral are introduced and we are told that Nicolás Maduro will place a replica of Bolívar's sword on the president's coffin. Maduro can be heard saying, 'Supreme leader of the Bolivarian revolution'. A vendor yells, 'Bacon, 10 bolivars!' The MC announces that Raúl Castro will lead the guard of honour.

Some minutes later, in a deep and plummy voice, the MC calls up on stage a number of sporting celebrities, ranging from baseball stars of the distant past to the winner of the gold medal in fencing at the last Olympic Games. Outside, people are now only yards from the casket but, because the progress of the queue has been held up by the official ceremonies, those still waiting will have to spend another few hours standing in line. Beneath a couple of parasols, pressed up against a crash barrier, a group of women watches what's unfolding on the giant screen. They arrived at ten o'clock the previous night and have got to know each other in the course of waiting. These chance friends all come from different parts of the country: the districts of Caricuao and La Pastora in Caracas, as well as the cities of Santa Teresa and Ciudad Guayana. Yéssica Reina, thirty-nine, who has smooth, dark skin and her hair bunched up under her cap, credits Chávez with giving her an education.

'I studied through the *Misión Rivas*. After I graduated, I got a job at PDVSA Gas, which was a closed shop before he opened it up to the people. I've been there now for five years. I continued my studies at the *Misión Sucre* and qualified in Business Administration and Management,' she explains.

'What's more, my mother is now getting her old age pension. Before, people weren't treated with respect and it took months before they actually received any money. Being here, getting cold, tired, hungry and too much sun: all in all, it's a small price to pay for what he gave us.'

Around her, a chorus of voices echoes her sentiments.

'He's the president of our hearts.'

'There's no one like him in the world.'

'Anything for the *Comandante*.'

'He died so we might live.'

'He gave us everything.'

'He gave us education, strength, a constitution.'

'He taught us not to be cowed by the lowlifes and imperialists.'

'He gave us opportunities.'

'To give' is more than a verb and its conjugation is a matter of emotion. The people here to mourn Chávez need to express their gratitude verbally in recognition of a debt. In a speech, later, Nicolás Maduro will refer to 'pure love'. This outpouring of sentiment seems to bypass rational consciousness: it appears to derive not from the intellect but from somewhere else. But, once the first impression fades away and you analyse the economic situation of Venezuela, doubts arise. Since Chávez first assumed power in 1999, the price of oil rose by a factor of six before levelling out at 100 dollars a barrel, and there was a fivefold increase in the size of the foreign debt, which reached 104 billion dollars in 2012. If calculated in bolivars, domestic borrowing was more than eighty times what it had been in 1999: then, it stood at 2.5 billion bolivars before rising to 216 billion bolivars fourteen years later. However, thanks to a devaluation of the local currency from 649 to the dollar to 63,870 to the dollar (in line with the US dollar/bolivar exchange rate in the parallel market at the end of 2013) that same domestic borrowing fell in dollars from 3.85 billion to approximately 3.38 billion. Over the same period, the number of employees working in the public sector rose until it comprised 20 per cent of the active population in formal employment, over two and a half million people. Most of whom are now dressed in red and here at the state funeral celebrations. Chávez's hardline support was essentially made up of people officially working for the government, or people hired to work for the government on a temporary basis.

At the very time the government was consolidating its economic power, its policies were destroying Venezuela's manufacturing and entrepreneurial capacity. Between 1999 and 2012, devaluation reached 900 per cent at the official rate within the restrictive system of foreign exchange controls but reached 3,400 per cent at the parallel black market rate, while average annual inflation topped 20 per cent. The consequences of this on the basic sector can be seen through data on food imports: the annual value in US dollars of imports of meat, rice, sugar, cooking oil, maize, wheat and milk rose from 1.5 billion in 1999 to 7 billion in 2012. This was due to the decline in Venezuela's agricultural capacity after many estates were subject to compulsory expropriation: according to figures provided by the National Federation of Venezuelan Ranchers (FEDENAGA), nine hundred plantations were sequestrated by the government in seven years. More than 40 per cent of the active population survives in the shadow economy. People like the Parada family, who hawk their wares on the street, but have no regular job and pay no taxes. With a black rucksack on his back and a plastic bag tied to his waistband, son Esteban holds a three-tier swivelling hanger system in his arms to display this season's product range: children's Chinese cotton T-shirts sporting an image of the late president. 'My mum makes them at home. Business is going well. Over the past few days, there's been loads of people,' he says, then shows me his best-seller: one of the *Comandante* wearing a beret and holding a crucifix, above the words 'Chávez forever'. A few yards further along, Wilmer Vera is selling posters. Between him and Esteban, there's a peddler every couple of feet along the line of people queuing and there are four lines like this one at the avenue's widest point. On Thursday, there was a new addition to the range of items on sale: a poster of Maduro to go with those of Chávez. 'They're not going down too well,' says Vera, with a shake of his head, the sun shining directly onto his face. He tells me he buys his posters from a wholesaler in La Bandera for 8,000 old bolivars, then sells them on for 10,000, or 10 new bolivars.

'Do you have to pay for them upfront or does he let you have them on credit?'

'Credit?'

'Yeah, credit.'

'We haven't seen credit around here for a long time.'

'Which one do you like best?'

'I like all of 'em.'

'Have you got any at home?'

'I've got fifteen – I'm going to frame them. I'm a carpenter.'

Wilmer Vera is wearing the burgundy shirt of the Venezuelan football team.

'Who's the best player for you?'

'I support the whole team. Nobody's better than anyone else.'

In a country where half the population lives in overcrowded slums with no basic services, the government increased the amount it provided in subsidies at the very time Venezuelan productivity was beginning to contract. In 2003, ten thousand Cuban doctors were dispersed nationwide to treat those on the outer edges of the public health system when the *Misión Barrio Adentro* was rolled out. This was the first of the forty-two initiatives created with such names as the *Misión Robinson*, which lowered illiteracy levels from 9 to 5 per cent, and other missions such as *Hijos de Venezuela*, *Madres del Barrio*, or *En Amor Mayor*, the last of which still hands out cash. According to its own estimates, the state-owned oil and gas conglomerate, PDVSA, 'donated' more than 120 billion dollars to these projects. As a result of these operations, the Economic Commission for Latin America and the Caribbean (CEPAL) defined Venezuela, on the basis of figures provided by its government, as a country that had achieved a reduction in the proportion of its inhabitants that could be classified as 'living in poverty' from from 49.4 per cent to 27.8 per cent within ten years. Nevertheless, official figures from 2010 also reveal a disparity in the distribution of wealth, channelled through institutions and organisations set up by the president, with the poorest section of society receiving 5.4 per cent of the funds given out while the most affluent received

45.2 per cent.

When the easiest means of survival for the majority is based on government handouts, how seriously can we take the expressions of grief and unconditional loyalty from people who benefit from social policies that fail to generate employment? After a while, doubts kick in: are they just saying what they know they are expected to say? The state has rewarded unquestioned allegiance to the leader and punished dissent. In 2002, when PDVSA employees withdrew their labour, precipitating a general strike that culminated in a coup d'état which collapsed in a matter of hours, all employees who participated in the strike at head office or any of its subsidiaries – essentially most of the payroll – were sacked. In 2004, when signatures were collected to back a recall referendum against the president, a ruling-party minister, Luis Tascón, obtained from the National Electoral Council (the regulatory authority overseeing the elections) the full list of all those who signed the petition calling for Chávez to go, then published their names and details online. The list was then deployed to sack public sector employees and to deny all those who appeared on it any social rights and benefits. Later, the Maisanta List was drawn up. It included the names of fourteen thousand people on the electoral register classified according to their stance on Chavez's policies. It was a huge database that cross-linked the Tascón List with another that identified those who benefitted from social programmes, missions and other perks. It would appear that this list, or one like it, is still in force given that, when elections have taken place over recent years, the ruling party has arranged for their potential supporters to be picked up from their homes and ferried to the polling stations. During the 2013 elections, videos were released showing that every voter was being monitored. The International Labour Organisation received reports of harassment against public employees that went as far as maintaining surveillance on their social network profiles and the texts sent from their mobile phones. The slightest suspicion of disloyalty towards the apparatus of the state would be enough to get a person the sack. Regardless of whether this persecution be accurate or efficient, simply revealing its existence serves as an example and spreads fear. Two weeks after the elections, opponents of the government reported four thousand incidents of harassment. A month after that, on 16 May, Chávez's successor, Nicolás Maduro, confirmed he had a list containing the details of nine hundred thousand 'compatriots' who didn't vote for him in the April 2013 elections. So, could it be that the expressions of grief over Chávez's death and of loyalty to him and his successor are coloured not only by gratitude but also by the fear of losing what one has already been given or what one expects to receive?

As for the president's last rites, the show must go on. Once again, it's the turn of Gustavo Dudamel and the Simón Bolívar Symphony Orchestra, with their interpretation of '*Alma llanera*' [soul of the plains]. Beneath some trees, several boyish-looking members of the National Guard are now distributing cartons of fruit juice from a refrigerated truck. The juice was produced by Los Andes, a firm that was taken over by the state. One of the soldiers says, calmly and with pride: 'It's been nationalised – now it's really Venezuelan.' The 'fruit nectar' tastes very sweet. Over the PA, the catholic chaplain José Hernán Sánchez Porras, who also holds the rank of colonel in the army, can be heard intoning 'Rest in peace, amen'. Next to speak is the evangelical preacher from the Presidential guard of honour, Alexis Romero Varela.

Three officers from the Patrimonial Guard, which is responsible for looking after the parks, museums, theatres and squares and has been on active duty since Monday, are standing in the shadow cast by the statues of the founding fathers of independence. The second officer, Luis Lucas, estimates that there were a million people here when the funeral cortege first arrived on Tuesday. Since then, possibly another million will have turned up. According to him, numbers have fallen over subsequent days. 'We pray that the soul of Hugo Chávez finds peace,' can be heard over the loudspeakers. Once again, Nicolás Maduro takes the microphone. At the back of the line, it's difficult to hear what's being said over the shouts of the vendors offering a wide range of homemade and manufactured goods: soft drinks, corn on the cob, sandwiches, flags, pudding, sliced mango, *arepas* and fried chicken, photos, caps, pastries, hotdog and Nestea (iced tea) combos, umbrellas, fritters. On the screen, an American shot of Nicolás Maduro shows him raising his voice as he declaims, 'You were too much for them, *Comandante!*' At which point, the vendors and the patient mourners all applaud. The noise is deafening and unremitting.

That night, the people on their way back from viewing Hugo Chávez's corpse look more exhausted than grief-stricken. They don't follow the same route they took on the way in. The exit from the Military Academy's Chapel of Rest is on the opposite corner to the Fuerte Tiuna, the gargantuan military complex that not only divides the city in two but also serves to remind all its inhabitants of the privileges the military caste enjoys in Venezuela. The return journey takes them along a dirt and tarmac road that runs parallel to the River Guaire. People move forward in columns. Troops from the National Guard steer them over to the right. At the exit, where a group of soldiers refuses entry to any unauthorised vehicles, an average of sixty people a minute pass through the checkpoint in a constant flow, punctuated by the odd gap when some groups cluster together. The procession is broadcast live and uninterrupted on Venezolana de Televisión. The way out is also festooned with enormous screens on which people can be seen stopping for a moment to peer into the casket. No one has photographed Chávez's face. Only the state TV channel has access to the area. If anyone lingers by the coffin longer than a second or two it is because they are making the sign of the cross or some other gesture like kissing their fingers placing them on the glass. Any behavioural variation draws the attention of the soldiers, who immediately move towards anyone hanging around for longer than the minuscule amount of time allotted to them.

By 6.30pm, it's already starting to get dark in Venezuela, the only country in the world that defied the hegemony of time zones and, through a presidential decree in 2007, turned the clock back half an hour. It's getting cooler. An old lady stops and stoops to deposit a bulging bag, knotted at the top, on the ground. She's wearing dark trousers and a red blouse. Her hair is well groomed and she has small eyes in a haggard black face. Ilda Palacios is from the state of Miranda, arrived in Caracas at five o'clock yesterday evening, but didn't join the queue until this morning. People reaching the final stage of their pilgrimage at this time began to line up at around eight in the morning. 'His face didn't look any different,' she says, 'The *Comandante* looked just like he always does. He's not dead as far as I'm concerned.' Ilda Palacios picks up her bag, which has other knotted bags inside it. She says she has seven children. 'Chávez gave me my pension,' she asserts. 'My husband worked at the town hall and earned very little. But, these days, everyone's eating chops and steak. What did we have to eat before he came along?' Her younger sister, Carmen, approaches and says, 'It was like seeing someone you really love.' They both shuffle off unsteadily. A bit further on, they stop at a van handing out sandwiches and water.

The live broadcast from Venezolana de Televisión is now showing the build-up to the ceremony to swear in the presidential candidate and vice president

411

Nicolás Maduro as president-elect. It will take place before the head of the National Assembly, Diosdado Cabello, who is himself in line for the presidency according to the constitution. 'He looked asleep to us,' says Tina Yegues, who describes herself as a 'social campaigner' for a 'communal council'. She's middle-aged and accompanied by her young son, who has a doll dressed in an olive-green military uniform. 'Such a lovely face,' she says. They come from Cumaná, some six hours away from the capital, and have been waiting for their turn since nine in the morning. In a bag, they've got a soft drink and some bread they were given at a help point on the way out. Sonia comes over and remarks, 'He seemed sad,' Tina Yegues disagrees and, together, they make their way down the unlit street.

ANY OLD S

CARLOS SANDOVAL
Translated by Montague Kobbé

To Alfredo Romero and Gonzalo Himiob, ombudsmen.

DAY 1

The only crime – the only real crime – S was guilty of was curiosity. He was on the ground floor, listening to a number of his neighbours speak to a journalist from one of the daily newspapers about the incursion of the National Guard on Avenida Páez that morning, at about seven. They arrested the lady from apartment 15Λ, who'd just gone out to exercise, and the janitor – a witness said – when they both sought shelter from the tear gas in the building's guardhouse. They were dragged out of the shed, which according to the Law of Horizontal Property is part of the communal grounds – in other words, a building within the boundaries of the residential complex. And all because people were shouting at the officers from inside, calling them 'Cubans', 'pigs', 'murderers'; a natural reaction by civilian society to the abuses they had witnessed as armed forces tried to smother the protests that had taken place over the past month.

The tear gas still hangs in the air; S winces and hears a soft litany that soon turns into an uproar:

413

'*colectivos, colectivos*'. The warning comes from the balconies of Tower B; next to S, someone screams: 'They've jumped the fence.' Everyone runs: towards the pergolas, towards the small central square, towards the park. Out of the corner of his eye, S sees a man wearing a red shirt pointing a gun at him; behind that one, a black shirt chases him frantically, wielding a shotgun. S heads for the underground car park but soon realises the gate won't open in time. Potential safety lies on the other side of the wall. He hears a shot, can't tell whether he's been hit. He grabs the edge of the wall, the man in the red shirt hauls him back: S falls roughly five metres, lands awkwardly: his ankle cracks. He slows down, thinks he's safe. Suddenly he sees them climbing up to the first floor. He continues his escape as best he can. Maybe he can find a way out through one of the gates – there are four buildings in the complex – of the third level of the car park. The pain in his leg isn't subsiding. He stops: the gates are locked.

The man in the red shirt rests the end of the barrel on his head: 'On your knees.' S begs for his life. 'On your knees,' the nine millimetre insists. The other one, the one with the shotgun, turns the butt of his weapon into a club and strikes S on his side. S falls, of course, to his knees. They use improvised plastic handcuffs to hold his arms behind his back. They lift him to his feet, and S cries: the pain is unbearable, reaching up above his thigh. His captors force him to run backwards, pull him from the shackles digging into the flesh on his wrists. From the buildings people are throwing bottles, cans of tuna, flower pots. S feels the moment last forever. Then, on reaching the entrance of the complex, he sees the contingent of guardsmen, all geared up, take their positions aiming at the source of the clattering saucepans.

The one in red – or the other one – hands him over to some uniformed men on a motorcycle. Squeezed between the driver and the passenger, on his way to the command post, he is repeatedly thumped by their helmets: the driver jerks the back of his head like a whip; his colleague does the same thing in the opposite direction, while he screams: 'We are the National Guard, you're in the hands of the National Guard now, you cocksucker.' They almost crash into a bus. They won't let him rest his feet on the bike's footpegs so, in a tight curve, his injured ankle strikes the kerb. S can't help but let out a shocked howl.

They have to help him limp into the reporting office, where he's thrown onto a bench. A guard takes his details and once he has complied with the procedure shouts: 'Ready, Sir.' The man in the red chemise reappears, looking sharp, in jeans and trainers (expensive, S thinks); he shuts the door and asks how many people were there blocking the road, their whereabouts and names. S explains that he was only being nosey, that he lives in a different block, Tower A, and that he started running instinctively as soon as he heard the terrifying cry of *colectivos* in his own backyard, since the small square is but an extension of the apartments (it's all part of the private grounds, together with the flower beds, the gardens and, of course, the car park). But the lieutenant isn't interested in reasons, and demands names and places; S doesn't understand what the officer's talking about, he repeats again 'curiosity', 'fear', '*colectivos*' until a spasm near his left nipple knocks the wind out of him: it's a Taser, the lieutenant has discharged an electric shock. The sequence of questions begins again. S breaks down in tears. He denies everything, insists he knows none of the answers. The Taser is used again, this time on the right side of his chest. A uniformed woman enters and asks the lieutenant to move S to the room next door.

S tries to stand up but is unable to do so. He tells the lieutenant, who lands a hook in his ribs that lifts him from the chair. He lands on his cuffed hands; one of them, the left one, breaks. The officer orders him to go to the room next door. S begs for help. The man rests his boot on the lad's chest and walks over him, given that, apparently, he's part of the floor. S can't stop crying, especially after the kicks to his broken ankle. Suddenly, the so-and-so comes up with an idea: 'Crawl'; S reaches the other room, at last, like a worm.

From the ground he sees a high-ranking officer enquiring about the state he's in. Someone informs him. The captain, or major, or whatever (S doesn't catch the rank) fires instructions to have him transferred to the Military Hospital where he is to receive the most elementary first-aid treatment. 'Once he's been seen to,' he makes clear, 'he must be taken back to the detention centre.' Two guards load him into a Jeep; as soon as they start moving the one on the passenger seat pulls his gun out and warns S that if he complains even once he'll put a bullet through his leg that will finish it off.

The traffic is gridlocked.

The cadets or corporals chat and fiddle with their mobile phones. The one who threatened to shoot S asks him if he wishes to make a call. S, astounded, reels off a number; the guard barks: 'Look, we have your boyfriend with us, we're taking him to hospital... I don't know, find out.'

At A&E they fit him with splints and immediately throw him back in the 4x4. Back at the command post, a public prosecutor takes record of all the detainees; when she sees S she speaks to the guards about the legal repercussions they could face if the injuries to his extremities get any worse. The major or captain sends S back to the hospital: the doctor on guard deems both fractures require an operation and he is allotted a bed in the orthopaedic unit.

DAY 2

They call this eighth-floor ward 'Chinatown', because it's where criminals are held: legs pinned to metal bars, kept straight by counterweights cunningly built with recycled bottles by ingenious relatives. S couldn't sleep, he spent the whole night talking to his watch guard, a lad from Maracaibo of roughly his age, whose dream is to find a profession that would allow him to get out of the armed forces. The other guard sleeps outside, in the cold of a balcony that faces a hillside choked with shacks. Discomforted by the handcuffs, S observes the three patients in the room, notices their snoring and that of the visitors by their sides, lying on mattresses such as the one his mother shares with the sister of the guy across the room.

He's been prescribed painkillers but the nurse forgets to administer them as soon as she discovers his alleged crime. S suffers the pain until his spirit is humbled; after several requests, he is finally given a dose. Halfway through the morning a doctor surrounded by students shows up and asks S how he got his injuries. 'This one isn't one of our patients,' he says, as he turns away from him. But he backtracks – a fit of professionalism? – and checks the bandages, the ghoulish flesh beneath the rudimentary splints. He gives instructions to have X-rays taken and to carry out further surgical tests, in keeping with the preliminary instructions given by the resident at A&E. The watch guard asks if, in fact, an operation is necessary and relays the news to his superior.

The law states that S must be charged within forty-eight hours of him being arrested. If he has to undergo surgery, it's going to be difficult for the prosecution to move him to a court of law, so the barristers push to have the hearing at the hospital. Calls come and go between an intricate bureaucracy of prosecutors and lawyers, guards and judges. It is already noon and the uncertainty surrounding the procedure persists; the guards, neglected by their garrison, accept the food

S's aunt offers them and laugh at the jokes told by the old Andean man on the bed to the right, who for the past three months has been saving for a prosthetic for his pelvis, wrecked by a stampede of rushing passengers at the Plaza Venezuela metro station.

Going to the toilet entails a painful effort. Held by precarious crutches, S empties not only his body but also the overwhelming sadness lodged in his throat. 'Is something the matter, mate?' someone asks, 'Does it hurt?' He's scared. From the next cubicle emerges a man in a wheelchair, his leg in a cast. 'The trick is to be patient,' he says. 'I've been here for seven weeks and I still don't know when they're going to operate because I don't have enough money to buy my femur replacement; you can be certain as soon as I get the sum – 60 mil – the price will have gone up. Sometimes you have the spare parts, and then there's no room in the operating theatre   that's what happened to my roommate. But we have a homeland, don't we bro?' he says smiling. Outside the toilet, S finds two nurses: they discuss whether to make their grandchildren an album with 'everything about Chávez' or, better still, to buy the special-issue magazine published by *Últimas Noticias* with fifty photos of the *Comandante*.

The guards don't change until after two in the afternoon: seven hours behind schedule. One of them is from Elorza, the other from San Cristóbal. They assume their positions indifferently, visibly bored. His aunt wins them over in no time: coffee and cookies, the newspaper and some water. The plainsman loosens his tongue: they're tired of orders and counter-orders;

above all, they're tired of political speeches. They haven't had a day off in thirty days and a week. The one from Táchira is told that they have just arrested his cousin in a roadblock. He makes a few calls and – pleased – announces, 'They'll let him go now.'

The patient at the end of the room to his right explains he fell from a scaffold nineteen days ago; he prays to kingdom come for a quick intervention: 'If it gets to a month, there'll be no helping me.' His sister in-law provides the medical and economic details, places all her hopes on an NGO; S nods and looks at the TV, which shows a 'limited time offer'. That's when a committee of minor officials and sergeants enters to take S (twenty-eight hours after the fact) to the forensic clinic. But mobility is an issue: there isn't an ambulance available – or even a wheelchair. S has only the precarious crutches to rely on. They load him into a Jeep packed with other prisoners.

Strictly speaking, the check-up takes exactly seventeen minutes; it's the journey to the crime lab in the centre of Caracas which has taken an eternity, because the president – together with the actor Danny Glover – is handing over an unfinished housing block, part of the *Misión Vivienda* initiative, right next to the police station. As the sun dies beyond the windscreen, they reach the facility where S will have to provide his fingerprints – but the lifts aren't working. Three guards carry him up five floors. Once they have climbed the final step, one of the sergeants faints. Clumsily they place S on a chair so as to attend to their unconscious comrade, whom they slap around the face roughly and nervously. As soon as the lad comes to, they start mocking him. S watches them without joining the fun.

Back in the hospital, S gives the *arepa* his indefatigable aunt has bought him to the ashen young man in uniform, his face pale with hunger and shame. Grateful.

Day 3

The complaints from the Andean guy who refused to have an IV kept S from sleeping. The foibles of old age, he thinks, as he wallows in the yellow light of distant streetlamps and the uncertain hue of dawn. A male nurse makes the final round of the night, double checks the level of the solution – 'Good luck,' he bids, in lieu of goodbye. S knows that the day has come, *his* day. In a few hours he will know if further woes await him: him, the innocent bearer of a strange fate.

The defence lawyer explains the dynamics of his appearance before the judge; S obsessively learns every detail. It's still unclear whether or not he will have to be taken to the Palace of Justice. By lunchtime a member of the defendant's team informs them – straight from the courts – of the magistrate's position: the decision to move the prisoner to the court will hinge on the medical report. S's mother consults the nurses at their station but they all claim not to know about the case. They call the house officer, who notices a number of the requested tests have not been performed and several rounds of painkillers have been skipped.

He's taken down to X-ray. In the queue at the hospital's imaging centre a sergeant major approaches the guard and asks him for the medical report. The corporal explains, 'This is one of those caught at the protests.' The sub-officer adds, 'These kids are fighting for you and me. Don't forget that.' The X-ray machine gets stuck. It takes one and a half hours to get them done. The plaster cast and more drugs arrive shortly thereafter, while the operation is added to the waiting list. There were no two ways about it: the court would have to raise or reject charges against S at the very hospital.

'If you say A, you have to stick to A. If they hit you, don't say B or C, always A, A, A. Shout it: AAAAA! This is the voice of experience speaking, judges are after contradictions.' It's the patient from across the room: some former buddies put four bullets into him; he claimed he was mugged for his motorcycle, so preventing any further investigations concerning his criminal record. He reminds S of his basketball teacher at school, who always talked up the fact that he grew up in Petare and kept boasting about how macho he was. At 1.12pm (S can't keep his eyes off his watch) a lawyer calls to collect his medical report. 'The court will be here between half past three and four o'clock,' she announces.

There's a new change of guards. The one from Maracaibo greets him warmly; the other one (from Ejido in Mérida) is too shy, simply smiles. The relief coincides with visiting hours. There are anecdotes and guffaws, a tin of biscuits, fizzy drinks. S wants to focus on the details revealed by the veteran across the room: he can't – the white sphere of his Casio keeps him on tenterhooks.

The entourage finally arrives at 4.55pm: the judge, a public prosecutor, two bailiffs, the court secretary and the two lawyers assigned to S by the bar. A soldier clears all the visitors from the ward, empties the hallway and orders the patients to go back to their beds. The act will take place in the presence of the three people who share the room.

Even though he's been advised to make use of his right not to testify, one of the lawyers entreats S to give an account of the events, given the severity of the charges he could face. Slowly but confidently S describes the most striking scenes of his life: the persecution inside the car park, ending in his capture. He skips the punches and the electric shocks. He keeps to himself the weight of the boot and the gun to his temple. He's afraid. The prosecutor lists the offenses that, according to the Public Ministry, S has committed. S doesn't understand the term 'collusion' and thinks about the word as he tries to follow the remaining accusations ('possession of flammable material', 'contempt of court'). All in all, there are seven crimes. Prosecution and defence commence their legal wrangling. S, in silence, recalls – he doesn't know why – the black Polo shirt worn by the man with the shotgun. He hears the dry tone of the judge's voice uttering 'sustained' several times.

In the end he is charged with five crimes, released pending trial and has to present himself at court every thirty days. A subtle sense of joy comes over the room (including the guards). S's mother cries; his aunt, seeks, confusedly, to thank the prosecutor, who looks at her coldly. S's lawyers shake hands and accept an embrace. With three fingers, S rubs his freed wrists.

That same night he is transferred to a clinic. He undergoes surgery the following afternoon. One week later he appears – in a wheelchair – in the Palace of Justice, making his debut in the dock.

A Chronicle of Scarcity

Willy McKey
Translated by Tim Girven

1

The hubbub of the market I remember has disappeared and I'm obsessed with getting to the bottom of this new silence. I haven't visited Catia market in months and, while it's true it's not a payday Saturday, the silence is evident and novel. Nevertheless, from what Josefina – my guide on this scarcity tour – tells me, the day of the week is no longer a determining factor. 'Money stretches to so little that it's all the same if it's payday or not. Every Saturday you go out with the cash you've got left to buy what you've run out of or couldn't find.'

'So you don't go shopping every fortnight?'

'Not any more. Going shopping twice a month died when the fortnightly wage-packet ceased to make any difference. If prices go up every week and you can't find half the things you want to buy, it makes no difference if you have the money or not.'

On the reverse side of a notice at one of the stalls I read: 'No merchandise above that's lacking below'. It's a written order to the staff of one of the many groceries in the market; but it reads like a spell. One of the employees explains that the phrase means that the goods on display should not be allowed to run out if there are still stocks in the stores, but Josefina's interpretation gives it a more Caribbean flavour: 'A proportion of the products that are scarce are reserved for standing clients and are hidden beneath the counter – and well, they're not to be exhibited for everyone to see.' Customer loyalty has become a safe passage in the midst of this supposed economic war.

'No merchandise above that's lacking below'. It's almost an 'As on Earth, so in Heaven'. Everyone reads scarcity from their own side of the counter.

2

One block down, in the boulevard that extends around and passes in front of the market, there is a truck selling chicken. It's part of one of the various initiatives that the central government has dedicated to the matter of foodstuffs, with the patronage – and leadership – of PDVSA, the state oil company. Nowhere does it say that it only sells one chicken per person, but that's how it is: just one chicken per person. The control appears strict: on an A4-sized, photocopied sheet of squared paper, splattered with the washed out, reddish tone left by defrosted blood, they take the names of those who buy the imported white meat at the regulated price:

'And what do you write down?'

'The full names and ID numbers of those who make a purchase. As they are sold at a regulated price, this list is to ensure that no one buys more than one chicken. Once they've paid, they're listed here. This way we avoid people buying more and abusing the system.'

'But with that information, how do you know if someone has already bought one?'

...

'I mean, you have a list of who has bought chicken here, right? Do you check on the list every time someone comes and asks for a chicken, to see if they've already bought one?'

'Well, the queue is about two hours long. I don't think anyone would want to come back and wait again, do you?'

She asks me like someone who has discovered, suddenly, that the system they've explained to her and which she has applied with determination for hours, doesn't work. That it never worked.

3

Oriana queues. It's her business. She finds out where there is toilet paper, corn oil, sugar, coffee, flour… and she queues as many times as her budget and the cashiers' memory permits. Strategically, she picks up an extra portion from the shelves and joins the queue behind another buyer who isn't using their full allowance, convincing them to pass through the tills 'as theirs' an item that wasn't originally on their list. In this way she can duplicate her acquisitions in just one go.

Oriana visits her family in the province of Los Andes every fortnight. She takes to the road with everything she's been able to accumulate as a result of her daily labours. And selling the goods there, she can double her outlay. She only resells non-perishable goods and some clients await her visits – and for one reason above all:

'Some touts take the Mickey and resell at four, five times the price they paid. I sell at a reasonable price, which also allows me to get rid of everything that much quicker.'

'And do you go there to sell as you can or do you also take orders?'

'Those customers who know me already have an idea what I'm likely to have and, yes, some make requests. It's good since then some of what I buy is pre-sold.'

'Has anyone helped you, here or there, since you started this?'

'I'm on my own with my daughter. But I'm always busy and I sort things out quickly and well.'

'And what makes you sell there rather than simply here in Caracas?'

'It's just that you can still get things here but there – well it's terrifying. My family live there and the truth is that you can't get anything. The queue to buy a chicken can be three hours long. It's as if it suits the authorities to keep Caracas more-or-less well supplied, ahead of the rest of the country…'

4

Where Josefina buys her goods there are more than thirty products on display, but only eight offer a choice between a couple of brands (and prices). There is also a rhythm that allows one to distinguish between regular customers and occasional buyers. The difference is in their patience, their capacity to wait. The regulars install themselves before the counter and wait, with no rush, until the merchant helps them with their purchases, while those who aren't skim past to ask if stocks *include such-and-such.*

Josefina writes on a scrap of paper while she asks the vendor what he has to sell. Another two ladies do the same. Between one thing and another, the butt of every joke that touches on the issue of scarcity is a government department.

It's curious: matters of hunger are usually sad, but everyone in the market laughs at the powers that be as if it allowed them to vent a legitimate – albeit at the same time resigned – rage.

We've been here half an hour and at least fifteen people have passed asking if the trader has the same product. I ask myself when we stopped using the imperative 'give me' to opt instead for the interrogative 'do you have' for a transaction as simple as buying a pound of flour. During these musings Josefina has finished her shopping. Or so it seems.

Before moving out of the way for the next person in line, Josefina gives the merchant a scrap of paper.

'How much did you spend at this store?'

'I don't know yet.'

'What do you mean, you still don't know?'

'He'll tell me just now, when he comes back to check the bags.'

'And what was that little piece of paper you gave the merchant, Josefina?'

Those who sell groceries have also had to turn themselves into some sort of agent for scarce products. After sorting out the orders for those products *available above and available below*, customers provide them with a list of the other things required to complete their shopping. This merchant doesn't have them here – neither above the counter nor below it – but he'll find what he can and charge his little extra.

'I can't say how much I've spent because that depends on whether or not they can find *the rest* for me. And of course, on how much whatever they find will cost me.'

'And if your money doesn't cover it?'

'I remove some of the things that I know are available and that you can get hold of elsewhere. Those things I can come back and buy whenever, but the ones that I wrote on my list…'

What she put on the scrap of paper wasn't the Iranian caviar that I was surprised to see available at one of the fishmongers, nor Iberian ham or Norwegian salmon (also available). They're products that form part of the shopping list of every family in the western hemisphere. Nevertheless, on reading that one of the favours that Josefina sought was a kilo of wheat flour to make a cake, one vendor exclaimed as if she were asking the impossible:

'You, darling, are going to give me kittens!'

5

A healthy number of peddlers mill around the chicken lorry and each has what everyone within the market is seeking. Jonathan and Gladys are husband-and-wife and part of the knot of people. A packet of corn flour for 20 new bolivars may seem excessive but to them it seems a fair price for having undertaken the necessary queuing. They know that price controls exist and that 20 bolivars is triple the amount established by the official gazette for those stores where you can obtain the product. It's an efficient cost structure and they hand over the re-sold goods in the bags from the same supermarkets where they themselves queued.

'You know that the price of flour is controlled, don't you?'

They laugh. In fact they double up with laughter.

'You've not had any problems with this?'

'If people wanted to buy it at the official price, they wouldn't come to us. But for that they'd have to find it first, then fight for it, and finally queue up to pay. And that includes the police. They always extort a few kilos but after that they pay at the same rate as everyone else.'

'So you benefit from the scarcity…'

'What scarcity? Go to a supermarket in Santa Fe, because this flour is from there. Listen, what happens is that in the poorer neighbourhoods there are more people and in the richer areas there are fewer, the food runs out sooner in the former than in the latter.

'And why do you think they send flour there and not here?'

'Because they want to mess with the government...'

'But isn't the Integrated System for Alimentary Control (SICA) a government scheme?'

...

'Do you know how the distribution of flour actually occurs?'

I have with me an annotated pamphlet with the mission statement of SADA, the National Agricultural Depot and Storage body, and I tell them what SICA is responsible for. The logical conclusion arrived at by Gladys reveals that our reality is more coherent than it appears:

'Oh, so they do the same with flour as they do with electricity, right?'

6

Negation cohabits with prices on the market's brightly coloured signs. Between the displays of white cheese and mozzarella there's a small cardboard sign that reads, 'There is no butter,' similar to others at each and every one of the dairy stalls. Rejection appears to be a foregone conclusion, but Josefina receives a text message from another of her merchants:

'We'll sort out the butter early…'

'There isn't any. None of the stalls has any butter.'

She smiles. Before my eyes she shows all her experience, purposefully striding to a precise destination. We arrive at a fridge and from within comes a brown packet that Josefina unwraps knowledgeably. The golden paper of the bar makes it appear like an ingot. 'It's imported and Danish,' she's informed, as they pass her a ticket with the cost of the acquisition – an expense quadrupled by the magical-realist gem that price controls have become.

'Imported and Danish, but the one I really like is the one they make in Maracay.'

'Or *used to*… because we haven't received any in some time.'

7

I ask myself what Josefina might be leaving until last to buy. 'Candles and my flowers. The flowers are a luxury but I like to have them in my home. I'll buy a rose for Saint Barbara and flowers for my mother at least. The candles are an essential so I try and buy good ones.'

'And what makes for a good candle?'

'The fact that it lasts longer…'

The only pause in this constant strategic movement is to have a cup of herbal tea after buying the little fruit she'd planned to get today. A red apple – also for Saint Barbara – half a papaya, a melon and two kilos of passion fruit. Heading for the plums, she pulls up short. They're priced two for 50 bolivars:

'Hey! Why have the plums gone up so much?'

'Three words, 'Fina: imported, contraband and Colombia.'

'Damn... well, there'll be no plums. And give me the small herbal teas.'

8

At one of the butchers, along with the prices on the blackboard there are photos of the deceased Hugo Chávez in military uniform and of Henrique Capriles Radonski with his yellow, blue and red baseball cap. Both are present, politicising the prices that aren't those which one pays at the till. A political portrait of the country, as fictional as the prices for tripe, kidneys, beef tongue, a whole chicken... the thigh and the breast of which serve to frame the photos. Impossible numbers. As impossible as the notices requesting that the question of prices not be politicised: that the one not be linked to the other... that food – ultimately – doesn't belong to either side. But there they are, between the lesser meats and the butchered joints, two possibilities that right now are much less immediate than the anguish arising from the harsh truth that the pennies simply won't reach. And when the stomach rumbles, patience and hope make themselves scarce.

9

The last stop on Josefina's rounds is for vegetables. Osvaldo and Isabel are siblings and work at the stall that their parents ran many years ago. They greet her affectionately but a complaint regarding last week's potatoes, which were hard, immediately comes to the fore. She asks:

'What could have happened to those potatoes, Osvaldo?'

That's something that will never be known for sure but his years in the business help him draw a conclusion: 'It's the shambles of imports and low productivity. That and the fact that there are about a thousand government entities which say they're responsible for agriculture. And the result is that something which should be everyone's ends up being no one's…'

All the traders with whom we chat are well informed as to what is currently going on. Osvaldo explains his vision of the lack of planning. He tells me about seeds imported from Canada and the ineptitude that saw various Andean producers he knows in the cantons of Mucuchíes, Bailadores and Jajó lose an entire crop:

'Before they began sowing, a cargo of Ecuadorian potatoes – subsidised by the government – arrived at Puerto Cabello. That's the same government which is supposedly helping them grow potatoes. If they can't even come to an agreement among themselves as to which potato we're going to eat, how the hell are we supposed to know how much a kilo of veg is supposed to cost!'

'And was there a shortage of potatoes?'

'It was worse than that: there were potatoes aplenty but precious few of decent quality. One ends up forced to sell a poor-quality product because there's nothing else available. That month we sold some potatoes which clients told me they prepared in pressure cookers – but the only thing that went soft was the pot...'

'And is the cost of something like potatoes affected by the exchange rate?'

'This sack of little Colombian potatoes, the small ones, cost me 650 bolivars two months ago; the day before yesterday it cost me 1,000.'

'What do you think is happening here, Osvaldo?'

'They've stuck their fingers into oil, into business, into foreign exchange... but now they're taking food from people's plates. And that... well, it's not going to end well.'

10

I remain obsessed by the silence. It's not that I miss the hubbub, but it seems strange to me that the noise of Catia Market feels so much like a memory. We've undertaken an entire tour and given the merchant time enough to perform a miracle. And upon our return he's managed to get everything except toilet paper.

'You're going to have to wait for the imported one, 'Fina.'

'Indeed. How much do I owe you?'

And then I understood everything: it wasn't a sum-total that the merchant said to Josefina, but rather a whisper. It was as if the number had been transformed into an aggression one does not mean to commit, an unintentional insult, an embarrassment. I hadn't noticed it but the voice of the stall-holder leaning towards the ear of his client was part of the need to stand beside each other in the face of the terror of inflation. There lies, without doubt, the cause of this verbal apathy – this renunciation of the rowdiness of other times. In a place where the simplest of dealings consists in giving someone the price of something, the voice has become a weapon that evidences the craziness of everyday economics.

'Is it much more than last week?'

'Not much, but yes, it's more. And that was more than the week before. And so it goes.'

'What is it that costs you most in all this, Josefina?'

'What costs me most? Are you referring to what costs me most effort or what costs me most money?'

'Both. What is it that costs you the most?'

'Not knowing how much it will cost me to do all this again next week... or if I'll be able to get what I need.'

A COUNTRY POLES APART

BORIS MUÑOZ
Translated by Montague Kobbé

THE EXILES WHO CAME TO THE TROPICS

In a brief piece from 1992, the novelist Tomás Eloy
Martínez evokes the raucous country that welcomed
him in the small hours of one morning in June 1975.
'I felt unspeakable joy at having made it back to
Latin America alive.' Martínez had come to Caracas
escaping the deadly persecution of 'The Sorcerer'
José López Rega, knowing nothing of a country
'whose currency was oil'. He had no belongings other
than the clothes he wore, a few dollars in one pocket,
a tourist visa and some letters of recommendation
signed by his friends Carlos Fuentes, Gabriel García
Márquez and Juan Rulfo. That morning he discovered
that the historic centre of that tropical location was
a shapeless and charmless composition, some sort of
mottled Arab souk populated with an abundance of
colours and noise, itinerant vendors and fun-loving
people who would start dancing salsa in the middle
of the street for no apparent reason. The following
night a group of Venezuelan writers took him out to Il
Vecchio Mulino, a restaurant featured in the 1972 and
1973 editions of the *Guinness Book of Records* for
being the public establishment where most whisky
and gin had been consumed in the whole world. But

the true essence of his experience boils down to a sentence that captures the emotion that overcame him at the time more accurately than any anecdote could: 'All I wanted at the time was simply to taste the air of a stable Latin American democracy, but there weren't many of them left,' he wrote.

This is a familiar, even obvious, point. From Guatemala to Patagonia, Latin America was a region dominated by the heavy hand of despots and the military. It suffices to list the names: Somoza, Ríos Mont, Videla, Pinochet, Bordaberry, Stroessner, Velasco Alvarado, Operation Condor. Only a handful of nations still had functioning democratic systems. And among them Venezuela was, ahead of Mexico, Colombia and Costa Rica, not only a vibrant country undergoing significant modernisation, but a stronghold of prosperity and openness. A country caught between the brutal and repressive violence prevalent in Central America and the brutal and repressive violence prevalent in South America. Venezuela was the country of whisky and oil, but it was also the country of motorways, of developments in the steel industry and of the inclusion of exiled intellectuals and academics. These circumstances shored up the foundations of Venezuela's democratic system. Thanks to its oil reserves the country had been able to navigate the tricky waters of the Cold War. The democratic system had survived the guerrilla warfare, pacifying its main protagonists who, as a general rule, were now beginning to take part in representative democracy (though there were, of course, notable exceptions to that rule, who two decades later would be back for their dues). And the combination of all this produced – perhaps too soon – a positive self-perception in the Venezuelan collective imaginary of Venezuelan society as a garden of harmony, which in turn made its political system seem like an exemplary project, the democratic ideal of the region.

As a child I lived in that Caracas, in that society, in that seemingly harmonious country, so different to the city, the society, the country of resentment, fear and confrontation we find today. Cities change, so do societies, not to mention countries. Sometimes the change is evident almost instantly, from one day to the next, so to speak, even if in reality the change has been gestating underground for a long time, like a worm eating away at society from within.

THE MYTHS OF THE LOST DECADE

Venezuela in the 1970s was totally alien to the authoritarian rule by a military elite that it had left behind less than two decades earlier. As the decade reached its glorious peak the country recorded the highest income per capita in the world. While oil remained the most coveted commodity on the planet and its price did nothing but climb like a hot air balloon, propelled by the crisis in the Middle East, no one found it necessary to think that the party might come to an end. There was just boastful talk of full employment and the promises spelled out in the Fifth

Plan for the Nation. The mirage of the First World shimmered so near that it could almost be grasped in the skyscrapers and banking towers that sprouted like mushrooms in the city. And everyone imagined that the oil income would perform the miracle of granting us the global status we craved by means of divine intervention.

In 1979 Maritza Sayalero, a spectacular woman, became the first Venezuelan to be crowned Miss Universe. It was no minor event. Her triumph was the icing on the cake for a country that was already on the rise, and it added yet another archetype to the catalogue of myths that have substantially transformed the contemporary history of Venezuela: the country of beauty queens. In 1981 Irene Sáez, the ambitious blonde who less than two decades later would be running for president, repeated Sayalero's feat, confirming with great fanfare the successful archetype and feeding the fantasy of this being a radiant country, blessed by natural wealth and beauty.

That is why any effort to reconnect with those experiences becomes painful. To put it in more photographic terms, the country looked great from afar. But as soon as the old facades and hidden recesses of the lost Eden come under scrutiny we realise that it was all a simulacrum, an impressive yet fragile stage set. Modernity sought to erase all trace of the country's rural and violent past in order for little or none of it to be recalled. This new country of oil and power was being designed by visionary architects, but the running of its day-to-day affairs had been left to pompous and boastful rulers.

Have I failed to mention something significant in this regard? For instance, the fact that Venezuela's fall from grace took place in the wider context of a major Latin American economic crisis, dubbed the debt crisis, which sparked an attempt to change the economic model of a benefactor state in favour of a neoliberal approach. Not so coincidentally Chile became the main laboratory for this experiment, which years later would be tried in Venezuela with disastrous consequences. It could be argued that for Venezuelans the 'lost decade' was the most negative consequence of a series of factors extraneous to Venezuelan society: a historical streak of bad luck. But, does anyone really believe that had a close to two-decade-long era of cut-price oil rates not started in 1980 the country would have soared straight into the ranking of the most prosperous, egalitarian and democratic nations in the world, in other words, that it would have joined the banquet of Western civilization? That would have been ideal. Nevertheless, the answer to that question is anything but obvious.

Therefore, as rhetorical as the question 'At what precise moment did Venezuela go to the dogs?' might seem, we must ask it again. And since time travels in one direction and memory in another we must find a middle point to help us to understand how these events ruined Venezuela's modern history and ultimately set the country's future on a terribly dubious course.

The eighties didn't last ten years in Venezuela, but nine. Just as they didn't begin on 1 January 1980 but rather on 18 February 1983, they didn't end on the first day of 1990 but rather on 4 February 1992. So we need to begin with the late start to the decade.

That year, 18 February was a Friday. On Monday Venezuelans would read in the papers that their currency had been devaluated and that the government had imposed exchange controls. They woke up to a new reality for which they weren't prepared. The price of oil had been falling since the beginning of the decade and at this stage it was simply not high enough to keep financing the constant trips to Miami that over the years had popularised the sentence 'That's cheap, give me two' as a Venezuelan trademark. The demons of inflation and unemployment were unleashed and they brought with them the first signs of other, greater, evils which would prove harder to control, such as social resentment, classism and racism.

I was thirteen and I suspect I was still enjoying the final portion of a troublesome but ultimately sheltered childhood. One of those days I was riding my bike in my neighbourhood when I heard one of my friends say something that forever shattered the remnants of the atemporal innocence left in me: 'Things are screwed beyond repair.' And indeed they were. Mister Pedro León, the father of Oswaldo, one of my best childhood friends and our neighbour from Flat 3, was one of the first casualties of our own private economic meltdown. Mister Pedro was a high-ranking executive of a multinational pharmaceutical company but, from one day to the next, he was fired unceremoniously. What these days is called restructuring and has become a rather common phenomenon wasn't common at all in the distant 1980s.

My neighbours from the penthouse, Fausto and Liduvina, a Cuban couple who had arrived from Havana escaping the revolution, stopped travelling to Miami as frequently as they used to, and no longer parked Uncle Ernesto's enormous motorhome – a symbol if there ever was one that you had made it to the top of the social pyramid – before the gates of the building.

For those who, like me, never went to Miami, the inability to travel abroad was not the biggest problem. The biggest problem was everything else. At home, where two years earlier my mum had been left alone raising the family, everything else meant a drastic cut-down in the most essential goods, frequently discontinued electricity and telephone services due to late payment, and the unending nightmare of having to eat *arepas* with mortadella or Bologna sausage and Kraft Cheez Whiz instead of fresh ham with Edam or Gouda imported from the Netherlands. Seeing my mum, a university lecturer whose natural habitat consisted of laboratories, microscopes, books and classrooms, forced to sell mail-order underwear and cakes and bread – which she would stay up baking late into the night when everyone else at home was already in bed – was a truly bitter pill for me to swallow. But that's the way it was, because a lecturer's salary was no longer enough. Maybe childhood ends when you start to understand that whatever happens outside your home can drastically alter your existence.

But in reality many different things happened in 1983, including Tomás Eloy Martínez's departure from Venezuela. Coincidentally, this was the year of the bicentenary celebration of the birth of *El Libertador* Simón Bolívar, the mythical hero and patriarch of the nation. Huge budgets were allocated for this commemoration, as if the country had to settle a debt with the war Hero and with History, both with a capital H. Nevertheless, in the civil society Venezuelans had forged over the previous twenty-five years of democracy, Bolívar had become a figure confined to school text books, high-denomination notes and the protocol of military parades. He remained an essential historical point of reference, no one could deny that, but one whose potential had been exhausted. Or so we thought.

Had oil wealth changed the Venezuelan way of life at its core? Certainly: Venezuela was, for one fleeting moment, an island of democracy and prosperity. From an agrarian and deeply impoverished society known by the wise men of the first half of the century as 'the home of malaria', in the blink of an eye, the country turned into the symbol of all that money could buy. Riding on the exploitation of the land's vast mineral and energetic resources, its rulers dreamt up a model that followed the example of Japan. In order to prove it they deliberately elevated the word infrastructure to new heights, planting roads all over the country, building enormous hydroelectric power plants and furnishing cities with tall buildings and inventively named spaghetti junctions: the octopus, the centipede, the spider. But this was a public policy that didn't take root as a collective project in the minds of Venezuelans at large. On the contrary, the true legacy of Venezuela's Saudi period in the 1970s was the newfound national passion for unbridled consumerism which was reflected not only in an insatiable appetite for imported goods but also in the emergence of the mall as the public space par excellence.

The economic privation that characterised the 1980s exposed many other things. For instance, the fact that the 1970s had been the years of bonanza, of social ascent in which many, too many, had been left on the bottom rung of the ladder.

The flow of bad news concerning the economy started to swell. Day after day the oil price fell slowly but steadily while the price of the US dollar kept rising, as if propelled by a hydraulic mechanism; week after week inflation ate up salaries; month after month scepticism grew around the possibility of escaping disaster; year after year the politicians spoke a language that sounded ever more hollow. Luis Herrera Campins, the president at the time, claimed he had inherited a mortgaged country, so he proceeded to devalue the currency, taking a resolute step towards the abyss. He was replaced by Jaime Lu*Sí*nchi, the yes man, a good-natured doctor who liked his drink and who asked the country to say *Sí* – yes – to his promises to stay the course towards a social democracy. 'Jaime is like you' was the slogan of his presidential campaign, and regardless of whether or not he was, the fact remains that during his term the crisis worsened to such an extent that by the time he passed on the presidential sash in 1989 the public coffers were practically empty. That's why politicians were deemed to be the harbingers of everything that was wrong. The public had already heard of bloodbaths involving guerrilla fighters and peasants, as well as – though very little was known about this – an attempted military rebellion which had been nipped in the bud. In December 1988 the people voted overwhelmingly in favour of the return to power of Carlos Andrés Pérez, who in the collective imagination personified the years of the Great Venezuela, with its delusions of grandeur and its consumerist orgies in Miami. Nevertheless, the general feeling was one of gradually straying off course, which soon enough would be replaced by the more conclusive 'No future'.

The year 1989 is the other cardinal point of that nine-year-long decade which started in 1983 instead of 1980.

Leaving aside for a moment – or perhaps not so much – the direction in which the country was heading, one of the few ways in which Caracas could appeal to a lad who was trying to piece together the puzzle of what was going on around him was by paying attention to the art scene. Sometime in the mid 1980s the boulders on the side of the motorways mysteriously appeared coated in the yellow, blue and red of the national flag. So did the discarded scraps of wrecked cars and even some monuments. The man behind these urban misdemeanours was Juan Loyola, an eccentric artist with a sharp talent for provocation and scandal. In a society that was still recovering from the hangover of the 1970s his works and performances spoke up against corruption, the plundering of the nation and the country being effectively handed over to international financial institutions. On one occasion he entered the Palace of Justice with seven assistants, all of them impeccably dressed in white as the seven stars on the flag and carrying bags of yellow, blue and red paint which they poured all over each other as they crawled on the floor like victims of a massacre. But Loyola's obsession with the flag was interpreted by most critics in the narrowest of senses: it was seen not as the expression of a visionary talent but as an atavistic form of patriotism. Or rather, his work was too abstract, absurd, coarse and perhaps even prophetic to be taken seriously. It was often ridiculed with dismissive comments.

Loyola, who thought of himself as a rebel, had a shrill and whiney voice. To me he looked androgynous because it was hard to tell at first sight whether he was a man or a woman. He died unceremoniously in 1999 before he could witness the full rise of *Chavismo* (and to some extent the metastasis of the ideas and symbols represented in his work). Any memory of him has been lost without trace in the black hole of oblivion. But his oeuvre truly was taking the pulse of a powerful undercurrent that was shaking Venezuelan society, as was evidenced on 27 February 1989 (27-F), the day when some of the most underprivileged areas of Caracas erupted in a visceral popular explosion that quite literally contained a bit of everything:

celebration, rage, catharsis, looting, repression. The city was engulfed by riots, an official curfew and police raids that resulted in over three hundred dead according to government sources – or over three thousand according to the dark legend brazenly exploited by Chávez's regime for its own benefit.

The Russian poet Joseph Brodsky was envious of those who can look in the rearview mirror of their life and make out episodes, periods, cycles in the continuum of their existence. In my life, a murky collection of moments like anyone else's, I can, however, identify 27-F as a milestone, the defining event of the epoch. If you have to rationalise a collective experience such as that one, which seems to encapsulate the essence of pointlessness, its most significant aspect is that it confronted the country with the very substance that lay at its core: impoverished, chaotic, tribal, choleric, and violent. The government punished with ruthless brutality the protests against the rising cost of living and the adoption of an astonishing economic policy that effectively negated the great expectations awoken by the return of Carlos Andrés Pérez. The repression was excessive by any measure. From that day onwards the city became a necropolis and, as is evidenced in the ever-worsening murder statistics, it remains one to this day. But the showers of bullets sprayed by the National Guard and the so-called government security corps were not left unanswered. They were repelled with various degrees of intensity in different areas of the city, which proved that some groups were already armed and willing to fight fire with fire against the forces of law and order.

That 27-F is the emblem of a sudden transition is proved by the snowball effect it provoked. As the shock waves produced by 27-F spread further out they shattered more and more myths along the way. First on the list was the superiority complex of a country that thought itself destined to join the First World. Or, if you like, the myth of a solid nation certain of its progress towards a social democracy that had started to crack six years earlier. At the same time, down came the myth of a multi-layered class system with harmonious social mobility. The whole edifice of Venezuela's liberal and representative democratic system began to collapse that day, even if its ultimate downfall was only confirmed ten years later. The social breach could no longer be ignored and worse still, it kept growing. But so did the rift between those in government and those who were being governed.

There was tremendous mistrust and prejudice against the ruling establishment, embodied at the time by the government and major corporations. On a personal note, I remember that the Venezuelan Confederation of Workers (CTV) together with other unions called for a nation-wide strike that brought the country to a standstill on 18 May that year, with the notable exception of McDonalds, the only sizeable establishment to open its doors that day. I considered this a personal affront. I wanted to contribute my bit to the destruction of the hierarchies of power so with a group of friends I organised a peaceful demonstration before the fast-food chain. We called it 'a march against the McBourgeoisie'. When the agreed day arrived a handful of students and journalists met outside the restaurant, which was being protected by over one hundred members of the secret police, the most feared in the country, dressed in riot gear and looking like Robocop. We didn't even number thirty people, and the only weapons at our disposal, apart from our harmless leaflets, were a pair of megaphones we used to appeal to passing pedestrians and motorists with a slogan that to this day makes me smile: 'Say NO to the McBourgeoisie. Eat an *arepa*'. Clearly, we didn't get very far, but there was value in the gesture.

The other personal anecdote I relate to 27-F isn't exactly an event but rather the recollection of a diffuse but also dramatic transition which I can only describe as the disappearance of a feeling of security and the simultaneous appearance of fear. The shower of bullets was replaced by a bout of panic. What were we afraid of? The Other. The disenfranchised are the Other and the bourgeoisie is the Other of the Other; the uneducated are the Other to professionals who in turn are the Other to entrepreneurs; politicians are the Other to the people. The Other constitutes a threat. I fear her, therefore she's my enemy. The end of the myth of a multi-layered class system gave way to a free-for-all scenario, the prelude, really, to the current every-man-for-himself.

At a time characterised by the reining back of military rule in Latin America and the transition towards civilian governments, Venezuela marched resolutely in the opposite direction. In some sense the events of 27 February 1989 transported us back as a country to a primordial chaos in which age-old resentments and longings for redemption came face to face with aspirations for order and hierarchy. And those longings were astutely identified by someone who for a long time had been lurking, getting ready to become the main protagonist of the following two decades.

A NOSTALGIC AND ARCHAIC UTOPIA

As Ana Teresa Torres reminds us in *La memoria de la tribu* [the memory of the tribe], no other country suffered greater devastation from the nineteenth century wars of independence than Venezuela. In a letter to his uncle, Simón Bolívar describes the destruction of the capital: 'You will find yourself in Caracas like a goblin arrived from the afterlife and you will realise that nothing is what it once was.' Torres notes: 'This text, we insist, encapsulates what would be the sentimental destiny of the patriots: the solace of glory in lieu of loss. Here we witness the genesis of an ethic, and the cornerstone of a national imagery.'

Hence, it comes as no surprise that faced with yet another disaster in Caracas, as was 27 February 1989, the response was to resurrect a nostalgic and archaic utopia. Nothing illustrates this longing for redemption like the apparition of Hugo Chávez on 4 February 1992 like a genie freed from a bottle. Chávez brought together in a single man the myth of the sentimental patriot and the epic hero, two of the cornerstones highlighted by Torres.

Chávez came clamouring that he would bring restitution to Venezuelan society for the trauma caused by a corrupt political system. In his famous speech after his arrest he took responsibility for failing in his attempt to depose the president and said new opportunities would arise to change the course of the fate of Venezuelans. Chávez presented his military and Bolivarian crusade as the catalyst of a creative destruction: the elimination of the so-called Fourth Republic and the creation of the Fifth Republic, which later on would morph into 'Bolivarian socialism' or 'twenty-first century socialism'.

The emergence of Chávez was greeted more with scepticism than with enthusiasm. His attempted coups (the one he led on 4 February 1992 and the one he orchestrated remotely from his prison cell in Yare on 27 November) piled more dead bodies upon the violence of those bloody years and people didn't take kindly to him trying to depose by force a president who, disliked as he might have become, had still been elected into office by popular vote. Nevertheless, clear signs appeared very early on that the military felon had touched a nerve deep in the Venezuelan psyche. Just weeks after the attempted coup, during the carnival celebrations of 1992, the most popular costume among children wasn't Batman, as it usually was, but rather the army fatigues and red beret worn by Hugo Chávez. There was the proof, if proof were needed, that the resurrected hero and military patriot had come to stay. Soon thereafter Chávez would also prove to be a skilful politician, tremendously shrewd, with a keen eye for strategy and, most importantly, a long-term political project.

4 February 1992 fell on a Tuesday. I'd just got back from the cinema at eleven at night when my grandmother phoned me. She sounded agitated. 'It's a coup. There's a coup underway,' she announced, like someone crying 'Fire, fire, call the fire brigade!' As I heard all hell breaking loose outside La Casona, the presidential residence which was just a few kilometres away from my home, I remembered that inside one of my desk drawers, in a grey paper envelope, I kept a document a friend of mine had given me to guard with great care and only make public if 'something' happened to him. At the time my friend was a university lecturer but his true calling was as a conspirator. In fact, from a very early age he had been a full-time conspirator. Some months earlier he had warned me that his frequent trips between Valencia and Maracay, the largest cities in the vicinity of Caracas, were because he was up to 'something'. More than once when we got together to have a drink in some bar or café we were interrupted by his 'friends' who came to see him and with whom he withdrew to a corner to speak almost secretly. In fact, we once spent hours driving around in a car with a gentleman with white hair and an equally white beard who was introduced to me as Kleber 'the Elder', much like you would speak of Alfonso X 'the Wise'. In the small hours of that February morning I could no longer keep

my curiosity in check so I pulled the document out of the envelope. It was a plan for a new constitution following a coup. I didn't really understand much of what was written there but I could never shake the memory of how it advocated for summary trials to execute anyone guilty of corruption. My friend was not among the conspirators detained by the secret police. After a year or perhaps even more I gave him back the document in the original envelope together with a note in which I made clear my relief at the failure of the insurrectionary adventure.

But had it really been a failure? In Yare prison, where Hugo Chávez spent a little over two years, he expanded his scope of action, attracting a number of outcasts from the intellectual and insurrectionary left who marched in and out of his cell on a daily basis without the least control from the authorities. In reality Chávez used the prison as his campaign HQ, preparing over the course of endless meetings his return to the political arena as the great exposer of the two-party system: the *deicide* of representative democracy.

As historians have been revealing, Hugo Chávez began shaping himself as a messianic leader as early as the 1970s, when he joined the Military Academy. In 1982, emulating the oath attributed to Simón Bolívar at Monte Sacro, he and a group of conspirators swore with dramatic solemnity under an old rain tree where Bolívar had apparently once had a siesta that they would bring to completion *El Libertador*'s unfinished work. In 1986 Chávez and a party of horsemen who all waved the black flag of the army led by independence war hero José Antonio Páez's crossed the county from the southern plains to the fields of Carabobo, where Venezuela's independence was secured in the final battle of June 1821. In every town he stopped at along the way Chávez placed a floral reef at the Plaza Bolívar and delivered a speech. These gestures, which you might be forgiven for considering rather dramatic, were taken totally seriously by him.

While he was held in Yare prison, history lent Chávez a distinctive helping hand: the same system that in 1983 had plunged into crisis and in 1989 had manifested its terminal illness was by 1992 in freefall.

In 1993, Carlos Andrés Pérez's exit from the presidential seat following a tumultuous trial for embezzlement, together with a banking crisis that brought to light the colossal scale of the fraud perpetrated by bank executives, was the final blow. But the problem wasn't merely economic.

You had to be blind not to see that the country was going to the dogs. The economic aspect of it was just a detail compared to the misgovernment and the insecurity that held the country to ransom day after day. It was the tragedy of a system that had entered into complete moral and political decadence.

The thousands upon thousands of dead bodies that these days overwhelm the country's morgues are not a new phenomenon. Already in 1993 it was a regular occurrence for a young man to fill another with bullets for a pair of trainers. Almost instinctively, hoards of people from my generation decided to leave the country. They were dubbed the 'flying rafters' because, like the Cuban rafters, the so-called *balseros*, they left by whatever means possible, with the difference that Venezuelans used planes instead of rafts. I looked for academic opportunities elsewhere myself, in impossible places like Japan. Ultimately I ended up going to New Jersey, chasing the illusion of the north. For those who stayed behind though, there weren't many options.

In fact, one of the very few sources of hope came from the beauty queen Irene Sáez, who had been elected Mayor of Chacao, a municipality in the eastern end of Caracas which during those years boasted being the wealthiest in Latin America. She did so well that in 1998, when the final collapse of representative democracy was about to be declared in Venezuela, she had the dubious honour of competing against Chávez in the general elections.

The beauty queen's discourse was technocratic, that of the warrior was vengeful. She evoked the feminine ideal, the old yearning for status and bourgeois comfort of the middle class, and, stretching her discourse, maybe the renovating potential of representative democracy. He appealed to the thirst for recognition of the impoverished majority, the historical revenge of the oppressed and the romantic Bolivarian redemption: an archaic and nostalgic utopia. The former Miss Universe was the favourite for most of the presidential campaign, but the lieutenant colonel ended up winning by a landslide.

In some sense, the rest is history and immortality. The greatest change Venezuela has witnessed over the course of the past forty years is too evident and (almost) self-explanatory.

In 1999, after a rushed constituent and re-foundational process set in motion and turbocharged by a Hugo Chávez in overdrive, the country changed its name from Republic of Venezuela to Bolivarian Republic of Venezuela. This was not merely a symbolic change. The adjective Bolivarian decidedly qualified the noun Republic. That was just the first of a series of changes in all aspects: real, material, ideological, structural, rhetorical and symbolic.

For instance, in terms of aesthetics. Looking back into the history of the forty years of democracy that preceded Chávez's regime, we see that a country that boasted a diverse, eclectic, modernist aesthetic went on to adopt a militaristic, official, deliberately archaic one based on the ubiquity of national symbols, army fatigues and the trademark red colour of Chávez's sympathisers.

It's true, the Bolivarian revolution turned many things on their head. It obliterated the previous political system, which after being demonised for over a decade was no longer publicly praised by anyone, not even its most emblematic survivors. Looking at it with a clear head and from an impartial perspective, though, the best years of the social democratic system had one major advantage over the Chávez era: its vision for the country's long-term future, faulty as it might have been, was the product of a social contract backed by various political figures and endorsed by the majority.

There is no doubt that Chávez recouped a platform of social assistance that the previous regime had neglected. Chávez enjoyed an oil-driven bonanza ten times greater than the one Carlos Andrés Pérez experienced during his first term in power (1974-79). He used the new oil boom of the start of the century to put Venezuela on the map of countries that advocate a social and economic model other than global neoliberalism. He promoted the emergence of left-leaning governments in the region with resounding success, as in the case of Bolivia and Ecuador, where other personalistic leaders rose to power. And he also benefited from Venezuela's economic influence to place himself at the epicentre of the regional political scene.

You could argue long and hard about the impact of Chávez and his twenty-first century socialism but you have to be prepared to face an uncomfortable question: in order to earn the loyalty of the majority and achieve those feats, modest as they were next to the enormous economic affluence that brought them about, did he need to spark social resentment and fall back on anti-politics? Did he need to erect an autocratic, hyper-centralised and egotistical regime that turns the screw ever tighter on its citizens? Did all imaginable corruption records need to be broken? Did he, after all is said and done, need to bring back to life the atavistic militarism that once again has pegged the future of the nation to the lust for power of one individual and his mediocre minions?

Chávez created a hybrid system: hierarchical-vertical-militaristic in its decision-making and democratic-populist-electoral in its mechanism of legitimation. Then he acted as the strong-arm leader of that very system. The one institution from the *ancien régime* in which Venezuelans kept faith, upholding it as the expression of their will and individual influence over the system, was the vote. Chávez understood this reality perfectly and held one election after another to reinforce the myth that he was the most democratic leader of them all, which in turn conferred on his entire project a semblance of legitimacy.

Nevertheless, as Alberto Barrera, co-author together with Cristina Marcano of *Chávez sin uniforme* [Chávez without uniform], the first serious biography of the strongman, told me in relation to the general elections of 2012: 'Chávez talks about himself and his personal tale all the time. So much that by now it's hard to tell what is and isn't true. More and more, his memory resembles a work of fiction. His main message is increasingly not the country or the revolution, but Chávez.'

Much has been written about Chávez, from all kinds of angles. As a journalist I saw him speak in public many times and I was always struck by his passionate patriotism and his sense of self-importance, evidenced in the ease with which he saw himself as a cog in the wheel of history.

He presented himself like that again on 1 July 2012 in Maracay when he launched his last political campaign. After the usual harangue against capitalism he spent a long time reflecting on Bolívar in order to plant the idea that he, Chávez, had been entrusted with the task of leading Venezuela towards its second independence from global imperialism. Tainting his oratory with deeply elegiac tones, filled with necrophilia and patriotic pathos, he promised his enemies that he would never be defeated, 'Never ever, because Chávez isn't just me, Chávez is an entire people – undefeated, invincible'. Obviously he was aware that death was hot on his heels, but when I listened to him I knew beyond the shadow of a doubt that he would keep up the show until the end, even if it cost him his life.

The other thing that struck me was the fervour with which he was venerated by his admirers. An expert seducer and flatterer of the masses, Chávez outlined for them an illusory country in which the state-owned oil constituted an inexhaustible supplier of material fulfilment. The poor could trust him to personally deliver justice or, if necessary, they would take it into their own hands, for in his eyes, as he said several times, stealing wasn't a bad thing if it was done out of necessity. 'Chávez is my brother, my husband, my friend, my mother and my father,' one woman told me, as she applauded by my side.

I heard those exacts same words again during his wake in the Military Academy of Caracas in March 2013. Among the thousands lamenting his death I spoke to many people who said they felt orphaned. When I was about to reach the coffin I stumbled upon a woman who claimed to be his secret wife – now she'd be his widow. 'Stand back, Death, be not so cruel, allow us to keep being protected by he who gave meaning to our lives!' she said. Perhaps Brodsky was right when he said that illness and death are the two single common denominators between an autocrat and his subjects. And I'm not so certain about illness.

As I left the Military Academy, marching with the crowd seeking the Metro, I posed myself the question that so many have asked before: what is Chávez's legacy?

After his physical disappearance Chávez has been exploited as a religious myth and instant pop icon, but his transubstantiation has not rendered the desired political effects. This is due to the fact that Chávez left Venezuela mired in a deep economic crisis, with a crime rate that can only be rivalled by the most violent nations in the world, and with an even more corrupt and dysfunctional state than the one against which he rebelled two decades earlier. While Chávez planted in the majority the yearning for justice, equality and welfare, the country he left behind is ever more distanced from the idyllic utopia he promised to his acolytes and edging ever closer to becoming a failed state.

In order to hold on to power without Chávez, the group that was left in charge of the country after his death has been forced to commit the most flagrant violations of the constitution. Venezuela is today in the hands of a mob of mediocre sidekicks who, ostensibly, are in charge of keeping the revolutionary values from being corrupted but whose true goal is to stay together in order to keep a close eye on one another, to keep the lid on the enormously shady dealings that have taken place under their command, and to avoid being punished for them.

POSTSCRIPT, 12 MARCH 2016

Chávez's death was the beginning of the end of *chavismo* as a ruling system, even if it has outlived him and it now seeks to hold on to power with further illegal and violent stratagems. But is there any point in wondering about Chávez's legacy at a time when the whole structure he created and of which he was the central figure is tumbling to the ground? This might seem like a rhetorical question but it isn't.

Venezuela is again on the brink of a major change and what is at stake is its survival as a nation. As deprivation spreads more and more widely it becomes evident that Chávez's legacy combines populism with the cult of the individual and the direct power lines inherent to the strong man at the helm – in other words, *caudillismo*. But there is a peculiar trait to *chavismo*: its nature is directly linked to authoritarianism, pillage and abuse of power, which is personified in the figure of the *malandro* – the wanton hoodlum. *Malandros* are always above the rule of law. *Malandros* promote the fiercest form of disorder because this enables them to impose their own order. *Malandros* rule in disorder not by imposing equal laws for everyone but rather by using force to rise above the law. This has been proved over the last decade by the emergence of *pranes*, prison dons fully in control of the penitentiaries they inhabit. *Pranes* demand blind obedience from their subordinates and even impose altruism through violence. Neither is it coincidental that President Chávez spent the greater part of his fourteen years in power issuing executive orders that placed him above any law or institution and spared him all scrutiny. For this same reason it should come as no surprise that over the course of seventeen years the Supreme Court has never ruled against the government – not once. Chávez's legacy is a highly disorganised society under complete control of the *malandro*: a form of systematised felony that cuts through the state vertically and horizontally, spilling over to the full extent of society.

Considering the will of the majority, reflected in the consistently high percentage of voter participation in recent elections, people in Venezuela still believe the country's future lies in democracy. Nevertheless, for this to be possible, it will have to be a democracy capable of convincing large sectors of the population to reach a compromise that would limit the unbounded power enjoyed presently by those very sectors. Only then can the *malandro* system of institutionalised felony imposed by Chávez be dismantled – a legacy that, like most of them, does not stem exclusively from him and his acolytes but also from his adversaries.

LIST
OF
CONTRIBUTORS

THE AUTHORS

Alberto Barrera Tyszka (Caracas, 1960). Writer and television scriptwriter. His novel *La Enfermedad* (2010, published in English as *The Sickness*) won the Herralde Prize and was a finalist of the Independent Prize for Foreign Fiction. In 2015, his novel *Patria o muerte* won the Tusquets Prize. He has also written short story collections, poetry and non-fiction books. His work has been translated into various languages. Together with the journalist Cristina Marcano he wrote *Chávez, sin uniforme* (2007), the first certified biography of the Venezuelan political leader. He has taught at the School of Literature (letras) at the Central University of Venezuela. As a scriptwriter, he has worked in Venezuela, Colombia, Argentina and Mexico.

Rodrigo Blanco Calderón (Caracas, 1981) is a writer, editor and university lecturer. He has published the short-story collections *Una larga fila de hombres* (2005), *Los Invencibles* (2007) and *Las rayas* (2011). His short stories have earned him recognition both in Venezuela and abroad. In 2007 he was selected for the group Bogotá39, which gathered the best Latin American writers under the age of thirty-nine. In 2013 he was guest author in the international writing programme of the University of Iowa. In 2014 his short story 'Emunctories' was included in issue number forty-six of *McSweeney's* magazine, titled *Thirteen Crime Stories from Latin America*. Presently he is completing a doctorate in linguistic and literary studies at the Université Paris XIII. *The Night* (2016), his first novel, was recently awarded the Prix Rive Gauche.

'**Clown**' was first published as 'Payaso' in *Las rayas* (Caracas: Punto Cero, 2011).

Israel Centeno (Caracas, 1958) is a writer of long and short fiction, creative literature instructor and cultural promoter. He has published approximately fifteen works in Venezuela, Spain and the United States. He was awarded the Consejo Nacional de la Cultura (CONAC) Prize and the Municipal Prize of Caracas in 1992 for his first novel, *Calletania*, and in 2003 won the short story competition of *El Nacional* for 'Según pasan los años'. His work has been included in anthologies in Venezuela, Spain and Slovenia. His collection of short stories *Bamboo City* (2012) and his novel *El Complot* (2002, published in English in 2014 as *The Conspiracy*) have been translated into English. He has translated into Spanish the works *Peru* by Gordon Lish, *El Jardín/Constance* (*The Front Yard*) by Constance Fenimore Woolson, *Un inconveniente* (*The Pitfall*) by Mary Cholmondeley and *Diario de un hombre de éxito* (*The Diary of a Successful Man*) by Ernest Dowson, all of them published in Spain by Editorial Periférica. He lives in Pittsburgh, where he was writer-in-residence at City of Asylum.

'The Expedition of the Dolls' is included as 'La expedición de los muñecos' in his collection of short stories *Según pasan los años* (New York: Sudaquia, 2012).

Doménico Chiappe (Peru, 1970) grew up in Venezuela, where his family moved in 1974. He has lived in Madrid since 2002. He holds a doctorate in humanities from Madrid's Universidad Carlos III, and focused his thesis on multimedia narrative. He has published the novels *Tiempo de encierro* (2013) and *Entrevista a Mailer Daemon* (2007), the short story book *Los muros* (2011), the collection of *crónicas Cédula de identidad* (2014) and the multimedia works *Hotel Minotauro* (2013-2015) and *Tierra de extracción* (1996-2007). As a researcher he focuses on journalism, photography and digital literature. He has published the essay *Tan real como la ficción. Herramientas narrativas en periodismo* (Laertes, 2010) and is working on *La visión multimedia. Apuntes para una narrativa electrónica* (2015-2016). In Venezuela he was cofounder of the newspaper *TalCual* and the magazine *Primicia*, and he worked in *El Nacional*. He is a contributor for the magazines *El Estado Mental, Fronterad* and *Letras Libres*. He works as publishing coordinator and teaches journalism at www.domenicochiappe.com.

'The Long Road to Nowhere' first appeared as 'Largo viaje inmóvil' in *Cédula de identidad* (Caracas: La Guaya, 2014) later published as *Largo viaje inmóvil. Crónicas de Venezuela* (Madrid: Círculo de Tiza, 2016).

Hector Concari (Montevideo, Uruguay, 1956), holds a degree in philosophy. He is film critic in the magazines *Encuadre, CineOja, Imagen*, the newspaper *TalCual* and various publications of the Cinemateca Nacional de Venezuela. He is the author of the novel *De prófugos y fantasmas* (2005) and the collections of short stories *Fuller y otros sobrevivientes* (2005) and *Yo fui el chofer de John Dillinger* (2008), all published in Venezuela. Presently he is a columnist in the Venezuelan daily newspaper *El Nacional*.

    'Blanes in Flashback' was originally published as 'Blanes en flashback' in *Yo fui el chofer de John Dillinger* (Caracas: Mondadori, 2008).

Victoria De Stefano (Rimini, Italy, 1940) read philosophy at the Central University of Venezuela (UCV). She worked in the university's Institute of Philosophy and taught aesthetics, contemporary philosophy and theory of dramatic structures in the UCV's faculties of Philosophy and Art. She is the author of the novels *El desolvido* (1970), *La noche llama a la noche* (1985), *El lugar del escritor* (1992), *Cabo de vida* (Planeta, 1994), *Historias de la marcha a pie* (1997), which merited her the Municipal Prize for Best Novel and was a finalist of the Rómulo Gallegos Prize, *Lluvia* (2002), *Pedir demasiado*

(2004), and *Paleografías*, (2010), which earned her the 2012 Critics' Award. She is also the author of the essays *Poesía y modernidad, Baudelaire*, (1984), winner of the Municipal Prize for Best Essay in 1984, and *La refiguración del viaje* (2005).

'**On a Bad Day in 1979**' is an extract of her novel *Historias de la marcha a pie* (Caracas: Todtmann Editores, 1997; El otro, el mismo, 2005).

Salvador Fleján (Caracas, 1966) holds an undergraduate degree in literature (Letras) from the Central University of Venezuela. He is the author of the collections of short stories *Intriga en el Car Wash* (2006) and *Miniaturas salvajes* (2012), the collection of *crónicas Ruedalibre: Crónicas inoxidables* (2014) and the book of *crónicas* and short stories *Tardes felices* (2016). His work has been printed in a number of domestic and international media outlets and his fiction is included in several anthologies both in the country and abroad. He has been awarded various literary prizes in Venezuela and has been a member of the jury of the yearly short story competition by the newspaper *El Nacional*, as well as of those by the Association of Venezuelan Authors and Composers (SACVEN) and the Metropolitan Polyclinic, among others.

'**Intrigue in the Car Wash**' was the title story of his *Intriga en el Car Wash* (Caracas: Random House Mondadori, 2006).

Miguel Gomes (1964) is the author of, among others, the works of fiction *Visión memorable* (1987); *De fantasmas y destierros* (2003); *Un fantasma portugués* (2004); *Viviana y otras historias del cuerpo* (2006); *Viudos, sirenas y libertinos* (2008); *El hijo y la zorra* (2010); and *Julieta en su castillo* (2012). He has been the recipient of the Caracas Municipal Prize for Literature for *Un fantasma portugués* and has twice won the yearly short story prize awarded by the Venezuelan newspaper *El Nacional*. As a critic he has written extensively about the essay in Latin America and about various poets and fiction writers. He studied in the University of Coimbra (Portugal), the Central University of Venezuela, and completed his PhD at Stony Brook University in New York. Since 1989 he lives in the USA, and currently is a lecturer at the University of Connecticut.

'**Christina Cries at Three O'Clock**' won the 2010 *El Nacional* short story prize and was published as 'Lorena llora a las tres' in his collection *Julieta en su castillo* (Caracas: Artesano Editores, 2012).

Freddy Gonçalves Da Silva (Caracas, 1981) was one of those children who would hide under the covers with a torch to read until the small hours of the morning. These days he just switches the lights on. He holds an undergraduate degree in literature (Letras) and a master's degree in children's and young adults' literature. He is a promoter of books and an academic at the Autonomous University of Barcelona and Bogota's Academy of Writers. He worked at Banco del Libro and was the creator of the youth jury of books Librogénitos. For eleven years he worked as scriptwriter for various television channels and he recently was coordinator of literature marketing at the Colombian publishing house SM. He has published the novels *Arañas de casa* (2015) and *María Diluvio* (2014), as well as a number of research papers for several specialised publications. He is the creator and director of the online YA literary magazine *PezLinterna* and its blog *Elhabatonka*.

'**Chasing Rabbits**,' originally 'Cacería de conejos,' is a previously unpublished short story.

Gisela Kozak-Rovero (Venezuela, 1963) is a novelist, short-story writer, essayist and academic researcher. She holds a PhD and undergraduate degree in literature (Letras) and is a lecturer at the Central University of Venezuela. Her books include *Venezuela, el país que siempre nace* (2008); *Ni tan chéveres ni tan iguales: el cheverismo venezolano y otras formas del disimulo* (2014); *En rojo* (2011); *Todas las lunas* (2011); *Latidos de Caracas* (2007); *Literatura asediada* (2012); *Rebelión en el Caribe Hispánico* (1993); *Pecados de la capital* (2012); *La catástrofe imaginaria* (1998). She has published opinion pieces in the national press and papers in specialised academic publications. She has taken part in international events, conducted seminars and delivered conferences at Stanford University, the

Latin American Faculty of Social Sciences (FLACSO, Dominican Republic), the Université de Paris VIII and Mexico's Universidad Nacional Autónoma (UNAM). She has also been a guest researcher of the DADD at the Latin American Institute of Berlin. Her critical and creative writing has been recognised with a number of domestic and international awards.

'**Passion**' was originally published as 'La pasión' in her collection of short stories *En rojo* (Caracas: Editorial Alfa, 2011).

Liliana Lara (Caracas, 1971) is a Spanish teacher and lecturer. She is the author of the collections of short stories *Los jardines de Salomón*, winner of the narrative prize of the XVI Literary Biennial José Antonio Ramos Sucre in 2007, and *Trampa – jaula* (finalist of the Oswaldo Trejo short-story prize organised by Equinoccio in 2012). In 2013 her book *Abecedario del estío* earned her a place among the finalists of the XIII Cross-Genre Prize of the Foundation for Urban Culture. Her articles and short stories have appeared in regular publications and anthologies in Venezuela, Mexico, Poland and Germany. She presently lives in Israel.

'**The Body**' was originally published as 'El cuerpo' by the Venezuelan online portal *Prodavinci* in 2009.

Eduardo Liendo (Caracas, 1941) is a novelist and short-story writer. He attended the secondary school Luis Espelozín in Caracas and studied at the Moscow Institute of Social Studies (1967-69) but his literary training came primarily as a voracious reader during his years as a political prisoner in the colonial Fortín El Vigía and the Island of Tacarigua (1962-67). He has worked as librarian, promoter and director of the Cultural Extension of the Venezuelan National Library (1976-2001), conducted the narrative workshop of the School of Literature (Letras) of the Catholic University Andrés Bello (1990-2005), was coordinator of the narrative workshop of the Centre for Latin American Studies Rómulo Gallegos on two occasions, and was guest lecturer at the University of Colorado Boulder (1996). He has been juror in several domestic and international literary competitions, and in 2015 he was made Doctor of Literature Honoris Causa by the Catholic University Cecilio Acosta of Maracaibo. He is the author of *El mago de la cara de vidrio* (1973); *Los topos* (1975); *Mascarada* (1978); *Los platos del diablo* (1985, winner of the Municipal Prize for Literature); *El cocodrilo rojo* (short stories, 1987); *Si yo fuera Pedro Infante* (1989, winner of the National Council of Culture Award the following year); *Diario del enano* (1995); *El round del olvido* (2002, winner of the Municipal Prize for Literature); *Las kuitas del hombre mosca* (2005); *Contraespejismo* (2007); *El último fantasma* (2008); *En torno al oficio de escritor* (essay, 2014); *Contigo en la distancia* (2014).

'**Patriotic Stuff**' is an extract of his novel *Las kuitas del hombre mosca* (Caracas: Alfaguara, Editorial Santillana, 2005).

Albinson Linares (Venezuela, 1981) is a journalist and writer. He is a graduate from the University of Los Andes (Táchira) and has worked in Venezuela's major newspapers and magazines, from *El Nacional's Papel Literario* to *Playboy* or *Prodavinci*, among others. He is a regular contributor to international publications such as *Etiqueta Negra, Ecos* (Germany), *Letras Libres, Reforma* (Mexico) and many others. He is the author of the books *Hugo Chávez, nuestro enfermo en La Habana* (2013), *El último rostro de Chávez* (2014) and *Caracas Bizarra* (2014). In 2012 he was included among the 'New Chroniclers of the Indies' by the Gabriel García Márquez Foundation for New Iberian-American Journalism. Presently he lives in Mexico City and works as editorial adviser for *Bizz* magazine, freelance editor for *NYT América* and web editor for *Information Week Mexico*.

'**The Living Ruins of the Tower of David**' was first printed as 'Las ruinas vivas de la Torre del Rey David' in *Exceso* magazine in February 2011.

Carolina Lozada (Venezuela, 1974), writer. Holds an undergraduate degree in literature (Letras) from the University of the Andes (Mérida, Venezuela). She is the author of *El cuarto del loco* (2014); *La culpa es* *del porno* (2013); *La vida de los mismos* (2011); *Los cuentos de Natalia* (2010); and *Memorias de azotea* (2007).

'**The Villagers**' was originally published as 'Los pobladores' and in 2014 won the sixty-ninth edition of the yearly short-story competition of the daily Venezuelan newspaper *El Nacional*.

Roberto Martínez Bachrich (Valencia, Venezuela, 1977) read literature (Letras) at the Central University of Venezuela, where he later lectured. He holds a master's degree in narrative technique from Scuola Holden in Turin and is presently completing his PhD in Hispanic language and literature at City University in New York (CUNY). He has been a contributor to several newspapers and magazines in Venezuela and has published three collections of short stories, *Desencuentros* (1998); *Vulgar* (2000); *Las guerras íntimas* (2011; 2013); the poetry collection *Las noches de cobalto* (2002); the *crónica La voz del animal* (2013), and the biographical essay *Tiempo hendido. Un acercamiento a la vida y obra de Antonia Palacios* (2012), which earned him the X Annual Cross-Genre Prize of the Foundation for Urban Culture. In 2011 he was named as one of the '25 best-kept secrets in Latin America' at the International Book Fair of Guadalajara (FIL).

'**While the Blood Dries**' was originally published as 'Mientras se seca la sangre' in BBC Mundo in 2011 and is included in the collection of non-fiction texts

479

titled *La prosa en ruinas. Escrituras de lector*, due out in 2016.

Willy McKey (Caracas, 1980), poet, cultural agitator, editor and educator specialised in non-fiction and cultural journalism. He is an adviser and analyst of political semiotics and the editor of *Newsweek*, the cultural magazine of the Venezuelan online portal *Prodavinci*. He has been awarded the 2007 Fundarte Poetry Prize for his collection *Vocado de orfandad* and the 2009 National Book Award for the poetry magazine *El Salmón - Revista de Poesía*. He is the author of the poetic-performative publishing experiences *Paisajeno* and *Nuestra Señora del Jabillo*.

'A Chronicle of Scarcity' was published as 'Una crónica de la escacez' by *Prodavinci* on 27 May 2013.

Juan Carlos Méndez Guédez (Barquisimeto, Venezuela, 1967) is the author of the novels *Los Maletines* (2014); *Tal vez la lluvia* (2009); *Una tarde con campanas* (2004); *El libro de Esther* (1999); and *Árbol de luna* (2000), among others. In 2013 his work *Arena negra* was named book of the year by the country's librarians. He has also published the collections of short stories *Ideogramas* (2012); *Hasta luego Míster, Salinger* (2007); and *Tan nítido en el recuerdo* (2001). He holds a PhD in Latin American literature from the University of Salamanca, and his books have been translated into French and Galician. His latest novel *El Baile de Madame Kalalú* was published in Spain in 2016.

'**The Briefcases**' is an extract of chapters twenty and twenty-one of the novel *Los maletines* (Madrid: Siruela, 2014).

Boris Muñoz (Caracas, 1969) is the Op-Ed editor for *The New York Times Español*. He has covered Venezuelan and Latin America affairs for a number of publications, including *Newsweek, The New Yorker, Prodavinci, Gatopardo, Clarín* and *El Malpensante*. In Venezuela, he was editor in chief of *Exceso* magazine and of *Nueva Sociedad*, a journal of current affairs. Boris holds a PhD in Hispanic American literature from Rutgers University. He is the author of *La ley de la calle* (1995), which focuses on the culture of youth violence in Caracas in the mid 1990s, and *Despachos del imperio* (2007), which compiles commentaries about American life at the turn of the century. His work has been included in several anthologies of Latin American literary journalism. He was a Nieman Fellow at the Nieman Foundation for Journalism and a visiting scholar at the Rockefeller Center for Latin American Studies, both at Harvard University. Muñoz is closely associated with the Gabriel García Márquez Foundation for New Journalism in Ibero America (FNPI)

'**A Coutry Poles Apart**' combines a reworked version of the *crónica* 'Un país en las antípodas,' included in the anthology *Crecer a golpes* (Chile: C. A. Press, 2013) and an abridged version of 'Postscript, 12 March 2016,' published in *Prodavinci*.

Leonardo Padrón (Caracas, 1959), poet, chronicler, columnist, scriptwriter for film and television. He is the author of the poetry collections *La orilla encendida* (1985); *Balada* (1993); *Tatuaje* (2000); *Boulevard* (2002); *El amor tóxico* (2006); *Los materiales humanos* (2010), and *Métodos de la Lluvia* (2011). His first book of *crónicas*, *Kilómetro Cero* (2013), sold over twenty thousand copies and was published in three different editions. In 2015 he published his new collection of *crónicas*, *Se busca un país*. He has been recognised with the Poetry Prize by the Catholic University Andrés Bello, the Essay Prize Fundarte, the Municipal Prize for Cinema, the National Association of Cinematographic Authors Award, and the Fundavisual Latina Prize. He was a member of the poetry group Guaire, which had a decisive influence on the Venezuelan literary scene in the eighties, before becoming one of the most successful writers in the television industry in Venezuela, earning more than twenty-five different awards. Over the past decade he has made a considerable impression on the air waves with his radio show Los Imposibles, which has been running for seven consecutive seasons and has been turned into the publishing best-seller *Los Imposibles, conversaciones al borde de un micrófono* (volumes 1-7). He is one of the most known and respected writers in the country and has been translated to a number of languages.

'**Variations on Goodbye**' was published as 'Formas del adiós' by *El Nacional* newspaper in February 2014.

Maye Primera is a Venezuelan journalist. She was editor-in-chief of the newspaper *TalCual* and worked as the Venezuela and Caribbean correspondent of the Spanish newspaper *El País*. She has published the books *La República Alucinada: conversaciones sobre la Independencia venezolana* (2011); *Rostros y voces contra la impunidad* (2010); and a biography of the Venezuelan politician *Diógenes Escalante* (2007). She is also the co-author of the anthologies of journalistic *crónicas*, *Mejor que ficción* (2012) and *Se habla venezolano* (2010). She presently resides in Miami and works as Latin America editor of Univision Noticias online.

'**I Want The Bones Of My Son**' is an extract from *Rostros y voces contra la impunidad* (Caracas: COFAVIC, 2010), published by the Committee of the Families of the Victims of the Events of February and March 1989.

Miguel Hidalgo Prince (Caracas, 1984) completed his undergraduate degree in literature (Letras) from the Central University of Venezuela. He is the author of the collection of short stories *Todas las batallas* *perdidas*, published in 2012 by bid & co and is presently working on a new collection.

'**Half Way There**' was first published as 'A medio camino' by the Venezuelan portal *Prodavinci*.

Ednodio Quintero (Trujillo, Venezuela, 1947) is a university lecturer, essayist, Japanese literature specialist, photographer and one of the most distinguished contemporary writers in Venezuelan literature. He is the author of eight books of short stories collected in two anthological volumes: *Combates* (2009) and *Ceremonias* (2013); eleven novels, including *La danza del jaguar* (1991), *Mariana y los comanches* (2004) and *El hijo de Gengis Khan* (2013); several book-length essays; a biography, *Akutagawa, el elegido* (2013); and a couple of film scripts. He has been recognised with the most significant literary awards in the country, such as the yearly short story competition by *El Nacional* (1975), the CONAC Prize for Narrative (1992) and the Miguel Otero Silva Prize awarded by the publishing house Planeta (1994). On two occasions he has taken part in year-long programmes by the Japan Foundation in Tokyo, where he has conducted research on the authors Junichiro Tanizaki and Ryunosuke Akutagawa. He also works on translations of contemporary Japanese literature into Spanish.

'**The Princess of Escurrufiní**,' originally 'La princesa de Escurrufiní,' is a previously unpublished short story.

Eduardo Sánchez Rugeles (Caracas, 1977) is the author of the novels *Blue Label / Etiqueta Azul* (2010), winner of the Ibero-American Novel Prize Arturo Uslar Pietri; *Transilvania, unplugged* (2011); *Liubliana* (2012), winner of the International Literary Prize Letras del Bicentenario Sor Juana Inés de la Cruz, and of Venezuela's Critics' Prize 2012; *Jezabel* (2013), and *Julián* (2014). He holds undergraduate degrees in literature (Letras) from the Catholic University Andrés Bello, and in philosophy from the Central University of Venezuela; he also holds master's degrees in Latin American studies from the Autonomous University of Madrid and in literary studies from the Complutense University of Madrid.

'**Ljubljana**' is an excerpt from the prologue of the novel *Liubliana* (Caracas: Ediciones B/Bruguera, 2012).

Carlos Sandoval (Caracas, 1964), literary critic, writer, editor. He is research fellow at the Institute of Literary Research of the Central University of Venezuela (UCV) and lecturer at the UCV and the Catholic University Andrés Bello. His latest publications include *De qué va el cuento. Antología de relatos venezolanos 2000-2012* (2013); *Servicio crítico. Despachos tentativos sobre literatura venezolana* (2013); *Propuesta para un canon del cuento venezolano del siglo XX* (2014; as coordinator, together with Carlos Pacheco and Luis Barrera Linares); *El rastro de Lovecraft. Cuentos misteriosos* *y fantásticos* (2015). He has been recognised with the Municipal Prize for Literary Research (2001), the I *crónica* competition by the magazine *Clímax* (2006) and the Short Novel Prize of the I Literary Biennial 'Julián Padrón' (2010).

'**Any Old S**' was first published as 'S cualquiera' by the Venezuelan portal *Prodavinci*.

Jesús Miguel Soto (Caracas, 1981) read media and communication as well as literature (Letras) at the Central University of Venezuela. He has experience working as a lecturer, copy editor and editor. He has published the collection of short stories *Perdidos en Frog* (2012) and the novels *La máscara de cuero* (2007) and *El caso Boeuf* (2016). He has been the recipient of a number of awards, including the 64th edition of the yearly short story competition by *El Nacional*, the VII National Short Story Award organised by the Association of Venezuelan Authors and Composers (SACVEN) and the XXIII edition of the Literary Competition Juana Santacruz (Mexico). His stories have appeared in anthologies, such as *Joven narrativa venezolana II* and *De qué va el cuento. Antología del relato venezolano 2000-2012*.

'**One of Many Potential Short Cuts**' was originally published as 'Uno de muchos posibles atajos' in *Perdidos en Frog* (Caracas: Lugar Común, 2012).

Francisco Suniaga (Margarita Island, Venezuela, 1954) is a lawyer specialised in international law. For years he worked as an academic and wrote columns in Venezuela's most respected newspapers. Between 2004 and 2009 he was the director of *Exxito* magazine, which focused on politics and economy. He has published the novels *La otra isla* (2005), which has been translated to German and French; *El pasajero de Truman* (2008); and *Esta gente* (2012). In 2010 Random House Mondadori also published the collection of autobiographical fiction *Margarita infanta*, a mural derived from his childhood in the Caribbean island of Margarita. Presently he is fully engaged in fiction writing and is planning to publish his next novel in 2016. He splits his time between Margarita Island and Caracas.

'**The Other Island**' is an extract from chapter XXII of the novel *La otra isla* (Caracas: Oscar Todtmann Editores, 2005).

Héctor Torres (Caracas, 1968) is a narrator and literary promoter. He is the author of the short-story books *El amor en tres platos* (2007) and *El regalo de Pandora* (2011), as well as of the novel *La huella del bisonte* (2008), which featured among the finalists of the 2006 Adriano González León Biennial, and of the *crónica* collections *Caracas muerde* (2012) and *Objetos no declarados* (2014). Formerly the editor of the website www.ficcionbreve.org he was also the creator of the Critics' Award to Best Novel of the Year, awarded by said portal. His texts have been included in a number of anthologies, and he has been a contributor to various print and online publications. He has taken part in workshops with the writers Santiago Gamboa, Leila Guerriero and Alberto Salcedo Ramos. Presently he is a regular contributor in the magazine *Clímax* and the portal *El Cambur*. He delivers literary workshops and since 2006 is the coordinator of the Short Story Prize for Young Authors of the Policlínica Metropolitana.

'What Do They Call Those Born in Chivacoa?' first appeared as 'Como se les llama los que nacen en Chivacoa' in *Caracas muerde* (Caracas: Punto Cero, 2012).

Gustavo Valle (Caracas, 1967) is the author of the books *Materia de otro mundo* (2003); *La paradoja de Ítaca* (2005); *Ciudad imaginaria* (2006); *Bajo tierra* (2009); *El país del escritor* (2013); and *Happening* (2014), which earned him the III Novel Biennial Adriano González León and Venezuela's Critics' Prize, as well as the XIII edition of the Cross-Genre Prize of the Friends of Urban Culture Society. He has written two feature film scripts, *El libro que no ganó el concuro* and *Peones*, both of which have merited him awards by the National Centre of Cinematography (CNAC). He is a regular contributor to a number of print and digital media in Argentina, Venezuela and Spain.

'**Corny or Porny**' first appeared as 'Lo cursi y lo porno' in the magazine *Letras Libres* in January 2004 and was later included in the *La paradoja de Ítaca* (Caracas: Ministerio de Cultura, 2005).

Federico Vegas (Caracas, 1950) completed his degree in architecture from the Central University of Venezuela (UCV) in 1976. He has taught architectural design in the UCV, design at Princeton University (1983) and was a visiting scholar at Harvard University (1995). He has published the following books on architecture: *El continente de papel* (1984); *Pueblos. Venezuela 1979-1984* (1986); *Venezuelan Vernacular* (1985); and *La Vega, una casa colonial* (1988). In the 1990s he began publishing collections of short stories: *El borrador* (1996); *Amores y castigos* (1998); *Los traumatólogos de Kosovo* (2002); *La carpa y otros cuentos* (2009); *Los peores de la clase* (2011); *La nostalgia esférica* (2014). He has also published six novels: *Prima lejana* (1999); *Falke* (2005); *Historia de una segunda vez* (2006); *Miedo, pudor y deleite* (2008); *Sumario* (2010); *Los Incurables* (2012); *El buen esposo* (2013). His newspaper pieces and essays are collected in the books *La ciudad sin lengua* (2001); *La ciudad y el deseo* (2007); and *Ciudad vagabunda* (2014).

'**The Tent**' was originally published as 'La carpa' in *La Carpa y otros cuentos* (Caracas: Alfaguara, 2009).

Slavko Zupcic (Venezuela, 1970), psychiatrist, occupational health doctor and writer. He is the author of the novels *Barbie, Círculo croata,* and *Pésame mucho,* all of which are included in the book *Tres novelas* (2006); he is also the author of the short story collections *Dragi Sol* (1989); *Vinko Spolovtiva, ¿quién te mató?* (1990); *583104: pizzas pizzas pizzas* (1995), and *Médicos taxistas, escritores* (2011; 2014). He has published the book of literary *crónicas Máquinas que cantan* (2005) and the children's book *Giuliana Labolita: el caso de Tepe Toledo.* In 2007 he was included in the group Bogotá39, selected by Hay Festival. His short stories have appeared in a number of anthologies in Venezuela and Latin America, and have been translated to English, German, Hungarian, French and Portuguese language. In 2015 he and Alejandra Costamagna published *Bogotana(mente)* with the publishing house Brutas Editoras. He presently resides in Valencia (Spain) and practices medicine in Castellón.

'**Literary Solutions to the Death of My Mother-in-Law,**' originally 'Soluciones literarias a la muerte de mi suegra,' is part of a new collection of short stories.

THE TRANSLATORS

Ollie Brock has translated authors such as Isabel Allende and Javier Montes, one of *Granta*'s Best Young Spanish-Language Novelists. His reviews have appeared in the *New Statesman*, the *Times Literary Supplement, Modern Poetry in Translation* and *TIME International*. He lives and works at the London Buddhist Centre, where he is training to join the Triratna Buddhist Order.

Ollie is the translator of '**The Tent**' by Federico Vegas.

Ruth Clarke is a translator working from Spanish, French, and Italian into English. She holds a degree in modern European languages from the University of Durham and a master's in translation studies from the University of Sheffield. Ruth has translated work by authors from Benin to Venezuela, and her translation of Cristina Caboni's best-selling debut novel *The Secret Ways of Perfume* will be published in 2016.

Ruth is the translator of '**Christina Cries at Three O'Clock**' by Miguel Gomes and '**Variations on Goodbye**' by Leonardo Padrón.

Lucy Foster is a translator from Spanish and French. She worked in editorial at Sceptre, the literary imprint of Hodder and Stoughton, for several years and before that lived on the west coast of Mexico, working as a dancer and in an art gallery. Lucy is doing a PhD in the literary and visual culture of the Mexican coastline, which fortunately necessitates quite frequent return trips to the beach.

Lucy is the translator of '**Chasing Rabbits**' by Freddy Gonçalves da Silva.

After graduating in Spanish and French, **Chris Lloyd** lived in Catalonia for over twenty years, besides brief spells in Bilbao and Madrid, where he worked as a teacher, in ELT publishing and as a translator. Now living in Wales, he works as a freelance translator and writer. He translates mainly academic and arts texts and has written a number of travel books for Rough Guides. He now writes the Elisenda Domènech series of crime novels set in Catalonia, the first of which, *City of Good Death*, was published in 2015.

Chris is the translator of the excerpt from Francisco Suniaga's novel ***The Other Island*** included in this collection.

Christina Macsweeney's translations of Valeria Luiselli's *Faces in the Crowd* (Coffee House Press, 2012), *Sidewalks* (Coffee House Press, 2013) and *The Story of my Teeth* (Granta, 2015) have received critical acclaim. Her work has appeared on such platforms as *Words Without Borders, McSweeney's, Quarterly Conversation, A Public Space* and *Litro Magazine,* plus the anthology *México20* (Pushkin Press, 2015), and she contributed an introductory text on Mexican literature for the *LBF Market Focus Guide*, 2015. Her translations of Daniel Saldaña París' *Among Strange Victims* and Eduardo Rabasa's *A Zero Sum Game* are forthcoming from Coffee House Press and Deep Vellum in 2016.

Christina is the translator of the chapter '**A Bad Day in 1979**,' taken from Victoria de Stefano's novel *Historias de la marcha a pie*.

Guillermo Parra (USA, 1970) is a poet and translator. His most recent translation is *Air on the Air: Selected Poems of Juan Sánchez Peláez* (Black Square Editions, 2016). He has also published a translation of José Antonio Ramos Sucre, *Selected Works* (University of New Orleans Press, 2012), which was included by *World Literature Today* in their list of '75 Notable Translations 2012'. He presently lives in Clearwater, Florida.

Guillermo is the translator of '**The Expedition of the Dolls**' by Israel Centeno and of an excerpt of the prologue to Eduardo Sánchez Rugeles' novel '**Ljubljana**'.

Jethro Soutar is a translator of Portuguese and Spanish. He has translated crime fiction from Argentina and Brazil for Bitter Lemon Press and novels from Equatorial Guinea for And Other Stories, picking up an Independent Foreign Fiction Prize shortlisting along the way. He is a co-founder of Ragpicker Press.

Jethro is the translator of the excerpt '**Patriotic Stuff**' taken from Eduardo Liendo's novel *Las Kuitas del hombre mosca.*

Occasional stand-up comedian and perennial experimental bass guitarist **Dave Swift** first studied Spanish under José Amodia at Bradford University in 1967. Subsequently, he has lived, laughed and somehow avoided having the shit kicked out of him in Spain, France, Mexico and Hungary. He currently resides in London with his imaginary family and even-more-imaginary friends.

David is the translator of '**Intrigue in the Car Wash**' by Salvador Fleján and of '**The Long Road to Nowhere**' by Domenico Chiappe.

THE EDITORS

Katie Brown has an unhealthy obsession with Venezuelan literature. She has recently completed a PhD on 'The Contested Values of Literature in the Bolivarian Republic of Venezuela' at King's College London. She now teaches Spanish and Latin American culture at University of Bristol. She runs www.venezuelanliterature.co.uk (@VenezuelanLit), posting news, information about published translations and her own translations, and has also contributed to the Palabras Errantes translation project.

Katie is the translator of '**Clown**' by Rodrigo Blanco Calderón, '**Blanes in Flashback**' by Héctor Concari, '**The Body**' by Liliana Lara, '**The Villagers**' by Carolina Lozada, an excerpt from Juan Carlos Méndez Guédez's novel '**The Briefcases**,' and '**Literary Solutions to the Death of My Mother-in-Law**' by Slavko Zupcic.

Tim Girven is the editor of a Latin America-focused commercial publication and a co-founder of Ragpicker Press. He has been involved with region for over 25 years.

Tim is the translator of Alberto Barrera Tyszka's foreword '**To Read a Country**,' Albinson Linares' '**The Living Ruins of the Tower of David**,' Roberto Martinez Bachrich's '**While the Blood Dries**,' Willy McKey's '**A Chronicle of Scarcity**,' and

Héctor Torres' **'What Do They Call Those Born in Chivacoa?'**.

Montague Kobbé is a German citizen with a Shakespearean name, born in Caracas, in a country that no longer exists, in a millennium that is long gone. He is the author of the novel *The Night of the Rambler* and the bilingual collection of flash fiction *Tales of Bed Sheets and Departure Lounges / Historias de camas y aeropuertos*. He has kept a column in Sint Maarten's *The Daily Herald* since 2008 and has translated over twenty photography books with Spanish publisher La Fábrica. His new novel, *On the Way Back* (Akashic, 2016) tackles issues of racial and social prejudice in Anguilla with a large dose of humour.

Montague is the translator of **'Halfway There'** by Miguel Hidalgo Prince, **'Passion'** by Gisela Kozak, **'A Country Poles Apart'** by Boris Muñoz, **'The Princess of Escurrufiní'** by Ednodio Quintero, **'Any Old S'** by Carlos Sandoval, and **'One of Many Possible Shortcuts'** by Jesús Miguel Soto.